CONNECTICUT/
WESTCHESTER COUNTY
HOME
BOOK

"HOME IS A NAME, A WORD, IT IS A STRONG ONE; STRONGER THAN A MAGICIAN EVER SPOKE, OR A SPIRIT EVER ANSWERED TO, IN THE STRONGEST CONJURATION."

Charles Dickens

Photo courtesy of **A. Karp Associates**
Photo by **David Todd**

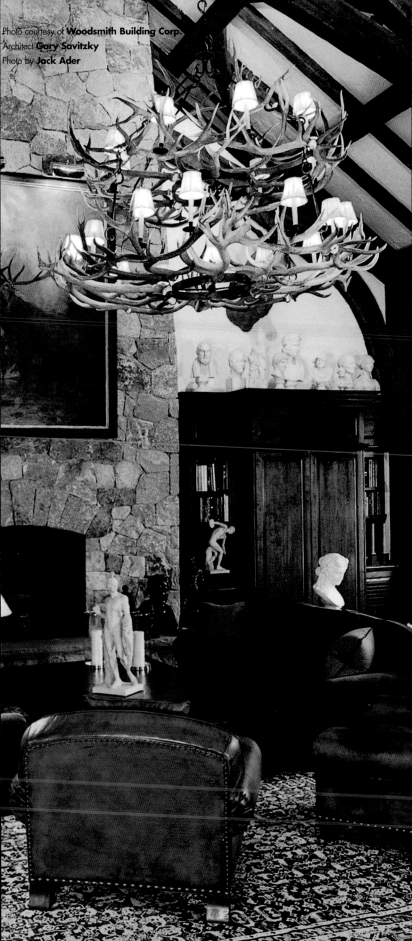

Photo courtesy of **Woodsmith Building Corp.**
Architect **Gary Savitzky**
Photo by **Jack Ader**

Photo courtesy of **Prosperity Interiors**

CONNECTICUT/ WESTCHESTER COUNTY HOME BOOK

A COMPREHENSIVE HANDS-ON DESIGN SOURCEBOOK FOR BUILDING, REMODELING, DECORATING, FURNISHING AND LANDSCAPING A LUXURY HOME IN CONNECTICUT/WESTCHESTER COUNTY AND SURROUNDING AREAS

Photo courtesy of **ACI General Contracting, Inc.**
Photo by **Brian Urso**

PUBLISHED BY

THE
ASHLEY
GROUP

Chicago   New York   Los Angeles

Las Vegas   Philadelphia   Atlanta   Detroit

Arizona   South Florida   Washington D.C.   Colorado

San Francisco   North Carolina   Dallas/Fort Worth

San Diego   Houston   Boston   Seattle   Kansas City

Orange County   Central Ohio   Connecticut/Westchester County

Published By
The Ashley Group
1234 Summer St.
Stamford, CT 06905
203.323.7400 FAX 203.323.5177

Reed Business
Information.
Reed Business Information
A Division of Reed Elsevier Inc

Copyright © 2002 The Ashley Group
All rights reserved. The Connecticut/Westchester County Home Book is published annually by the Ashley Group,
a Reed Business Information Company, which is a division of Reed Elsevier Inc.
No part of this publication may be reproduced in any way without written permission from the publisher.
The Ashley Group is not responsible for any errors or omissions.
All advertisers are totally responsible for their advertisements.

ISBN 1-58862-112-X

CONNECTICUT/WESTCHESTER COUNTY HOME BOOK

Publisher Andrea Greifenberger
Editor-in-Chief Dana Felmly
Managing Editor Laurence P. Maloney
Senior Editor James Scalzitti
Assistant Editor Alison M. Ishihara
Writer Carol White
Office Manager Wendy Boccuzzi
Account Executives Terri Riccio, Eric VanStone, Lauren Wendell
Production Director Paul Ojeda, Catherine Wajer
Production Manager Sean Kealey
Creative Director Bill Weaver
Senior Graphic Designer LN Vaillancourt, Rhonda Jackson
Ad Service Coordinator Michael Foley
Graphic Designers W. Keel, Jennifer Morris, Kate E. Meehan,
Amie L. Smith, Melissa Weinstein
Circulation Manager Christine Kurgan
Prepress Reed Prepress
Printed in Hong Kong by Dai Nippon Printing Company

THE ASHLEY GROUP

Group Publisher Paul A. Casper
Director of Publications N. David Shiba
Regional Director David Baldini
Group Controller Patricia Lavigne
Group Administration Nicole Port, Kimberly Spizzirri, Norma Olson

REED BUSINESS INFORMATION

Chief Executive Officer James Casella
Chief Financial Officer John Poulin
Executive Vice President Ronald C. Andriani
Vice President, Finance David Lench

Front Cover Hobbs, Inc. Photo by Steve Turner
Back Cover E.M. Rose Builders, Inc. and Sean O'Kane, AIA Architect Photo by John Olson

Photo courtesy of **Austin Patterson Disston Architects, LLC**

Photo courtesy of **Mingolello & Hayes, Architec**
Photo by **Rick Scanlc**

Note

The premier edition of **The Connecticut/Westchester County Home Book** was created like most other successful products and brands are - out of need. **The Home Book** concept was originally conceived by Paul Casper, currently Group Publisher of The Ashley Group. Paul, a resident of Chicago's North Shore, at one time was planning the renovation of his home. However, he quickly discovered problems locating credible professionals to help his dream become a reality. Well, Paul's dream did become a reality - it just happens to be a different dream now! Instead of Paul simply finishing his new home, he saw the need by consumers nationwide to have a complete home resource guide at their disposal. Thus, he created the distinct **Home Book** to fulfill consumers' needs for reliable and accessible home improvement information.

After three successful years, the **Home Book** drew the attention of Reed Business Information. In April 1999, Reed purchased it, and since then, the Home Book network has grown rapidly. By the end of 2001 there were **Home Books** in 14 markets nationwide. In addition to Connecticut/ Westchester County and Chicago, **Home Books** are available in Washington D.C., Detroit, South Florida, Colorado, Dallas Fort Worth, Los Angeles, Atlanta, San Diego, Philadelphia, Arizona, Las Vegas, Houston, Boston and North Carolina. By year's end, **Home Books** will be published in Seattle, Ohio and San Francisco, among other areas.

Public demand for quality home improvement services continues to increase. The Ashley Group recognizes this trend which is why we exact the same amount of dedication and hard work from ourselves that we expect from our **Home Book** advertisers. We hope our hard work rewards you with the quality craftsmanship you deserve, turning your dream house into a reality.

Congratulations on purchasing a **Home Book**. Now reward yourself by kicking back and delving through its pages. We hope you enjoy the inspiring ideas within.

Dana Felmly *Editor-in-Chief*

Laurence P. Maloney *Managing Editor*

Why
You Should
Use This
Book

Why You'll Want to Use the CONNECTICUT/WESTCHESTER COUNTY Home Book

At times, in this high-speed information-driven culture, we can easily become lost and disoriented. Where we find information, how we find it, and how credible this information is, has become critical to consumers everywhere.

The *Connecticut/Westchester County Home Book* recognizes and addresses these concerns, and provides ease of use and comfort to consumers looking to build, renovate or enhance their home. As a consumer, the anxiety of searching for trustworthy, experienced housing professionals can be overwhelming.

Relief is in Sight

The *Connecticut/Westchester County Home Book* puts an end to this stress. It offers you, the reader, a comprehensive, hands-on guide to building, remodeling, decorating, furnishing and landscaping a home in Connecticut/Westchester. The book also offers readers convenience and comfort.

Convenience

The *Connecticut/Westchester County Home Book* compiles the area's top home service providers with easy-to-read listings by trade. It also dissuades readers' fears of unreliable service providers by featuring many of the finest professionals available, specialists who rank among the top 10 of their respective fields in Connecticut/Westchester. Their outstanding work has netted them many awards in their fields. The other listings are recommendations made by these advertisers.

The goal of the *Connecticut/Westchester County Home Book* creators is to provide a high quality product that goes well beyond the scope of mere Yellow Pages. Its focus is to provide consumers with credible, reliable, and experienced professionals, accompanied by photographic examples of their work.

This crucial resource was unavailable to the founders of the *Connecticut/Westchester County Home Book* when they were working on their own home improvement projects. This lack of information spurred them on to create the book, and to assist other consumers in finding the proper professionals that suit their specific needs. Now, thanks to the team's entrepreneurial spirit, you have the *Connecticut/Westchester County Home Book* at your fingertips, to guide you on your home enhancement journey.

Comfort

Embrace this book, enjoy it and relish it, because at one time it didn't exist; but now, someone has done your homework for you. Instead of running all over town, you'll find in these pages:

* More than 700 listings of professionals, specializing in 40 different trades.

* Instructional information for choosing and working with architects, contractors, landscapers and interior designers.

* More than 1,000 photos inspiring innovative interior and exterior modeling ideas.

* A compilation of the area's top home enhancement service providers with easy-to-read listings by trade.

Excitement...*The Connecticut/Westchester County Home Book* can turn your dream into a reality!

Andrea M. Greifenberger

Andrea Greifenberger, *Publisher*

The premier resource provider for the luxury home market

About the Front Cover:
A majestic estate on a Connecticut
peninsula by Hobbs, Inc.

Contents

INTRODUCTION
11 Editors' Note
12 Why You Should Use
This Book
18 How to Use This Book
20 Design Update

54c ARCHITECTS
55 From Dream to
Drafting Table
61 Architects
74 Designing Dreams
97 Residential Designers
100 Architectal Illustrators

102a CUSTOM HOME BUILDERS
103 From the Ground Up
110 Custom Builders
118 Material Matters
169 Remodeling Specialists
176 Electrical Contractors
178 Roofing Specialists

180a INTERIOR DESIGNERS
181 Inner Expressions of Self
187 Interior Designers
210 Interior Design Spotlight

234a LANDSCAPING
235 Making the
Most of Nature
242 Landscape
Architects/Designers
248 Landscape Contractors
252a Timeline: Landscaping
Your Dream Home
256 Hardscape, Masonry
& Water Gardens
262 Swimming Pools/Spas
268 Decks &
Architectural Elements
273 Landscape Lighting
278 Automatic Gates

280a KITCHEN & BATH
281 Places to Unwind
288 Designers & Contractors
312a Timeline: Building Your
Dream Kitchen & Bath
314 New in the Showroom
316 Fixtures & Hardware
320 Appliances

Continued

22

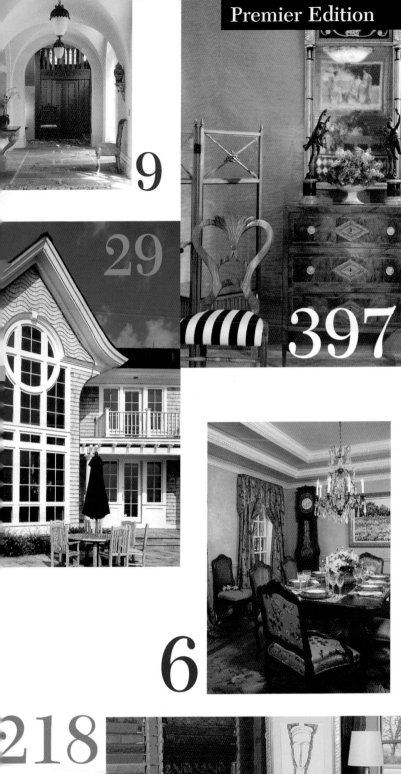

9

29

397

6

218

About the Back Cover:
A cozy living space created
by Diva Interiors, Inc.

Contents

**330a CUSTOM WOODWORKING,
METALWORKING,
HARDWARE & GLASS**
331 Paying Attention
to the Details
338 Custom Millwork
347 Custom Cabinets
354 Stairways
360 Hardware
360 Windows & Doors
367 Metalworking
371 Garage Doors

**374a FLOORING &
COUNTERTOPS**
375 Surfacing in Style
382 Carpeting & Area Rugs
386 Marble, Tile & Granite
390 Flooring

**396a HOME FURNISHING &
DECORATING**
397 The Finishing Pieces
404 Home Furnishings
411 Home Office,
Closet, Garage
417 Architectural Elements
419 Specialty Painters &
Wall Finishes

424 New in the Showroom
426 Window Coverings,
Fabric & Upholstery
431 Home Gyms
433 Billiards
436 Lighting
438 Fireplaces

440a ART & ANTIQUES
451 The Beauty of Rarity
446 Art Galleries
448 Framing
451 Antiques

**464a HOME THEATER &
TECHNOLOGY**
465 High Tech Comes Home
468 Home Theater Design
473 Integrated Home Systems

482a INDEXES
483 Alphabetical Index
486 Professional Index

482a

124

210

78

10

440a

How To Use

TABLE OF CONTENTS

Start here for an at-a-glance guide to the 12 tabbed categories and numerous subcategories. The book is organized for quick, easy access to the information you want, when you want it. The Table of Contents provides an introduction to the comprehensive selection of information.

INTERIOR DESIGN SPOTLIGHT

Dedicated to showcasing the elegance and vitality of some of the most beautiful residences in the area.

DESIGN UPDATE

Read what top home industry professionals think are the most exciting new styles, future trends and best ideas in their fields as we continue into the millennium. See even more inspiring photos of some of Connecticut/Westchester County's most beautiful, up-to-date luxury homes and landscapes. It's a visual feast, full of great ideas.

"HOW-TO" ARTICLES

Each tabbed section begins with a locally researched article on how to achieve the best possible result in your home building, remodeling, decorating or landscape project. These pages help take the fear and trepidation out of the process. You'll receive the kind of information you need to communicate effectively with professionals and to be prepared for the nature of the process. Each article is a step-by-step guide, aiding you in finding the materials you need in the order you'll need them..

This Book

DIVIDER TABS

Use the sturdy tabs to go directly to the section of the book you're interested in. A table of contents for each section's subcategories is printed on the front of each tab. Quick, easy, convenient.

LISTINGS

Culled from current, comprehensive data and qualified through careful local research, the listings are a valuable resource as you assemble the team of experts and top quality suppliers for your home project. We have included references to their ad pages throughout the book.

FEATURES

From Interior Design Spotlight to New in the Showroom, we've devoted attention to specific areas within the various sections. We've also gone in-depth, with feature articles in the Architects and Home Builders sections.

INDEXES

This extensive cross reference system allows easy access to the information on the pages of the book. You can check by alphabetical order or individual profession.

BEAUTIFUL VISUALS

The most beautiful, inspiring and comprehensive collections of homes and materials of distinction in Connecticut/Westchester County. On these pages, our advertisers present exceptional examples of their finest work. Use these visuals for ideas as well as resources.

Design

What are the hot ideas and attitudes that are shaping n
Update, where top local professionals tell what's happen

20

Update

SUBTLE HOME SYSTEMS

OPUS Audio/Video/Control, Inc.: "Many people believe
that even a modest home theater will dominate a multi-
use room. The homeowner, in consultation with the
architect, interior designer and builder, can make certain a
room's focus remains where it is desired, independent of
the scale of the room or the system."

Photo by **Scott Miles**

23

COMFORT AND LUXURY ARE FOREVER

Wright Brothers Builders: "Forget the seductiveness of the hottest trends. When it comes to being in vogue, comfort, luxury and quality never go out of style. Being at home with family and friends, enjoying the luxurious elegance and details inside and outside your home, combining quality materials with perfect craftsmanship – what could be more enduring?"

OLD WORLD AND MODERN

Girouard Associates, Inc.:"Luxury homebuyers are seeking masterful residences that blend Old World charm and traditional architecture with modern conveniences and amenities. Typical layouts include a master bedroom with a marble fireplace, spacious walk-in closets and an adjacent sitting area. Other desired features include mahogany-paneled libraries, workout/exercise rooms, billiards rooms, entertainment /recreation rooms, and large family and living rooms with high ceilings."

FIRST IMPRESSIONS COUNT

Colonial Collections of New England, Inc.:

"More people are realizing that the first impression about a home is what can first be seen from the outside. Accessories like an address marker or an upscale mailbox dress up any house. An address marker, stating the house number and the street name, adds elegance and that 'finishing touch' to a home."

24

BALANCING OLD AND NEW

Gullans & Brooks Associates, Inc.: "The challenge for today's architect, whether designing a kitchen renovation or a house from the ground up, is to find a balance between our modern lifestyle and our traditional roots. Consequently, the most successful project expresses a seamless integration of today's technology with a client's dreams and budget."

BASINS FOR TODAY

Sachs Plumbing Supplies:

"Homeowners want luxurious modern suites in the bathroom that thoughtfully combine form and function. Some of the best new designs use a large basin with its elegant elliptical form, and a drip catching rim that allows water to gently drain back into the basin."

SOFT AND COMFORTABLE

Jerry Liotta Decorative Artist: "Homeowners want maximum comfort in their libraries and reading rooms. This can be achieved through color coordinated wall techniques that provide monochromatic softness. Rich mahogany woodwork, complemented by hand-painted surface art on the walls with the look of suede, achieves a casual formality."

AT THE TOUCH OF A BUTTON

Audio Excellence: "Today, there is expanded exposure and usage of integrated home systems, or whole house automation. These systems are bringing together perimeter and internal security, environmental and lighting controls, and audio and home theater components under the control of a single system utilizing state-of-the-art components."

RENOVATED GARAGES

GarageTek: "With the price of home renovations today, many homeowners are taking a fresh look at upgrading a less expensive area of the house, their garage. Unfinished garage space can be transformed into an attractive, versatile, organized area that offers extra storage, living and work space."

UPSCALE WORKOUT

Home Gym Design, Inc.: "Gyms are coming home, literally. Creating custom fitness rooms in the home is the most convenient way to stay healthy and save precious time. People want home gyms that are not only equipped for their own unique needs and goals, but are also well decorated, enticing, motivating and comfortable. Home gyms are moving from dark, unfinished basements to bright, mirrored, soundproof rooms with great entertainment systems and a variety of fitness equipment adjacent to their master bedroom suites."

PREFERRED DETAILS
Cornerstone Building Services, LLC:
"Whether building a coastal estate or restoring a relic from the past, custom details are becoming a standard in fine home building. The traditional look of raised panel walls, wainscot, coffered ceilings, detailed moldings and natural wood trim are preferred by homeowners who want to enhance the beauty of their homes."

GETTING NATURAL
Le Barn:
"We're seeing more natural and rustic looks, utilizing materials like stone, linen, silk and fiber. Furniture is also less formal, incorporating warm wood tones and natural finishes."

Photo by **Scott Ash**

FROM MANICURED TO NATURAL

Femia Landscaping Inc.: "The demand is shifting from 'well-manicured' to a more natural landscape. With the right knowledge, expertise and creative intervention, a simple piece of ledge can be transformed into a functional, aesthetic part of the landscape."

OVERCOMING THE COMPLEXITY

The Electronics Connection: "HDTV, DVD, DTS …what does it all mean? With technology constantly changing, homeowners are becoming more knowledgeable about selecting systems that fit their needs, whether it's multi-room audio/video, home theaters, home automation or another aspect of home electronics technology."

CLEAN KITCHENS

Vigneau & Associates/Architects, LLC: "No two clients are the same, nor are any two projects. When remodeling a kitchen, off-white cabinets can make a kitchen bright and clean. Tiles and counters in hues of blue-green can continue a water theme. Hard, durable Brazilian cherry can be used in the kitchen to provide warmth."

Photo by **Olson Photographic**

THE GREENING OF THE HOME

Dujardin Design Associates, Inc.: "One of the most important trends in design today is sustainability and the use of 'green' materials, such as recycled and reforested woods and non-toxic paints and building materials. Many of the best designs incorporate natural light and open floor plans, with the use of natural fibers and sustainable materials, making for a healthy and distinct living space that still appeals to the eye."

SOHO NORTH

Gregory Allan Cramer & Co.: "'Soho chic' has come north to Westchester and Connecticut. Area homeowners are discovering fabulous pillows, accessories and antiques, among other treasures, that were once only the province of New York City dwellers."

Photo by **Dawn Glover**

Photo by **Jack Weinhold**

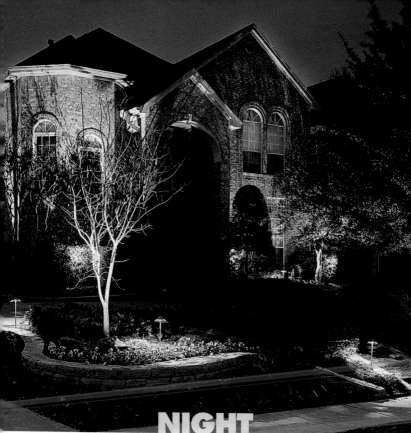

NIGHT COMES FIRST

Custom Landscape Lighting: "An experienced lighting designer has the ability to create an effect that will complement and transform darkness into beauty. It is a misconception that a pretty lighting fixture will yield a nice effect of light. The truth is, the right fixture should be chosen to give the proper effect, and the look of the fixture in the daylight should be secondary."

TODAY'S HOMEOWNER
American Development Corp.:
"Today's homeowners are more in tune with what they want, being more understanding of the process it takes to achieve the home they desire. The relationship forged by a client and builder, spending day after day together, allows people to grow, in turn improving the design process for each person."

WHOLEHOUSE SYSTEMS

HomeTronics Lifestyles: "Homeowners want home integration systems that fit their lifestyle. Wholehouse audio, for example, means you don't have to blast the stereo to listen to music throughout the house, or even install a CD player, radio, cassette player or receiver in every room. With one main equipment source and wires run to in-wall or bookshelf speakers, you can even listen to music on the deck or by the pool, using the same source. In-wall speakers please the eyes as well as the ears. They sit flush with the wall and can be painted to match. Outside, hide the speakers in terra cotta planters or disguise them in the garden as rocks."

Photo by Olson Photographic

LIVING MATERIALS

Architects Guild: "When we talk about architectural materials, we tend to speak about static materials such as masonry, lumber and glass. There is a great wealth of other materials that create architecture, materials that change with an environment to shape a place, such as stacked firewood under a shed roof, corn in a corn crib, and plates and glasses sitting in a drying rack. Rich design is manifest by things that undergo transformation. The clothing in a laundry room, heaped in baskets, washed, folded, and hung, become a prop in life's drama. Put them among stainless steel countertops and integral sinks, combined with a vinyl checkerboard floor pattern, and you have a living space that echoes the service rooms of classic estate residences."

WARM & NATURAL

Bedford Stone & Masonry Supply: "Natural...like it's been there forever, is what's popular in landscaping in our area. Whether creating a formal entrance, rustic wall, or a simple garden path, people are looking for warm colors and the natural look of stone."

BUILDING SMART

Kling Brothers Builders, Inc.: "Busy homeowners today want systems that save time. Smart homes can not only make your coffee, cook your meals, and light your path from garage to any room in the house, systems today can also provide wireless data ports in every room, so a homeowner can walk from room to room with a laptop and never get disconnected. Security systems alert owners from the moment a car approaches the driveway. And when it's time to relax, entertainment systems can provide central surround sound throughout the entire house. Even when nobody's home, such as on long vacations, temperature control systems save on fuel and can be programmed to heat up the house the moment before the owners arrive home."

AGE OF THE INDIVIDUAL

Kitchens By Deane: "It's the time of the individual and personal touches – combinations of finishes and textures, multiple work stations, second sinks, cabinetry and appliances to suit your personal lifestyle."

LIKE A MANET
Handwright Gallery & Framing: "Be it for the discriminating collector or the amateur photographer, museum-quality materials make a difference in framing, whether the frame is for a unique shadow-box, a child's first masterpiece, or an Impressionist painting purchased from auction."

30

KITCHENS OF NEW ENGLAND

Kitchen & Bath Center: "People today spend a great amount of time in their kitchens. The kitchen is seen as a gathering room that happens to be functional. The preferred kitchen is warm and welcoming with a classic New England look."

ELEGANCE REVISITED
A Matter of Style: "Attention to architectural details, including layered moldings, handmade carvings, decorative accents and state-of-the-art appliances, creates 'fine kitchen furniture.' Woods are finished in rich glazes and accented by custom paint colors. Architectural craftsmanship of the past has elegantly returned."

NOT JUST ANOTHER BRICK IN THE WALL

Christianson Lee Studios, Inc.: "Murals are enhancing walls, ceilings, and niches in a variety of ways. A small foyer has become the open vista of a seaside garden. A dark dining room was brightened by a panoramic landscape of the English countryside. An oddly-shaped attic bedroom was transformed into a child's underwater fantasy. Murals can be bold and dramatic like the classical Renaissance style, or quiet and romantic in the manner of 18th century English landscape painting."

Photo by **Olson Photographic**

BRINGING THE PAST TO LIGHT

Benchmark Builders, LLC: "When it comes to remodeling, homeowners want to open their living spaces and use rich architectural detail to add charm. The warmth of hand-planed millwork, plaster, and wide-plank floors are increasingly coveted as essential. Homeowners want the character and custom detailing of the past to infuse the space and light of today."

THE TEST OF TIME

Huestis Tucker Architects, LLC: "The influx of new technology is changing a lot of what goes into today's houses, but it hasn't changed what most people want from their house. People want a home that is comfortable and livable with a little bit of elegance and classic, timeless detailing. The trick is to marry the technology into the design so that when it is all done you feel like you are in a house that has already stood the test of time."

OLD STYLE HOMES

Turnkey Associates: "Old style features and qualities are what people are looking for. They want to have all-new construction and amenities with all the style and charm of yesteryear, a new house that looks and feels 100 years old."

DRAWING CONCLUSIONS

The Red Sun Studio: "Drawing has always been a fundamental and ever-present companion throughout our history, and it is an art form that has been used in home decorating for centuries. It has become increasingly evident that the ability to manipulate computer software has overshadowed the all-important and very critical ability to draw by hand. Although the computer certainly has its place in art, it isn't nor should it ever be a substitute, but rather a complement to the creative process. Drawing will always be an irreplaceable and critical element in the communication of thought, vision and creative passion."

Drawing by **André Paul Junget**

SIMPLICITY OUT OF COMPLEXITY

Robin McGarry & Associates: "The information age has transformed our lives to unprecedented stress levels. The need for spaces that emit harmony, balance and tranquility has become a priority, and the quest for sumptuous rooms filled with expensive things has lost its appeal. People need more simplified spaces, paring away unnecessary details and keeping the things they love. Simplicity can be a complex process, but it yields a serene vision and tranquil space, a place to rejuvenate the soul after an intense day of work and responsibilities."

Photo by **Bob Capazzo**

33

PERIOD PIECES

G. Sergeant Antiques:
"Period accessories such as candlesticks, tea caddies and decanters lend elegance and value to any collection. Home-owners today have a vast array of materials available to them, including bronze, ormolu, brass, marble and rock crystal, each with its own charm and style."

Photo by **Olson Photographic**

CHOOSING UNIQUE COMBINATIONS

Audrey Morgan Interiors, Inc.: "Homeowners are creating a modern look by combining antiques with abstract art. Whether it's the textures, colors or media of fabrics, the diversity of lighting options, or the array of carpeting and flooring possibilities, the defining term is choice."

BETTER THAN A PRIVATE BOX

A.P. Savino, LLC: "Homeowners want their building projects to be like going to the symphony. The com-poser (architect), conductor (builder), and musicians (tradesmen and manufacturers) work in harmony for the enjoyment of the audience (homeowner). All interact in a creative endeavor of problem solving."

Photo by **Walter Putrycz**

CRYSTAL CLEAR ELEGANCE

American Frameless:
"As so many baths are now designed with the beauty, comfort and expanse of a contemporary spa, the aesthetic application of structural glass for bath and shower enclosures is of great and rising significance. Frameless glass enclosures provide an understated elegance and visual clarity in today's designs."

ROARING AHEAD

Davenport Contracting: "Clients want their home to look 'like it's been there forever.' Incorporating certain materials highlights craftsmanship from a bygone era. Examples of this include plaster with oak beams, paneling, hand-cut rusticated siding, and chimney designs featuring a brick and stone pattern. The 1920s is an era often looked to for inspiration."

KEY WORD: SIMPLIFY!

SBD Kitchens, LLC: "Clients are looking for much simpler design, for a kitchen that welcomes friends and family in a warm and informal way. Homeowners are selecting traditional designs, like the 1920s door styles with recessed panel insets in quality woods. Key design words are casual, cozy, simple, warm."

Photo by **Peter Leach** Photography

KNOWING ASIA

Asian Collectibles & Design:

"A lot of people have the wrong idea about Asian furniture and art. The early pieces in China were always contemporary-looking, not ornate or lacquered in any way. And early pieces never used nails; they either simply fit together or used pins (an inspiration for the Arts & Crafts style). What's most important are the woods used. The Chinese have a tendency to stain their woods various colors, so the way to identify a wood is by the grain. Hong mu translates to the West as a redwood (or blackwood), and a yellow flower pearwood called huang hua-li is also popular."

NO WASTED SPACE

Palladio Interior Design:

"The 'living room' in most American homes has become an obsolete idea. This is the space that we simply walk past to get to another area of the house. These truly wasted spaces can be turned into warm and inviting libraries, music rooms or offices, to the delight of the homeowner."

Photo by **Olson Photographic**

CASUAL ELEGANCE

Building Designs, LLC: "Casual comfort is what people want to incorporate into their home design today. They want to do away with the formal living areas and make one large, great room where there is more family interaction. The idea is to make this room the most usable room in the home, dressing it with casual elegance, but making it functional as well."

LIKE A SYMPHONY

Blansfield Builders, Inc.: "The trend in construction today is all about teamwork. The best results come from a well-orchestrated, collaborative effort from all members of the design and construction fields. Each home varies with the individual tastes of the home-owner, but the execution of design is all about details and the use of the latest products, together with the strengths of the design/ construction team."

DISTINCTIVE SUITES

Grayson Construction: "The trend toward a master bedroom suite has never been stronger or more in demand. Homeowners want comfort and function in a luxurious space. Carpeting and colors can unify the rooms, while they still retain their own ambiance. For example, the bedroom may be filled with mahogany English antiques and art, while the sitting room is furnished with French antiques and soft silk pillows."

THE ANTIQUE FEEL

Kitchen & Bath Creations: "The newest trends are Old World. The feel of antique furniture pieces is extremely popular in the Northeast. The mixing of heights and colors give a more personalized and custom appeal. The proper placement of decorative appliqués and molding treatments can change the look of any kitchen."

Photo by **Jennifer Simpson**

LET'S GO ANTIQUING

Harbor View Center for Antiques: "Homeowners enjoy visiting upscale antique centers. These centers have evolved from their flea market origins into today's show-rooms, where clients can view merchandise of various periods and styles. Now, what traditionally took days or even weeks to view can be done in one afternoon."

LANDSCAPING IN STYLE

Barchella Contracting Co., Inc.: "Today's homeowners seek serenity from the demands of daily life. To achieve this, landscapes must play along with the house aesthetically. Formal homes should be surrounded by a formal landscape, with mitered, symmetrical, tightly pruned plants. A looser, billowing, bushy landscape would suit less formal homes, lending them more grace and filling space."

SERENE GARDENS

Fishe Bros Merchants of Interest, LLC: "The urge to build a private sanctuary is stronger than ever, and where else can you find that kind of serenity, but in your garden? Today's homeowner is bringing that theme indoors. After all, an armillary is equally beautiful in a garden room as well as a sunroom. There are more options than ever for container gardeners – fiberglass, cast-aluminum, polyethylene, terra cotta, and glazed pottery – something in every weight and style."

THE MATRIX OF LIFE

Eric Michaels Architects: "Clients often ask how they can get proper flow into their homes. Proper flow is achieved through the careful organization of real-life requirements and practical living spaces. It's important to talk about the matrix of life that occurs in all homes: how we transition between utilitarian and formal functions, and the proximity of public and private areas. By carefully crafting where and how these intersections occur, the home will achieve a balance and lend itself to feelings of comfort and flow."

THE IMPORTANCE OF COLOR

Pierre Gagnon Interiors: "Color is everything. It is light, shadow, how we get up in the morning, how we respond to objects surrounding us. It's the music of the eye, the core of our soul. Good color treatments are like the discovery of a stained glass in the silence of a cathedral. They work together, allowing the other to be."

Photo courtesy of Viking

SEAMLESS STYLE

Albano Appliance & Service, LLC: "Today's kitchens are continually becoming more customized with specialty built-in items that give each space a unique look and feel. Kitchen connoisseurs love 'hidden surprises.' Many new designs incorporate an overall seamlessness or integration between the appliances and cabinetry, especially with refrigeration items, dishwashers, warming drawers and hoods. A built-in coffee system, for example, not only looks sleek, but also frees up counterspace. There is also a trend toward combining professional cooking equipment (which tends to be bulky) with the built-in look."

Photo by **Bob Capazzo**

YOUR OWN STYLE

Beautiful Home: "Homes should be true expressions of yourself. One of the best ways to accomplish your own style is through custom-designed furnishings. These one-of-a-kind pieces are uniquely your own. Through custom designs, people are collecting the antiques of tomorrow with their own personal history of today."

A TIMELESS AMERICAN

Brad Demotte Architects: "Shingle is one of the timeless architectural styles that will never lose its appeal. It lends itself easily to reinterpretation, while still retaining the essence of the style. A renewed interest in traditional American vernacular styles signifies a return to traditional detailing, both on the exterior and throughout the interior."

SAFE HAVENS

Contadino Architects: "'Home' has become a comfortable safe haven that offers refuge from our complex, hectic world and lifestyles. People want living spaces that reflect the traditional styles and values of the past, while fulfilling their need for simplicity, functionality and self-expression. Through changing times, architectural design should accommodate the different stages of people's lives."

THINKING STORAGE

Classy Closets: "Homeowners want a smarter way to get organized faster. Customized closet and storage solutions are now offering an elegant and sleek way to do so, as they are designed around the homeowner's needs. The accessories are right where homeowners want them, and clothes storage is given ample space."

SOPHISTICATED OWNERS

Sean O'Kane, AIA Architect, PC: "Today, there is a greater emphasis on detail and quality of fixtures, fittings and finish across the board. Homeowners are increasingly sophisticated in their taste for design and architecture, and they demand from home building professionals greater knowledge and experience with historical styles."

Photo by **Brian Urso Photography**

MAKE IT LESS HECTIC

ACI General Contracting, Inc.: "Today's home-owners look to their builder/contractor to create living spaces to accommodate their hectic lifestyles. They want spacious family room/kitchen combinations where the whole family can gather, luxurious master baths for pampering, and home offices wired to accommodate today's technology."

TREASURE CHESTS

Briggs House Antiques:
"To dress up their living areas, homeowners are looking to furniture that's weighty without being ostentatious. Chests of drawers such as the classic Louis Phillipe may be often used in an entry foyer with a mirror, but can also be found in the living room with an oil painting above, matching the buffet's rich color and lending a glow to the area. Some even use it in the bedroom where it was originally intended to be placed."

42

TANKS FOR THE BIG FISH

House of Fins: "Homeowners are asking for aquariums today on a grand scale. Designs can go as large as 15 ft. long coral reef tanks that cost $150,000 to design, install and stock, complete with 1,500 lbs. of live rock, anemone and other invertebrates. Most large-scale designs involve salt-water tropical fish. The amount of water involved is staggering, as well. A 900-gallon marine aquarium costing $100,000 is high-end, but not an entirely unusual request."

COMFORT, SIMPLICITY, FUNCTION

Connecticut Design Center: "Our clients are seeking the basics of comfort, simplicity and function. Comfort speaks for itself – you need to have comfort in your seating. Simplicity means uncluttered with a strong single focus. Function is how you live and how you do what you do in each of your spaces."

STYLES TRUE TO TRADITION

Moisan Architects:
"While designs may tend toward traditional residential architecture, the Classical style can be carefully blended with the present day vernacular. A design or renovation that seamlessly blends with the desired architectural tradition is of primary importance."

HISTORIC HOMES

Karp Associates, Inc.: "Mixing Old World charm with New World conveniences is what families are looking for today. Expanding kitchen and dining rooms, or adding a three-car garage, a family room and a children's playroom can better accommodate modern families. Classic details such as antique oak floors, older-style doors with glass knobs, raised panel walls and extensive moldings are just a few touches that help preserve the greater elegance and special atmosphere not commonly found in a newly built house."

Photo by **David Todd**

ONE-COLOR BACKDROP

Paramount Stone: "Monochromatic use of texture, with the mixing of medium, allows interest and design without the permanent introduction of multiple color palettes. With the permanent work remaining timeless, the space gains the freedom to take on new dimensions with the addition and deletion of color in fabrics, wallpaper and other accents."

FREESTANDING PIECES

Rose Adams Design Cabinetry: "Dramatic color and fine, freestanding furniture are extending the domain of the kitchen in homes today. 'Behind-the-doors' kitchens are a thing of the past. Handcrafted, unfitted elements, such as freestanding hutches, enhance the kitchen's connection to the overall home décor."

Photo by **Tim Lee**

PRIORITIES AT HOME

The Connecticut Fencemen, Inc.: "Privacy, security, protection and aesthetics are the priorities of most homeowners these days. Especially popular are automated driveway gate systems with high tech access controls."

44

UPGRADING IN STYLE

Fenimore Plumbing Supply Showroom: "Renovations in bathrooms today are featuring an upgrade to high style, high end fixtures. Homeowners are taking small bathrooms and transforming them into luxurious spacious bathrooms. They are finishing these rooms with pedestal sinks, custom countertops, vanities, water closets, and unique and hard-to-find faucets and accessories."

SAFE AND COMFORTABLE

Prosperity Interiors, Inc.: "The recent strong desire for security and comfort has made upholstered walls fashionable. There is a trend toward beautiful moldings, elaborate wainscoting and ornate paneling. People today want to feel the safety and stability of the past, which makes traditional furniture styles, both fine reproductions and antiques, the style of choice for today's elegant homes."

TODAY'S KITCHEN & BATH

Creative Bath of Danbury: "Homeowners today are creating the kitchens and baths they've always imagined with features such as whirlpools, body sprays, pedestals and under-mount sinks. All it takes is the right combination of design, color, function and quality."

Photo by **Rick Scanlan**

UNTOLD TREASURES

Bloom Design, LLC: "When client needs and the designer's insight mesh, wonderful interior spaces result – spaces and furniture that can be imagined but not easily found."

COLOR & LIGHT

Vandamm Interiors: "Although traditional styles will always be popular, variations to these themes can be realized by experimenting with the subtleties of color. Add to that the effects of variety of lighting techniques, and homeowners will find it is an exciting time to be giving their homes a new look."

OPEN FOR VIEWING

Austin Patterson Disston, Architects: "Many Georgian houses are defined by a series of arches that afford views from the library through the foyer to the living room. Homeowners who enjoy entertaining often for large gatherings may want the library, generally an enclosed space, to be open to the dining room and foyer, allowing for a more expansive flow. This openness creates an easy, comfortable setting for the homeowner to pursue a passion, whether it be reading, playing pool, or some other activity."

A TOUCH OF EUROPE

Wilton Lamp & Shade: "Old World European looks seem to be making a reappearance. Especially with crystal and iron combinations, Tuscan finishes such as bronze, and patinas with gold and silver leaf are being used to show depth, age, and that European feel."

Photo by **Durston Saylor**

Photo by **Georg Müeller-Nicholson**

GRACE BEYOND TIME

Budd & Allardyce Interiors, LLC: "More than ever, people today want a home that is not only functional, but also gracious and timeless. Homeowners are more appreciative of the effects of professional creative design to help achieve these goals."

PAYING ATTENTION TO DREAMS

Chary & Sigüenza Architects, LLP: "Homeowners want an architect that exhibits the keen attentiveness required to translate their dreams and wishes into structures that are timeless and enduring."

LUXURY BY THE POOL

Construction Concepts: "A guest/pool house can be as comfortable and extraordinary as a permanent home. Bedroom suites equipped with full baths and built-in furniture, large central great rooms with fireplaces and luxurious stone floors, open kitchens with beautiful poolside views – all features of a pool house that affords complete privacy for guests and homeowners alike."

Photo by **Rosemarie Stiller**

BACK TO THE GARDEN

Walpole Woodworkers:
"Homeowners' passion for gardening is looking up. With exciting new options in handcrafted garden arbors, obelisks, lattice panels, pergolas and trellis, enthusiasts can create arrays of color at eye level. A favorite climbing plant intertwined with a graceful spindle arbor is the height of beauty."

GOOD AS GOLD

Thornwood Architectural Millwork:
"'The woodworker is the goldsmith of the trades,' is an old adage. In the kitchen, library, entrance and dining room, woodwork stands out. From quiet painted paneling to spectacular vaneers and finishes, never before has such a range of woods, detailing and design been available. Whether sleek cutting-edge, or period and classic, woodwork is an exciting and durable element throughout today's interiors."

LOOK UP AND DREAM

E.M. Rose Builders, Inc.: "The decoration of ceilings suffered a serious decline in the 20th century. Ironically, with a decline in the quality of building materials in the 1990s there came a renaissance in the use of plaster moldings and design motifs. With the return of plaster as a finish material, we have seen a resurgence in the decoration and detailing of ceilings. Look up and ask your architect what he or she can imagine!"

49

FEEL THE DIFFERENCE
Drexel S. Frye, Inc.: "Cabinet buyers are paying more attention to the fine details of quality cabinets: the inclusion of dovetail joints, the feel of the drawers closing by themselves, the touch of fine wood finishes. Whether creating a $50,000 kitchen or a $150,000 kitchen, the most important principle is the quality of the furniture. Fancy hardware for blind corners that folds out to a set of shelves, hidden drawers behind pilasters for spice racks, wine coolers, under-counter refrigerators, foot-operated plumbing for faucets, and pot-filling faucets located above the range are just a few of the modern conveniences people are integrating into their kitchens today."

A PERSONAL HOME
Geitz Design Associates, LLC, Architects: "Whether it be a coffee bar in the master bedroom, an ice cream parlor for the children, or a computerized lighting system, the need among homeowners to create a personal environment is always evident."

FIRST IMPRESSIONS
Ed's Garage Doors, Ltd.: "Often the first view of the home as you pull up to it is the garage doors. Garage doors no longer have to be plain, basic paneled doors. The top-of-the-line choice is Honduran mahogany, which doesn't need to be cut with the grain and almost always yields an excellent piece of wood. Other popular wood choices include western red cedar and Spanish cedar, African mahogany, and Meranti mahogany, a coarse textured wood with a wavy interlocked grain pattern, which has a pale creamy-red color and is light but strong."

BUILDING DREAMS
Clarke Builders, Inc.: "Homeowners today want timeless, classic designs. They also want their homes built to architects' plans and specifications, whether building their dream home or making their current residence a dream home."

NATURAL OUTDOOR LOOKS
Giorgio's Upholstery Interior Decorating, Inc.: "Bring the outdoors inside with classic natural materials. White rough marble fireplaces with emerald pearl granite mantels, combined with hardwood floors and safari prints in the upholstery can give a room that outdoor look."

THE BUILT-IN EFFECT

Brindisi & Yaroscak: "Today, we are seeing more knock-downs and renovations than new construction. Average house sizes are starting to come down as well, reflecting the losses in the financial markets. As a result, people want to utilize and maximize space as much as possible. They're doing that by specifying custom built-in cabinetry in many of the rooms. In mud rooms, built-ins store boots, jackets and hats. Built-ins afford a place for videotapes, DVDs, and audio/video equipment in home entertainment centers. Libraries use built-in cabinetry to store computer equipment, while kitchens take advantage of built-ins to hide small appliances."

ADD OBJECTS TO THE MIX

Diana Sawicki Interior Design, Inc.: "Our lives today are an eclectic mix of so many different elements, and our homes should reflect all of our interests. As a result of this complexity, I advocate a mix of contemporary, antique and mid-century objects, as a natural development of today's lifestyle. The current trend includes the use of 1940s office furniture for rooms throughout the home. Steel f actory and store stools from this period are now being used around kitchen counters, and aluminum lamps are being used for home offices and desks."

CONCRETE ART

Connecticut Bomanite System: "When planning patios, walkways, driveways, pool decks and court-yards, homeowners want a surface that's an expression of their lifestyle and personality, of elegance and creativity. New surfacing materials today, replicating slate, granite, lime-stone, sandstone, cobblestone and other natural stones, are far more than just imprinted and colored concrete. Because of their many patterns and textures, these paving materials can be used as a palette for art."

SOUTH AMERICAN BEAUTY

51

Phoenix Hardwood Flooring: "Exotic wood species have become more available and less cost prohibitive in recent years. Jatoba, Santos mahogany and many other South American woods are now milled to standard flooring specifications. These 'exotics' offer varied and vibrant colors, and they are generally much harder and more dimension-ally staple than North American species."

STAIRWAY TO ELEGANCE

New England Stair Co.: "Today's home buyers realize that the stairway is often a main focal point of the home, which is why grand scale and dramatic detail are becoming more popular. The box newel, because of its stately appearance and ornamentation possibilities, is in great demand. Increasingly, homeowners are specifying exotic wood species and specialized stairway and balustrade designs. The growing selection of balustrade components dwarfs that which was available only a few years ago."

Home Books

12 Tips
For Pursuing Quality

1. Assemble a Team of Professionals During Preliminaries.
Search out and value creativity.

2. Educate Yourself on What to Expect.
But also be prepared to be flexible in the likely event of set-backs.

3. Realize the Value and Worth of Design.
It's the best value for your investment.

4. Be Involved in the Process.
It's more personally satisfying and yields the best results.

5. Bigger Isn't Better – Better is Better.
Look for what produces quality and you'll never look back.

6. Understand the Process.
Be aware of products, prices and schedules, to be a productive part of the creative team.

7. Present a Realistic Budget.
Creative, workable ideas can be explored.

8. Create the Right Environment.
Mutual respect, trust and communication get the job done.

9. There Are No Immediate Miracles.
Time is a necessary component in the quest for quality.

10. Have Faith in Yourself.
Discover your own taste and style.

11. Plan for the Future.
Lifestyles and products aren't static.

12. Do Sweat the Details.
Establish the discipline to stay organized.

CONNECTICUT/
WESTCHESTER COUNTY
HOME
BOOK

1234 Summer St., Stamford, CT, 06905 203-323-7400 fax 203-326-5177

Free Product
&
Service Information

By filling out the survey below and selecting any number of advertisers, you will receive of a copy of a Home Book in one of the US markets listed below — a $39.95 value free of charge. Just check the box next to the market of the Home Book you'd like to receive. (There is only a limited amount of books available, so please fill out this card and send it in as soon as possible.)

CONNECTICUT/ WESTCHESTER COUNTY
HOME BOOK

Name _____

Address _____

City _____

State _____ Zip_____

Phone_____

Fax_____

Email _____

☐ I would like to receive one 2002 Home Book from the market checked off here:

☐ Chicago   ☐ Los Angeles   ☐ Detroit

☐ New York   ☐ South Florida   ☐ Colorado

☐ Atlanta   ☐ Dallas/Ft. Worth ☐ Philadelphia

☐ Arizona   ☐ San Diego   ☐ Las Vegas

☐ Houston   ☐ North Carolina   ☐ Boston

☐ Ohio   ☐ Washington, D.C. ☐ Kansas City

☐ Connecticut/Westchester County ☐ Orange County

How often do you need and use Home Book-oriented professionals?_____
_____
_____
_____
_____

Have you contacted any professionals you saw featured in the this book? _____ Yes _____ No

If so, who?_____
_____
_____
_____

Do you like the size and format of the Home Book?
___ Yes ___ No

How did you receive a copy of this book?
___ Bought in store   ___ Received in mail
___ Specifically ordered ___ Sent by a friend
___ Other _____

Besides your own area, what other areas of the US would you like to see a Home Book printed in?
_____
_____
_____

Would you be interested in seeing next year's volume of your area's Home Book, or do you think this has offered you all the information you need?
___ Yes, I'd like to see next year's book
___ No, this book was sufficient.

What aspect of the book would encourage you to order other editions?_____
_____
_____
_____

Would you be interested in participating in a focus group for the Home Books?
___ Yes ___ No

Would you be interested in participating in an advisory council for the Home Books?
___ Yes ___ No

Please be sure to fold and seal the envelope before mailing. If you prefer, please fax both sides to 630-288-7949, Attn: Editorial Dept.

Be sure to fill out the survey completely to receive your free Home Book!

NO POSTAGE
NECESSARY
IF MAILED
IN THE
UNITED STATES

BUSINESS REPLY MAIL
FIRST-CLASS MAIL   PERMIT NO. 18   DES PLAINES IL

POSTAGE WILL BE PAID BY ADDRESSEE

The Ashley Group

PO BOX 5080
Des Plaines IL 60019-9583

oto courtesy of **Gullans & Brooks Architects**
oto by **John Kane**

ARCHITECTS

55
**From Dream to
Drafting Table**

61
Architects

74
Designing Dreams

Masterpiece – THE SYNTHESIS OF
FLOW, ACTIVITY AND DESIRE
A UNIQUE AND DISTINCTLY CRAFTED
WORK OF ART

WE CREATE ARCHITECTURE THAT WILL
SHAPE AND SIMPLIFY YOUR LIFE
ENVIRONMENTS THAT ARE STIMULATING
AND SENSUAL
CLASSIC ELEGANCE THAT EXCEEDS
EVERY EXPECTATION
... YOUR MASTERPIECE

RESIDENTIAL • COMMERCIAL • RESTORATION

ERIC MICHAELS

ARCHITECTS, LLC

115 MAIN STREET • WESTPORT, CT
203-221-3005

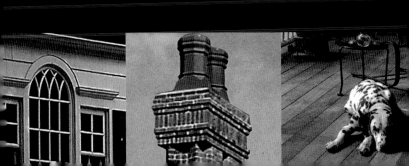

BANKS
DESIGN
ASSOCIATES
LTD

CT
SOUTHPORT
203.259.8899

ME
PORTLAND
207.781.8899

w w w . b a n k s d e s i g n a s s o c i a t e s . c o m

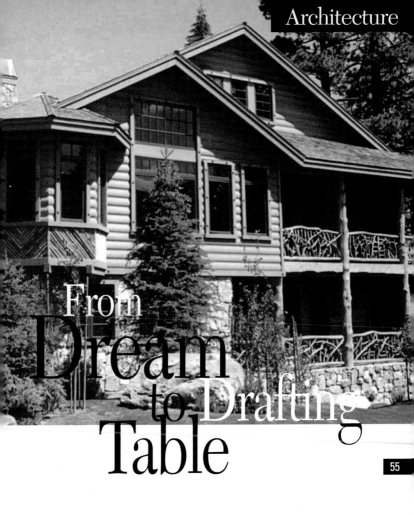

From Dream to Drafting Table

Architects are at once artists and engineers. At their best, they are dreamers of extraordinary vision. They pride themselves on knowing how their clients want to live, even when that vision may be hard to articulate. An architect's art is supported by strong grounding in technical knowledge: mechanical engineering, materials, finishes, and environmental awareness.

When you hire an architect, you hire a professional who will see the building process through from start to finish. Site checks are standard operating procedure for architects; you won't have to worry about a design that looks great in blueprints, but is ruined in the execution. We have the privilege of featuring the finest of these creative, technically proficient problem solvers to help you bring your ultimate home to life.

Photo courtesy of **Chary & Sigüenza Architects**
Photo by **Georg Mueller-Nicholson Photography**

YOUR OWN DREAM TEAM

Whether you're building your dream home in the city, a second vacation home, or remodeling your home in the suburbs, it takes a team to design and build a high quality residential project. A team of an architect, builder, interior designer, kitchen and bath designer, and landscape architect/designer should be assembled very early in the process. When these five professionals have the opportunity to collaborate before ground is broken, you'll reap the rewards for years to come. Their blend of experience and ideas can give you insights into the fabulous possibilities of your home and site you never considered. Their association will surely save you time, money and eventually frustration.

THE ARCHITECT – MAKING THE DREAM REAL

Licensed architects provide three basic, easily defined tasks. First, they design, taking into account budget, site, owner's needs and existing house style. Second, they produce the necessary technical drawings and specifications to accomplish the desires of their clients, and explain to a contractor in adequate detail what work needs to be done. Lastly, architects participate in the construction process. This straightforward mission requires more than education.

It requires listening. The best architects have gained their status by giving their clients exactly what they want – even when those clients have difficulty articulating what that is. How? By creatively interpreting word pictures into real pictures. By eliciting the spirit of the project and following that spirit responsibly as they develop an unparalleled design.

It requires experience. Significant architects, such as those included in your Home Book, maintain a reputation for superiority because their buildings are stunningly conceived, properly designed and technically sound. If a unique, steeply pitched roof was custom-designed for you by a licensed architect with an established reputation, you can be confident that it is buildable.

Suggestions by an experienced architect can add value and interest to your new home or remodeling project. He or she may suggest you wire your home for the technology of the future, frame up an attic for future use as a second floor, or build your countertops at varying levels to accommodate people of different heights.

This area is blessed with many talented architects. It's not uncommon for any number of them to be working on a luxury vacation retreat in another country or a unique second home in another state. Their

WHY YOU
SHOULD
WORK WITH
A TOP
ARCHITECT

1. They are expert problem solvers. A talented architect can create solutions to your design problems, and solve the problems that stand in the way of achieving your dream.

2. They have creative ideas. You may see a two-story addition strictly in terms of its function - a great room with a master suite upstairs. An architect immediately applies a creative eye to the possibilities.

3. They provide a priceless product and service. A popular misconception about architects is that their fees make their services an extravagance. In reality, an architect's fee represents a small percentage of the overall building cost.

vision and devotion to design set a standard of excellence for dynamic and uncompromising quality.

WORKING WITH AN ARCHITECT

The best relationships are characterized by close collaborative communication. The architect is the person you're relying on to take your ideas, elevate them to the highest level, and bring them to life in a custom design that's never been built before. So take your time in selecting the architect. It's not unusual for clients to spend two or three months interviewing prospective architects.

In preparation for the interview process, spend time fine-tuning your ideas. Put together an Idea Notebook (See the sidebar 'Compile an Idea Notebook'). Make a wish list that includes every absolute requirement and every fantasy you've ever wanted in a home. Visit builders' models to discover what 3,000 sq. ft. looks like in comparison to 6,000 sq. ft., how volume ceilings impact you or what loft living feels like. Look at established and new neighborhoods to get ideas about the relationship between landscaping and homes, and what level of landscaping you want.

GOOD COMMUNICATION SETS THE TONE

The first meeting is the time to communicate all of your desires for your new home or remodeling project, from the abstract to the concrete. You're creating something new, so be creative in imprinting your spirit and personality on the project. Be bold in expressing your ideas, even if they are not fully developed or seem unrealistic. Share your Idea Notebook and allow the architect to keep it as plans are being developed. Be prepared to talk about your lifestyle, because the architect will be trying to soak up as much information about you and your wishes as possible.

• Be frank about your budget. Although some clients are unrestricted by budgetary concerns, most must put some control on costs, and good architects expect and respect this. Great ideas can be achieved on a budget, and the architect will tell you what can be achieved for your budget.

• However, sticking to your budget requires tremendous self-discipline. If there's a luxury you really want, (a second laundry room, a built-in aquarium) it's probably just as practical to build it into your design from the outset, instead of paying for it in a change order once building has begun.

• Ask lots of questions. Architects of luxury homes in

WHAT'S YOUR LIFESTYLE?

(Your architect will want to know.)
• Who lives in your house now?
• Who will live there in the future?
• Who visits and for how long?
• Do you like traditional, contemporary or eclectic design?
• Why are you moving or remodeling?
• What aspects of your current home need to be improved upon?
• Do you like functional, minimalist design, or embellishments and lots of style?
• Do you entertain formally or informally?
• How much time will you spend in the master bedroom? Is it spent reading, watching TV, working or exercising?
• What are the primary functions of the kitchen?
• Do you need a home office?
• Do you like lots of open space or little nooks and crannies?
• What kind of storage do you need?

57

the area are committed to providing their clients with information up front about the design process, the building process and their fees. These architects respect the sophistication and intelligence of their clientele, but do not necessarily expect them to have a high level of design experience or architectural expertise. Educating you is on their agenda.

• What is the breadth of services? Although this information is in your contract, it's important to know the level of services a firm will provide. There is no set standard and you need to be sure if an architect will provide the kind of services you want – from basic "no-frills" through "full service."

• Find out who you will be working with. Will you be working with one person or a team? Who will execute your drawings?

• Ask for references. Speak to past and current clients who built projects similar to yours. Ask for references from contractors with whom the architect works.

• Does the architect carry liability insurance?

• Ask to see examples of the architect's work – finished homes, job sites, and architectural plans. Does the work look and feel like what you want?

• Find out how many projects the architect has in progress. Will you get the attention you deserve?

• Decide if you like the architect. For successful collaboration, there must be a good personal connection. As you both suggest, reject, and refine ideas, a shared sense of humor and good communication will be what makes the process workable and enjoyable. Ask yourself, "Do I trust this person to deliver my dream and take care of business in the process?" If the answer is anything less than a strong and sure, "yes!," keep looking.

UNDERSTANDING ARCHITECTS' FEES AND CONTRACTS

Fees and fee structures vary greatly among architects, and comparing them can be confusing, even for the experienced client. Architects, like licensed professionals in other fields, are prohibited from setting fees as a group and agreeing on rates. They arrive at their fees based on:

(A) an hourly rate
(B) lump sum total
(C) percentage of construction cost
(D) dollars per square foot
(E) size of the job
(F) a combination of the above

The final quoted fee will include a set of services

COMPILE AN IDEA NOTEBOOK

It's hard to put an idea into words, but so easy to show with a picture. Fill a good-sized notebook with plain white paper, tuck a roll of clear tape and a pair of scissors into the front flap, and you've got an Idea Notebook. Fill it with pictures, snapshots of homes you like, sketches of your own, little bits of paper that show a color you love, notes to yourself on your priorities and wishes. Circle the parts of the pictures and make spontaneous notes: "Love the finish on the cabinets," "Great rug," "Don't want windows this big." Show this to your architect, and other team members. Not only will it help keep ideas in the front of your mind, but will spark the creativity and increase understanding of the entire team.

that may vary greatly from architect to architect. From a "no frills" to a "full service" bid, services are vastly different. For example, a no frills agreement budgets the architect's fee at two to seven percent of the construction cost; a full service contract budgets the architect's fee at 12 to 18 percent. Some firms include contractor's selection, bid procurement, field inspections, interior cabinetry, plumbing and lighting design, and punch list. Others don't.

One concrete basis for comparison is the architectural drawings. There can be a vast difference in the number of pages of drawings, the layers of drawings and the detail level of the specifications. Some include extra sketchbooks with drawings of all the construction details and in-depth written specs which call out every doorknob and fixture. Some offer impressive three-dimensional scale models to help you better visualize the end result, and computerized virtual walk throughs.

The benefit of a more detailed set of drawings is a more accurate, cost-effective construction bid. The more details noted in the drawings and text, the fewer contingencies a contractor will have to speculate on. The drawings are the sum total of what your contract with a builder is based upon. If a detail isn't included in the drawings, then it's not part of the project and you'll be billed extra for it.

Services should be clearly outlined in your contract. Many local architects use a standard American Institute of Architects (AIA) contract, in a long or short form. Some use a letter of agreement.

Have your attorney read the contract. Be clear that the level of service you desire is what the architect is prepared to deliver.

THE DESIGN PHASE

The architect will be in communication with you as your project progresses through the phases of schematic design, design development, preparation of construction documents, bidding and negotiating with a contractor, and contract administration (monitoring the construction). If any of these services will not be supplied, you should find out at your initial meeting.

The creativity belongs in the first phases. This is when you move walls, add windows, change your mind about the two-person whirlpool tub in favor of a shower surround, and see how far your budget will take you.

The time involved in the design process varies depending on the size of the project, your individual availability, and coordinating schedules.

Think practically. Consider what you don't like

ADD MORE LIVING SPACE

What might it cost to add a 15 x 20 ft. family room and rehab a kitchen and powder room? Here is a typical breakdown, incorporating a brick and stone exterior, classical frieze board, with copper gutters and cedar shingles or slate roofing. The family room's interior features 5/8 in. drywall with poplar base and crown moldings and herringbone clear oak flooring.

Family Room:
• Exterior and Interior: $90,000
• Entertainment cabinetry: $10,000

Kitchen & Powder Room Rehab:
• Cabinetry, custom: $47,500
• Appliances: $18,000
• Stone countertops, backsplash & tilework: $15,000
• Plumbing, Electrical & HVAC: $26,000
• Demolition & construction: $18,000

• Contingency (10%): $ 22,450
• Architectural fees (15%): $ 33,675

Total: $280,625

59

AMERICAN
INSTITUTE OF
ARCHITECTS

**American Institute
of Architects**

**1735 New York
Ave., NW
Washington, DC
20006
800.AIA.3837
Fax:
202.626.7547
www.aia.org**

AIA is a profes-
sional association
of licensed archi-
tects, with a
strong commit-
ment to educating
and serving the
general public. It
frequently spon-
sors free seminars
called, "Working
with an
Architect," which
feature local
architects speak-
ing on home
design and build-
ing. AIA has also
produced an edu-
cational package
including a video
entitled,
"Investing in a
Dream," and a
brochure, "You
and Your
Architect." It's
available at many
local libraries
throughout the
area.

about your current home. If noise from the dishwasher bothers you at night, tell your architect you want a quiet bedroom, and a quiet dishwasher. Think about the nature of your future needs. Architects note that their clients are beginning to ask for "barrier-free" and ergonomic designs for more comfortable living as they age or as their parents move in with them.

A key role architects can play is in the planning for a secure home. Your architect can perform a security assessment, which will determine what is to be protected, what is the risk level and nature of the potential threat, what are the property's vulnerabilities, and what can be done to achieve the desired level of protection.

BUILDING BEGINS: BIDDING AND NEGOTIATION

If your contract includes it, your architect will bid your project to contractors he or she considers appropriate for your project, and any contractor you wish to consider. You may want to include a contractor to provide a "control" bid. If you wish to hire a specific contractor, you needn't go through the bidding process, unless you're simply curious about the range of responses you may receive. After the architect has analyzed the bids and the field is narrowed, you will want to meet the contractors to see if you're compatible, if you're able to communicate clearly, and if you sense a genuine interest in your project. These meetings can take place as a contractor walks through a home to be remodeled, or on a tour of a previously built project if you're building a new home.

If your plans come in over budget, the architect is responsible for bringing the costs down, except, of course, if the excess is caused by some item the architect had previously cautioned you would be prohibitive.

Not all people select an architect first. It's not uncommon for the builder to help in the selection of an architect, or for a builder to offer "design/build" services with architects on staff, just as an architectural firm may have interior designers on staff. ∎

Architects

ALBIS TURLINGTON ARCHITECTS, LLC ....**(203) 772-1212**
175 Orange Street, New Haven   Fax: (203) 773-1212
See Ad on Page: 71
Principal/Owner: Francis J. Albis Jr., AIA
Website: albisturlington.com e-mail: falbis@albisturlington.com
Additional Information: Albis Turlington Architects is an award winning full service firm with 20
years of experience in residential architecture.

ANTHONY TOTILO, ARCHITECT ....**(203) 968-8529**
43 Greenwood Avenue, Darien   Fax: (203) 461-9165
See Ad on Page: 90
Principal/Owner: Anthony Totilo
e-mail: atotilo@optonline.net
Additional Information: High-end residential, renovations, additions and new homes.

ARCHITECTS' GUILD ....**(203) 791-8778**
137 Greenwood, Bethel   Fax: (203) 791-8875
See Ad on Page: 94
Principal/Owner: Peter K. Eckert, AIA
Additional Information: We are a small firm specializing in high-end residential design. We are
committed to the integrity of good design in every detail. Client involvement is an ongoing part
of our design process.

AUSTIN PATTERSON DISSTON ....**(203) 255-4031**
376 Pequot Avenue, Southport   Fax: (203) 254-1390
See Ad on Page: 89
Principal/Owner: Judith C. Proctor

BANKS DESIGN ASSOCIATES, LTD ....**(203) 259-8899**
368 Center Street, Southport   Fax: (203) 259-1703
See Ad on Page: 57
Principal/Owner: Linda A. Banks, David C. Dumas
Website: www.bankdesignassociates.com
Additional Information: Since 1984, Banks Design Associates has been creating beautiful archi-
tecture and interiors for families who appreciate tradition, quality and creativity.

BUILDING DESIGNS, LLC ....**(203) 544-0011**
16 Old Mill Road, P.O. Box 813, Georgetown   Fax: (203) 544-0022
See Ad on Page: 98, 99
Principal/Owner: Lynne Persan
Website: lynneprsnacs.com
Additional Information: Specializing in both residential and commercial design, we are always
attentive to balance and proportions while providing you with a full wide range of services for
your convenience.

CHARY & SIGÜENZA ARCHITECTS, LLP ....**(914) 234-6289**
460 Old Post Road, Bedford   Fax: (914) 234-0619
See Ad on Page: 95
Principal/Owner: Andrew Chary & Teo Siguenza
Website: www.chary.com e-mail: dream@chary.com

COLE HARRIS CH2K ARCHITECTURE INTERIORS ....**(203) 226-1830**
111 Main Street, Westport, Simsbury, New York   Fax: (203) 226-8917
See Ad on Page: 64, 65
Principal/Owner: Paul Harris

CONTADINO ARCHITECTS, AIA ....**(203) 861-9007**
436 East Putnam Avenue, 2nd Floor , Cos Cob   Fax: (203) 861-6504
See Ad on Page: 86
Principal/Owner: Louis Contadino
Additional Information: Offering personalized and creative design services committed to the indi-
vidual expression of each client's needs and vision.

DANIEL L. COLBERT, ARCHITECT ....**(203) 661-1739**
309 Greenwich Avenue, Greenwich   Fax: (203) 661-1786
See Ad on Page: 91
Principal/Owner: Daniel L. Colbert
Additional Information: Single-Family, Residential Architecture

61

continued on page **66**

- Architecture
- Interiors
- Historic Restoration

Photographs: Rick Scanlan
121 West Main St.
Clinton, CT 06413
860.664.0673

Mingolleo & Hayes
ARCHITECTS

Greenwich, CT • Tel: 203-618-9820 • www.mh-architects.com

cole harris / ch²k

architecture & interiors

SEAN OKANE A.I.A. ARCHITECT P.C.

412 Main Street

Ridgefield, CT 06877

tel: 203.438.4208

email: s.okane@snet.net

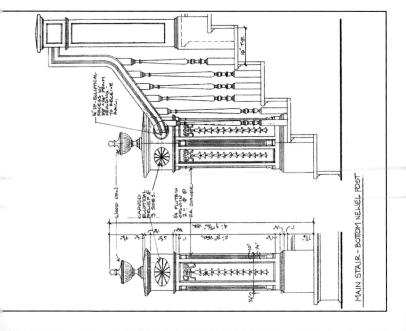

MAIN STAIR – BOTTOM NEWEL POST

V

VIGNEAU
& ASSOCIATES

*Residential & Commercial
Architecture steeped in traditio
Elegantly proportioned.
Meticulously detailed.*

NANCÉ J. VIGNEAU AIA
PRINCIPAL

Toll-free 866-226-4412
Fax 203-227-8209
www.vigneauandassociates.com

ARCHITECTURE & INTERIOR DESIGN
ESTPORT, CT   MILLBROOK, NY   PALM BEACH, F

Albis Turlington Architects, LLC

175 Orange Street
New Haven, CT 06510
203.772.1212 voice
203.773.1212 fax
www.albisturlington.com

Moisan Architects
PO Box 266

203 263.3141   494 Main Street South
Fax 263 4141   Woodbury, CT 06798

203 531.1794   77 Sherwood Avenue
Fax 263 4141   Greenwich, CT 06830

Specializing in traditional, residential
architecture that carefully blends the classical
with the present day vernacular.

Designing
DREAMS

W hat is your lifestyle, your family size, the architecture you love? Answering these and other questions in close collaboration with your architect can be the beginning of a most satisfying design experience.

To prove this point, Home Book editors asked four area architects to tell us about some of their favorite design experiences.

Arch

Photo courtesy of **Moisan Architects**

75

This newly built mini estate in the English country style evokes a time gone by.

Design Directions

Mark P. Finlay, president of Mark P. Finlay Architects, designs from the inside out. To Finlay, well lit, comfortable interiors come from careful orientation to the unique qualities of the home site environment: where the sun comes up, the direction of the wind, the natural surroundings and topography.

tects

76

This elegant yet comfortable cherry wood library is the heart of a large family home.

Photo courtesy of **Gullans & Brooks Associates, Inc.**
Photo by **John Kane**

Arch

Where Finlay designs from the inside out, Andrew Chary and Teo Sigüenza, principals of Chary & Sigüenza Architects, endeavor to bring the outdoors in. For a Westchester client, they created a home where every room steps away from the next, so each affords a different view. For another, they guaranteed their clients a 125-mountain view by conducting an extensive survey of local building requirements.

Warm and welcoming, this magical home beautifully blends the charm of an English cottage and the whimsical spirit of a beloved cartoon residence.

Photo courtesy of **Chary & Sigüenza Architects, LLP**
Photo by **Georg-Müeller-Nicholson Photography**

77

tects

In this vacation ski house dining room/kitchen,
natural fir walls celebrate the beauty of nature.

Arch

Photo courtesy of **Moisan Architects**

This informal dining area off the kitchen is also the perfect spot for watching sailboat races on Long Island Sound.

Rick Moisan, principal of Moisan Architects, is often called upon to create a new house that looks 100 years old or to renovate an original so it matches the existing structure. Not surprisingly, a design or renovation that seamlessly blends with the home's age or architectural tradition is of primary importance.

A Perfect Fit

Upon discovering that their client wanted a magical house that blended the charm of an English cottage and the whimsical spirit of a Smurf's cartoon residence, Chary & Sigüenza designed a home that is truly enchanting. This lakeside shingle and stone home boasts a front door with an eyebrow arch and an exuberant roof that sweeps and curves.

For Connecticut clients who asked that their new home overlooking the Long Island Sound have a 100-year-old look and a comfy, summery feel, Moisan designed a traditional, shingle-style house. To make the home seem smaller and more welcoming, he designed a cozy, wrap-around porch. As well as enhancing the front entry, it boasts an informal dining area with a fireplace off the kitchen.

tects

When Louise Brooks and Vincent Falotico, principals of Gullans & Brooks Associates, Inc., were asked to make a very large house with two poorly designed additions into a warm and cozy residence, they faced both architectural and design challenges. The additions were torn down, then carefully rebuilt in a manner that perfectly matched the original main section. To house new electronics, the second floor interior was gutted, then reconstructed with higher ceilings. Enhanced with architect-designed millwork and plaster detailing, the finished home is now open and flowing, welcoming and comfortable-just right for the young family who lives in it.

Rooms with Reason

At times, a client's desires and needs will inspire a truly spectacular room design. This was the case when Finlay was asked to create a one-of-a-kind library to house the homeowner's personal collection of 70,000 books and numerous art works. Although rooted in tradition, the open, three-story area is enhanced with many unusual features. A floating, structural glass bridge serves as an entrance. Stairways feature etched glass handrails. And crowning it all, a barrel vaulted ceiling acts as a projection screen displaying an infinite array of art and video images.

From the fieldstone walls and working fireplace to the high tech appliances and gleaming granite countertops, this kitchen fulfills both aesthetic and functional desires.

Photo courtesy of **Gullans & Brooks Associates, Inc.**
Photo by **John Kane**

Arch

Photo courtesy of **Gullans & Brooks Associates, Inc.**
Photo by **John Kane**

81

**Enhanced with architect-designed millwork and an elk
antler chandelier, this child's bedroom is a delight.**

Large libraries can also be warm and comfortable. Brooks and Falotico's
clients wanted the library to be the heart of their new family home. The
result is a gracious room made entirely of cherry wood. Designed so the
open two-story area is warm and comfortable, the second floor is lined
with the homeowner's personal collection of books and features an elegant,
coffered ceiling. This family-friendly space also offers upstairs access to the
master suite as well as downstairs entry to the lower level billiard room,
wine cellar and home theater.

As these favorite design experiences confirm, a new home is a personal
expression of the people who will live in it. An architect is dedicated to
making your vision a reality. Share your dreams. ■

tects

Bourke&Matthews -Builder.

Hobbs Inc.-Builder, John Mandela-Photographer

Hobbs Inc.-Builder

Gullans and Brooks Associates, Inc.

Architects ◆ Designers

87 Main Street New Canaan, CT 06877
Ph: 203 966 8440 Fax: 203 966 3191
www.gullansandbrooks.com

Hobbs Inc.-Builder

Hobbs Inc.-Builder, John Kane-Photographer

is Custom Builders-Builder, Photograph as seen is Renovation Style Magazine

Dave Improta Inc.-Builder, John Kane-Photographer

Gullans and Brooks Associates, Inc.

Architects ◆ Designers

87 Main Street New Canaan, CT 06877
Ph: 203 966 8440 Fax: 203 966 3191
www.gullansandbrooks.com

Hobbs Inc.-Builder, John Kane-Photographer

MARK P. FINLAY ARCHITECTS, AIA

1300 POST RD., SUITE 101, FAIRFIELD, CT 06824
(P) 203-254-2388 (F) 203-254-1704
email: mpfaia@markfinlay.com www.markfinlay.com

RICHARD F. HEIN
A R C H I T E C T S
ARCHITECTURE/LANDSCAPE

"We see the garden in the architecture,
we see the architecture in the garden"

138 Larchmont Avenue • Suite 4
Larchmont • NY 10538
t: 914.834.1414 • f: 914.833.9569
rfhdesign@hotmail.com

CONTADINO ARCHITECTS   AIA

436 EAST PUTNAM AVENUE • 2nd FLOOR • COS COB, CONNECTICUT 06807
PHONE: 203-861-9007   FAX: 203-861-6504

HAVERSON ARCHITECTURE·AND DESIGN:PC

63 CHURCH STREET ▪ GREENWICH, CT 06830
203.629.8300 ▪ FAX 629.8399
www.haversonarchitecture.com

ERIC MICHAELS

ARCHITECTS, LLC

RESIDENTIAL • COMMERCIAL • RESTORATION

115 MAIN STREET • WESTPORT, CT • 203-221-3005

AUSTIN PATTERSON DISSTON

ARCHITECTS

376 Pequot Avenue, Southport, CT 06490 • (203) 255-4031
4 Midland Street, Quogue, NY 11959 • (631) 653-1481
www.apdarchitects.com

ANTHONY TOTILO ARCHITECTS AND ASSOCIATES

43 Greenwood Ave., Darien, CT 06820
(203) 968-8529

DANIEL L. COLBERT, ARCHITECT
309 GREENWICH AVENUE, GREENWICH, CT 06830
(203) 661-1739 FAX 661-1786

H U E S T I S ▪ T U C K E R

A R C H I T E C T S

L.L.C.

(2 0 3) 2 4 8 - 1 0 0 7   FAX 2 4 8 - 3 8 8 4

www.huestistucker.com

Photography by: Olson Photographic, LLC

GDA

■ ■ ■

Geitz Design Associates, LLC
Architects

50 Riverside Avenue   Westport, CT 06880   203.227.4878   GDADESIGN@aol.com

■ ARCHITECTS' GUILD ■

137 Greenwood Ave   Bethel, CT 06801
(203) 791-8778

CHARY & SIGÜENZA

ARCHITECTS L.L.P.

460 OLD POST ROAD BEDFORD, NEW YORK 10506

(914) 234-6289 www.chary.com

Rosenblum
Architects

307 7th Avenue
23rd FL
Phone 212•352•0001
Fax 212•352•0002

Photos by: Durston Saylor

Architects

MINGOLELLO & HAYES ARCHITECTS ....**(203) 925-1991**
90 Huntington Street, Shelton   Fax: (203) 925-8263
See Ad on Page: 62,63
Principal/Owner: A. Joseph Mingolello./R. Neil
Website: www.mh-architect.com e-mail: mh.arch@snet.net

MOISAN ARCHITECTS ....**(203) 263-3141**
494 Main Street South, Woodbury   Fax: (203) 263-4141
See Ad on Page: 72,73
Principal/Owner: Richard C. Moisan
Website: www.moisanarchitects.com e-mail: rmoisan494@aol.com
Additional Information: Specializing in traditional, residential architecture that carefully blends the
classical with the present-day vernacular.

ROSENBLUM ARCHITECTS ....**(212) 352-0001**
307 7th Avenue, Suite 2301, New York   Fax: (212) 352-0002
See Ad on Page: 96
Principal/Owner: Elliot Rosenblum

SEAN O'KANE AIA ARCHITECTS PC..**(203) 438-4208**
412 Main Street, Ridgefield   Fax: (203) 438-6495
See Ad on Page: 68,69
Principal/Owner: Sean O'Kane
e-mail: s.okane@snet.net
Additional Information: Seven-person architectural firm specializing in high-end residential work.

VIGNEAU & ASSOCIATES ....**(203) 226-0581**
64 Post Road West, Westport. CT   Fax: (203) 226-8209
See Ad on Page: 70
Principal/Owner: Nancy J. Vigneau
Website: www.vigneauandassociates.com
Additional Information: Full service architect/interior design firm with offices in Westport CT,
Millbrook NY and Palm Beach FL.

97

Architectural
Designers

BUILDING DESIGNS, LLC ....**(203) 544-0011**
16 Old Mill Road, P.O. Box 813, Georgetown   Fax: (203) 544-0022
See Ad on Page: 98, 99
Principal/Owner: Lynne Persan
Website: lynneprsnacs.com
Additional Information: Specializing in both residential and commercial design, we are always
attentive to balance and proportions while providing you with a full wide range of services fo

BUILDING DESIGNS, LLC.

Commercial • Residential
Building • Remodeling
16 Old Mill Rd P.O. Box 813, Georgetown, CT 06829
(203) 544-0011 • Fax (203) 544-0022

Architectural
Illustrator

RED SUN STUDIO, THE ....**(203) 878-3345**
26 Knollwood Road, Milford   Fax: (203) 878-3415
See Ad on Page: 101
<u>Principal/Owner</u>: Andre Paul Junget
<u>Additional Information</u>: My studio's reputation has been built upon creating distinctive, tradtional handcrafted pen and ink illustrations. Residential and commercial designs, as well as personal commissions are considered. In addition, pencil and colored pencil illustrations are also provided.

THE RED SUN STUDIO • ANDRE' PAUL JUNGET • ILLUSTRATOR
26 KNOLLWOOD ROAD MILFORD CONNECTICUT 06460
203•878•3345 • FAX:203•878•3415
WWW.THEREDSUNSTUDIO.COM

Finally...
Connecticut/
Westchester County's Own
Home & Design
Sourcebook

The **Connecticut/Westchester County Home Book** is your final destination when searching for home remodeling, building and decorating resources. This comprehensive, hands-on sourcebook to building, remodeling, decorating, furnishing, and landscaping a luxury home is required reading for the serious and discriminating homeowner. With more than 500 full-color, beautiful pages, the **Connecticut/Westchester County Home Book** is the most complete and well-organized reference to the home industry. This hardcover volume covers all aspects of the process, includes listings of hundreds of industry professionals, and is accompanied by informative and valuable editorial discussing the most recent trends. Ordering your copy of the **Connecticut/Westchester County Home Book** now can ensure that you have the blueprints to your dream home, in your hand, today.

Order your copy now!

Published by
The Ashley Group
1234 Summer St., Stamford, CT 06905
203-323-7400 fax 203-326-5177
E-mail: ashleybooksales@ReedBusiness.com

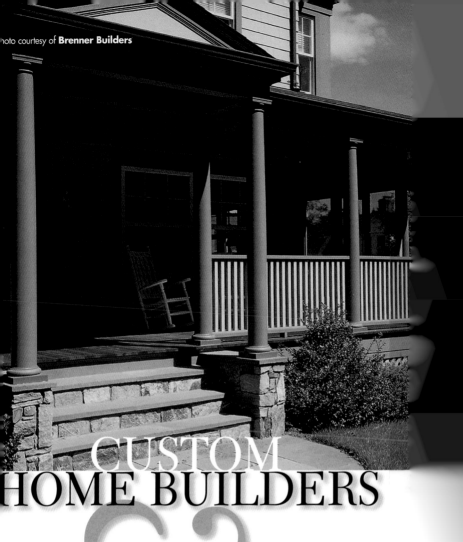

photo courtesy of **Brenner Builders**

CUSTOM
HOME BUILDERS

&

REMODELERS

103
**Bringing It
Together**

110
Home Builders

118
Material Matters

171
Remodeling

178
Roofing Specialists

GIROUARD ASSOCIATES, INC.

CUSTOM HOME BUILDER

62 Main Street, New Canaan, CT 06840   P 203.972.6580   F 203.972.5850
www.girouardassociates.com

Architect: Sean O'Keane, AIA
Photo by: Olson Photographic, LLC

2000 Connecticut Remodeling Project of the Year
When Quality is Your Priority

E.M. ROSE BUILDERS, INC.

9 Business Park Drive, Suite 12
Branford, CT 06405
tel. 203.481.4550   fax 203.481.1927

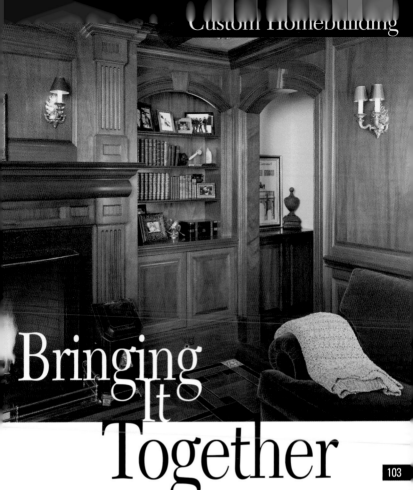

Bringing It Together

103

Once you've envisioned your dream home, you need a builder in order to turn that dream into a place you can live. Builders create new realities. They can take your ideas and turn them into the house that you will call home.

While design/build teams of architects and builders are becoming increasingly popular, the home in which you will be living will be the direct result of your contractor's efforts and expertise. Depending on the breadth of your project, you and your builder will be in a working relationship that could last as long as a year or two. Therefore, it is essential to choose a company or individual with whom you have a good rapport, who has excellent references as well as experience with your type of project. Seek out a builder whose attention to quality detail, willingness to listen to your concerns, and in-depth knowledge of the trades assures you a smooth road on the way to your new home.

Photo courtesy of **Wright Brothers Builders**
Photo by **Tom Young Photography**

WHICH COMES FIRST – THE ARCHITECT OR THE BUILDER?

Answering this question can seem like the "chicken or the egg" riddle: Do you hire the builder first, the architect first, or choose a design/build firm, where both functions are under the same roof?

If you work first with an architect, his or her firm will recommend builders they know have a track record in building homes of the same caliber you desire. Most likely, your architect contract will include bidding and negotiation services with these builders, and you may expect help in analyzing bids and making your selection. Your architect contract also may include construction administration, in which the architect makes site visits to observe construction, review the builder's applications for payment, and help make sure the home is built according to the plans.

Perhaps you've seen previous work or know satisfied clients of a custom home builder, and wish to work with him. In this scenario, the builder will recommend architects who are experienced in successfully designing homes and/or additions similar to what you want. The builder will support you, and the architect will cost-control information through realistic cost figures, before products are integrated into the house.

If you like the idea of working with one firm for both the architectural design and building, consider a design/build firm. Design/build firms offer an arrangement that can improve time management and efficient communication, simply by virtue of having both professional functions under the same roof. There is also added flexibility as the project develops. If you decide you want to add a feature, the design/build firm handles the design process and communicates the changes internally to the builder. When you interview a design/builder firm, it's important to ascertain that the firm has a strong architectural background, with experienced custom home architects on staff.

All scenarios work and no one way is always better than the other. Make your choice by finding professionals you trust and with whom you feel comfortable. Look for vision and integrity and let the creative process begin.

FINDING THE RIGHT CHEMISTRY

The selection of a builder or remodeler is a major decision, and should be approached in a thoughtful, unhurried manner. Allow plenty of time to interview and research at least two candidates before making your choice. Hours invested at this point can save months of time later on.

TEN GOOD QUESTIONS TO ASK A BUILDER'S PAST CLIENTS

1. Are you happy with your home?
2. Was the house built on schedule?
3. Did the builder respect the budget and give an honest appraisal of costs early on?
4. Did the builder bring creativity to your project?
5. Were you well informed so you properly understood each phase of the project?
6. Was the builder accessible and on-site?
7. Does the builder provide good service now that the project is complete?
8. How much help did you get from the builder in choosing the products in your home?
9. Is the house well built?
10. Would you hire the builder again?

At the initial interview, the most important information you'll get is not from brochures, portfolios, or a sales pitch, but from your own intuition. Ask yourself: Can we trust this person to execute plans for our dream home, likely the biggest expenditure of our lifetime? Is there a natural two-way communication, mutual respect, and creative energy? Does he have the vision to make our home unique and important? Is his sense of the project similar to ours? Will we have any fun together? Can we work together for at least a year?

If you answer "Yes!" you've found the most valuable asset – the right chemistry.

CHECK REFERENCES, GET INVOLVED

The most distinguished builders in the area expect, even want, you to check their references. More luxury home clients are taking the time to do this research as the move toward quality workmanship continues to grow.

Talk to clients. Get a list of clients spanning the last three to five years, some of whom are owners of projects similar to yours. Call them and go visit their homes or building sites. Satisfied customers are only too happy to show you around and praise the builder who did the work. If you can, speak with a past client not on the builder's referral list. Finding one unhappy customer is not cause for concern, but if you unearth a number of them, cross that builder off your list.

Visit a construction site. Clients who get the best results appreciate the importance of the sub-contractors. Their commitment to quality is at the heart of the job. Do the subcontractors appear to be professional? Are they taking their time in doing their work? Is the site clean and neat?

Contact subcontractors with whom the builder has worked. If they vouch for the builder's integrity and ability, you'll know the firm has earned a good professional reputation. Meeting subcontractors also provides a good measure for the quality of workmanship you'll receive.

Visit the builder's office. Is it well-staffed and organized? Does this person offer the technology for virtual walk-throughs? Do you feel welcome there?

Find out how long the builder has been in business. Experienced custom builders have strong relationships with top quality subcontractors and architects, a comprehensive knowledge of products and materials, and skills to provide the best service before, during and after construction.

Ask how many homes are currently being built and how your project will be serviced. Some builders work on several homes at once; some limit their total to 10 or 12 a year.

CAN YOU TELL THE DIFFERENCE?

Manufactured stone (also called cast stone, since the product is poured into molds in a liquid form) can provide the same look and feel of natural stone. In some instances, such as in driveways and walkways, manufactured stone or concrete cast in the shape of say, cobblestone, can be the better alternative, due to its uniformity. Natural stone shapes have to be cut and carved by hand, which involves a great deal of labor and expense. The price of cast stone varies depending on the style and level of detail, but it generally costs about half as much as natural products.

LAYING A FOUNDATION FOR SUCCESS

Two documents, the contract and the timeline, define your building experience. The contract lays down the requirements of the relationship and the timeline delineates the order in which the work is done. While the contract is negotiated once at the beginning of the relationship, the timeline continues to be updated and revised as the project develops.

THE CONTRACT

The American Institute of Architects (AIA) provides a standard neutral contract which is widely used in the area, but some firms write their own contracts. As with any contract, get legal advice, read carefully, and assume nothing. If landscaping is not mentioned, then landscaping will not be provided. Pay careful attention to:

• Payment schedules. When and how does the builder get paid? How much is the deposit (depends on the total cost of the project but $10,000 to $25,000 is not uncommon) and will it be applied against the first phase of the work? Do you have the right to withhold any payment until your punch list is completed? Will you write checks to the builder (if so, insist on sworn waivers) or only to the title company? Remodeling contracts typically use a payment schedule broken into thirds – one-third up front, one-third half-way through the project, and one-third at completion. You may withhold a negotiated percentage of the contract price until you're satisfied that the terms of the contract have been met and the work has been inspected. This should be stipulated in the contract. Ten percent is the average amount to be held back, but is negotiable based on the overall size of the project.

Builders and remodeling specialists who attract a quality-minded, high-end custom home client are contacted by institutions offering attractive construction or bridge and end loan packages. Ask your contractor for referrals if you want to do some comparative shopping.

• The total cost – breakdown of labor and materials expenses.

• Change order procedures. Change orders on the average add seven to 10 percent to the cost of a custom home. Be clear on how these orders are charged and the impact they eventually will have on the timetable.

• The basic work description. This should be extremely detailed, including everything from installing phone jacks to the final cleaning of your

CREATE A RECORD

You have a team of highly qualified professionals building your home, but the ultimate responsibility is on your shoulders. So keep track of the project. Organize a binder to keep all of your samples, change orders and documents together. Make copies for yourself of all communication with your suppliers and contractor. Take notes from conversations and send them to the contractor. This can help eliminate confusion before a problem occurs.

TRUTH ABOUT CHANGE ORDERS

The building process demands an environment that allows for changes as plans move from paper to reality. Although you can control changes through careful planning in the preliminary stages of design and bidding, budget an extra seven to 10 percent of the cost of the home to cover change orders. Changes are made by talking to the contractor, not someone working at the site.

home. A comprehensive list of specified materials should be given, if it hasn't already been provided by your architect.

• Allowances. Are they realistic? This is one place where discrepancies will be evident. Is Contractor A estimating $75,000 for cabinets while Contractor B is stating $150,000?

• Warranty. A one-year warranty, effective the date you move in, is standard in this area.

THE TIMELINE

This changeable document will give you a good indication if and when things will go wrong.

Go to the site often enough to keep track of the progress according to the timeline. Do what you need to do to keep the project on schedule. One of the main causes of delays and problems is late decision-making by the homeowner. If you wait until three weeks prior to cabinet installation to order your cabinets, you can count on holding up the entire process by at least a month. (You'll also limit your options to cabinets that can be delivered quickly.)

BUILDING SUPPLIER: EARTH

Some of the most popular materials around today are those that have been here forever. While our homes may contain the modern technology and up-to-date amenities, natural materials, such as marble, granite, stone and rich woods, provide the backbone for these homes. Italian tile can bring you a piece of that Tuscan villa you dream about, granite surfaces or heavy wood cabinetry can bring a bit of nature into your otherwise sleek and modern kitchen, and the visible use of certain types of stone throughout your home can pay tribute to the architectural heritage of the area.

Keep in mind, though, that whatever materials you are using, different times of the year dictate different prices. The cost of lumber, for example, traditionally goes up in late spring to mid-summer. Good builders might also be able to predict when there will be occasional shortages in such products as drywall and brick, and plan accordingly. They will also know when to buy certain items in bulk to decrease your overall costs. Also ask your builder about new products, such as manufactured, or faux, stone, which yield many of the same benefits of its natural counterpart, but at a reduced cost.

CREATING A CUSTOM HOME

While every home project is different, here's one example of some of the costs involved in building a custom home. This one is for construction of a 10,000 sq. ft. home with brick and stone veneer and a slate roof.

• Rough Lumber and Exterior Trim: $110,000
• Carpentry: $100,000
• Steel and Ornamental Iron: $12,500
• Windows: Skylight, $1,500 Windows and doors, $75,000
• Slate Roof: $140,000
• Radiant Heat: $12,500
• Security System: $5,000
• Masonry Veneer: $215,000
• Wood floors: $30,000
• Tile: Ceramic tile, $30,000 Hearth and surround, $10,500
• Cabinets and Vanities: $125,000
• Interior trim: Mantel, $10,900 Wine rack, $3,000 Closets, $8,000

SOURCE FOR HISTORIC PROPERTIES

**The National Trust for Historic Preservation
1785 Massachusetts Avenue, N.W. Washington, DC 20036
202.588.6000**

Having a home listed on the National Register doesn't restrict homeowners from demolishing or making changes (local restrictions do that), but offers possible financial assistance and tax credits for renovations, and limited protection against federal 'takings.' The organization sponsors programs, publishes newsletters and books, and advocates preservation.

108

THE TEAR-DOWN TREND

Land for new residential construction is getting harder to find, and "tear-down" renovations are becoming more common. There are often mixed emotions in an existing neighborhood as old structures come down. If you are considering a "tear-down" property, be sure you work with a builder and architect who are sensitive to the character of the neighborhood, and will help you build a home that fits in.

THE SECOND TIME'S A CHARM

Renovating a home offers the unique excitement of reinventing an old space to serve a new, enhanced purpose. It's an evolutionary process, charged with creative thinking and bold ideas. If you enjoy a stimulating environment of problem solving and decision making, and you're prepared to dedicate the needed time and resources, remodeling will result in a home which lives up to all of your expectations. You'll be living in the neighborhood you love, in a home that fits your needs.

A WORD ABOUT FINANCING OF REMODELING PROJECTS

Payment schedules in remodeling contracts typically require a deposit or a first payment at the start of the project, with subsequent payments due monthly or in conjunction with the progress of the work.

It is within your rights to withhold a negotiated percentage of the contract price until you're satisfied that the terms of the contract have been met and the work has been inspected. This should be stipulated in the written contract. Ten percent is the average amount to be held back, but is negotiated based on the overall size of the project.

Remodeling specialists who attract a quality-minded clientele are kept abreast of the most attractive remodeling loans on the market by lenders who specialize in these products. Ask your remodeler for referrals to these financial institutions.

RESTORE, RENEW

Many homeowners at the beginning of the new century are attracted to the historic architecture in older neighborhoods. Maturity and classicism are factors that persuade homeowners to make an investment in an old home and restore, renovate or preserve it, depending on what level of involvement interests them and the significance of the house. Renovations include additions and updating or replacing systems in the house. Restorations involve restoring the building to the specifications original to the house. Preservation efforts preserve what's there.

Like any remodeling project, it's an emotional and personal experience, only more so. Staying within the confines of a certain period or style is difficult and time consuming. That's why it's crucial to find an experienced architect and builder who share a reverence for tradition and craftsmanship. At your interview, determine if his or her portfolio shows competence in this specialty. It's vital to find a professional who understands historic projects and knows experienced and qualified contractors and/or subcontractors who will do the work for you. Ask if he or she knows experienced contractors who work in historic districts and have relationships with knowledgeable, experienced craftsmen. If you want exterior features, like period gardens or terraces, ask if they will be included in the overall plan. Make sure he or she has sources for you to find period furnishings, sconce shades or chimney pots.

There are many construction and design issues particular to old homes. The historic renovation and preservation experts featured in the following pages bring experience, creativity and responsibility to each project.

THESE OLD HOUSES

Before you fall in love with an old house, get a professional opinion. Find out how much is salvageable before you make the investment. Can the wood be restored? Have the casings been painted too many times? Is the plaster wavy and buckled? Can the house support ductwork for central air conditioning or additional light sources?

Notable remodelers are often contacted for their expert advice prior to a real estate purchase, and realtors maintain relationships with qualified remodelers for this purpose. They also keep remodelers informed of special properties suitable for custom renovations as they become available.

LEAVING HOME

Remodelers overwhelmingly agree their clients are happier if they move to a temporary residence during all, or the most intensive part, of the renovation. The sight of the roof and walls being torn out, the constant banging and buzzing of tools, and the invasion of privacy quickly take their toll on children and adults who are trying to carry on family life in a house full of dust. Homeowners who are well-rested from living in clean, well-lighted temporary quarters enjoy better relationships with each other, their remodeler and subcontractors.

Common hideaways are rental homes, suite-type hotels, the unoccupied home of a relative, or a long vacation trip. ∎

HOME BUILDER SOURCES

Home Builders & Remodelers Association of Fairfield County
324 Elm St.
Monroe, CT 06468
203.268.7008
www.fairfield-countyhba.com

National Association of the Remodeling Industry (NARI)
847.298.9200
www.nari.org

SOURCES FOR HISTORIC PROPERTIES
Connecticut Trust for Historic Preservation
940 Whitney Ave.
Hamden, CT 06517
203.562.6312
www.national-trust.org

109

CLEAN UP TIME:
Now or Later?

Your remodeling contract should be specific about clean-up. Will the site be cleaned up every day, or at the end of the project? Everyday clean-up may add to the price, but is well worth the extra expenditure.

Custom
Homebuilders

ACI GENERAL CONTRACTING, INC. ....**(203) 661-6209**
33 Meeting House Road, Greenwich Fax: (203) 869-1708
See Ad on Page: 128, 129
Principal/Owner: Lawrence Kendall
Website: www.acigeneralcontracting.com e-mail: ACIGC1@aol.com
Additional Information: Designer, builder, construction management, renovation and restoration specialist.

A.P. SAVINO LLC ....**(203) 698-1147**
3 West End, Greewich Fax: (203) 637-0936
See Ad on Page: 133
Principal/Owner: Tony Savino
e-mail: apsavinollc@aol.com
Additional Information: Our building team is ready to work with you, whether a custom home or remodeling your existing home. Our job is to handle budgets, quality control, and schedule. You focus on the realization of your plans. With experience and integrity, we build by process.

AMERICAN DEVELOPMENT CORPORATION ....**(845) 621-1521**
12 Lupi Court Suite 5, Mahopac Fax: (845) 621-2843
See Ad on Page: 166, 167
Principal/Owner: Christopher Amundson
Website: www.americandevelopmentcorp.com
Additional Information: American Development Corporation excels at high-end home construction and renovation, combining a meticulous attention to detail with superior building and management techniques to deliver products and services that surpass the expectation of our clients.

ARTISANS, INC. ....**(203) 831-9716**
149 Rowayton Avenue, Rowaton Fax: (203) 838-1267
See Ad on Page: 114, 115
Principal/Owner: Christopher A. Phillips
Website: artisanshomebuilders.com e-mail: chrisphillips@artisanshomebuilders.com
Additional Information: High-end custom home builder with a reputation for customer satisfaction.

BARRINGTON BUILDING COMPANY, LLC..**(203) 227-5862**
215 Post Road East, Suite 108, Westport Fax: (203) 227-6430
See Ad on Page: 143
Principal/Owner: Scott Buddenhagen
e-mail: Barringtonbldg@aol.com

BLANSFIELD BUILDERS, INC. ....**(203) 797-9174**
2 High Fields Drive, Danbury Fax: (203) 730-9381
See Ad on Page: 116, 117
Principal/Owner: James J. Blansfield
Website: www.blansfieldbuilders.com
Additional Information: High-end residential and commercial renovation and new construction.

BOURKE & MATHEWS ....**(203) 622-0100**
779 North Street, Greenwich Fax: (203) 622-6995
See Ad on Page: 157
Principal/Owner: Matt Mathews

BRENNER BUILDERS..**(914) 763-0035**
18 Ebenezer Lane, Pound Ridge Fax: (914) 763-0036
See Ad on Page: 138,139
Principal/Owner: Kevin Brenner
Website: brennerbuilders.com

BRINDISI & YAROSCAK LLC ....**(203) 656-1948**
39 Leroy Avenue, Darien Fax: (203) 656-2511
See Ad on Page: 141
Principal/Owner: John Brindisi & Christopher
Additional Information: Experienced in every facet of custom building and remodeling.

110

continued on page **132**

CANNONDALE

BUILDING AND DESIGN

WE WOULD BE HONORED TO DESIGN

AND BUILD YOU A HOME OF CLASSICAL

BEAUTY—A HOME THAT WILL PROUDLY

STAND THE TEST OF TIME.

41 RUSCOE ROAD, WILTON, CONNECTICUT 203.762.3608 WWW.CANNONDALEDESIGNBUILD.COM

Wright Brothers builds
prestige, quality, luxury and beauty
into every home.

Custom Home Building and Renovations

WRIGHT
BROTHERS
BUILDERS, INC.

325 Post Road West, Westport CT 06880
Phone: 203-227-8215 Fax: 203-227-0408 Greenwich: 203-637-3210
Web Site: http://www.wrightbuild.com E-mail: wbb@wrightbuild.com

ARTISANS, inc
Home Builders

Rowayton and Wallingford, CT
Phone: (203) 831-9716 • FAX: (203) 838-1267

ARTISANS, inc
Home Builders

For over two decades, Artisans has been providing
high quality Construction services to architects
and homeowners throughout Connecticut and
Westchester County, NY

Artisans' clients enjoy competitive pricing,
accurate estimates, old-fashioned craftsmanship
and on-target completion dates.

Rowayton and Wallingford, CT
Phone: (203) 831-9716 • FAX: (203) 838-1267

Blansfield Builders, Inc.

2 High Fields Drive, Danbury, CT 06811

Phone: 203-797-9174   Fax: 203-730-9381

www.blansfieldbuilders.com

Material
MATTERS

Today's building materials and techniques are remarkable. Architecturally correct classic columns are made from fiberglass. Ceiling beams are being aged in microwave kilns. One hundred-year-old stone walls can be perfectly recreated.

HomeB

This newly renovated, 1910 Georgian is one of the
original great estates of Greenwich, Connecticut.

Photo courtesy of **ACI General Contracting, Inc.**
Photo by **Brian Urso**

uilders

Because they work with these and other materials, four area custom builders were asked by Home Book editors to describe those they most often employ.

Recreating the Past

Gary Neil Savitzky, architect, and Ronald Parlato, president of Woodsmith Building Corporation, utilized modern technology when asked to build an authentic Adirondack room inside an existing 100-year-old home in Westchester County. For the ceiling, new oak beams were cut to size, hand-hewn and sandblasted in Vermont. They were then trucked to Ohio where they were microwaved in a large kiln for six weeks. Back at the site, these same beams were stained and antiqued. Using nail-free, pegged construction-much like the Amish did 100 years ago-they now grace a new room that seamlessly matches the rest of the home.

Repairing old homes can present problems, as Matt Matthews, president of Bourke & Matthews Companies, well knows. When renovating a spacious stone mansion in Westchester County, he was faced with a predicament: the antique, Ludowici tile roof was leaking and some of the old, irregular-edged clay tiles had to be replaced. Happily, Matt was able to locate these unique tiles and age them so the repair was invisible.

Larry Kendall, principal at ACI General Contracting, specializes in restoring unique homes in Westchester County and Connecticut. To a 1910 miniature castle in Greenwich, Kendall added a new master bathroom. This addition necessitated building a new 20 in. thick stone exterior wall that perfectly matched the original.

For the total renovation of a historic, 20,000 sq. ft. Georgian, Kendall had custom windows made in Europe and used standing seam copper for the roof. He also reconstructed an elegant lower level with marble floors and columns. This level boasted a gym, a sauna, a summer kitchen, an indoor pool, and a wine cellar and tasting room, as well as access to the outdoor pool, Italian gardens and bocci ball court.

Maintaining the Past

Ask a top builder and he'll tell you that often, architectural elements from the past can be preserved. Walter Cromwell, president of Country Club Homes, had clients who felt bad about having to tear down an old, Early American house to make way for their new residence. Although most of the home was unsalvageable, Cromwell was able to retain the original mantle wall in its entirety and incorporate it into the new, shingle-style home.

A custom home builder may even, unknowingly, locate antique materials that have a personal history. One example is the Art Deco bronze elevator door and surround that Matthews located for a client. Upon reading the inscription, "The Provident Loan Society of New York," the client smiled and told Matthews that he had to have it; this door was from the same company that had refused a loan to his soon-to-be-wealthy relative in 1920.

Constructed from local fieldstones, this dry stack stone fireplace lends focus and warmth to this highly detailed Adirondack room.

Photo courtesy of **Woodsmith Building Corporation**
Photo by **Jack Ader**

121

uilders

An antique, remilled heart-of-pine floor completes this gracious foyer.

Photo courtesy of **Bourke & Matthews Companies**
Photo by **Leonard Lampe**

For a 50-acre horse farm in Connecticut, Matthews went all the way to Vermont. There, he dismantled five existing18th and 19th century timber-frame buildings and transported them to the site. Using wood from three of the original homes, Matthews built a spacious, 10,000 sq. ft. main house. These 100-plus-year-old materials were also used to construct a separate 2,000 sq. ft. cottage and a bicycle shed. For the windows Matthews chose a combination of modern technology and authentic style by installing weather-friendly, thermopane windows made from antique restoration glass.

Shingle-Style Versatility

Cromwell has loved shingles since he first saw them on a family vacation in Europe. "Wood shingles have a timeless beauty, sculptural style and versatility that is unmatched," he said. "Whether they're natural, stained or painted, used alone or mixed with stone work, shingles can enhance the exterior of any style home."

HomeB

The beams in this expansive Adirondack-style great room were aged and stained, then installed with 18th century, nail-free, pegged construction.

Photo courtesy of **Woodsmith Building Corporation**
Photo by **Jack Ader**

uilders

124

A wrap-around porch with a beadboard ceiling circles the open bottom of this intricately shingled tower; at the top is a sitting room.

Photo courtesy of **Country Club Homes**
Photo by **Olson Photographic, LLC**

HomeB

A thoughtful statue welcomes one to the beautifully restored Italian gardens of this 1910 mansion.

As an example, Cromwell cited the 'Dream House' that he built in Connecticut. Designed in a 'U' shape, this 6,000 sq. ft. residence is a shingle-style delight. The gables are graced with brackets and cornice detailing, the wrap-around porch has a beadboard ceiling, and the tower is enhanced with both fish-scale and diamond-shaped shingles.

Modern Techniques, Classic Look

On newly built homes, Kendall appreciates the durability of low maintenance, architecturally correct fiberglass columns. An elegant combination of aerospace technology and authentic classical column design, these columns are virtually indistinguishable from the real thing, he maintains.

As these area builders have shown, anything is possible in today's new and remodeled homes. So pursue your dream, whatever it may be. The builders and building materials are here to make your dream come true. ■

uilders

CORNERSTONE BUILDING SERVICES, LLC

PO BOX 428 EASTON, CT 06612
203.261.1551 Fax 203.261.1993
INFO@CORNERSTONEBUILDINGSERVICES.COM

ACI

General Contracting

Renovation Specialists

Remodeling,

Home Building,

Construction Management

(203) 661-6209   (914) 273-7888
Greenwich, CT   Armonk, NY
www.acigeneralcontracting.com

Photo by Kurt A. Dolnier

Photo by Kurt A. Dolnier

Photo by Kurt A. Dolnier

Photo by Kurt A. Dolnier

Photo by Kurt A. Dolnier

PERDIKARIS-CONSTANTINE
DEVELOPERS, INC.

M.P.O. Box 247 Purchase, NY 10577
914.251.1346 Fax 914.251.1347

Custom
Homebuilders

CANNONDALE BUILDING & DESIGN ....**(203) 762-3608**
41 Ruscoe Road, Wilton   Fax: (203) 762-7787
See Ad on Page: 111
Principal/Owner: Andrew LaSala

CLARKE BUILDERS INC. ....**(203) 637-4135**
60 Hillcrest Park Rd, Old Greenwich   Fax: (203) 637-8126
See Ad on Page: 140
Principal/Owner: Jes / David Dall
Website: www.clarkebuilders.com
Additional Information: Clarke Builders Inc. has been building in Greenwich CT, Fairfield County
CT and Westchester County NY for over 35 years. Architects, realtors and homeowners have
known us as a leader in new construction and renovations. Choose from
hundreds of designs or let us create one just for you. We also build to your architect's
plans and specifications on time and on budget. Clarke Builders is your source for prompt, professional service.

CORNERSTONE BUILDING, LLC ....**(203) 261-1551**
P.O. Box 428, Easton   Fax: (203) 261-1993
See Ad on Page: 126,127
Principal/Owner: David Solway
Website: www.cornerstonebuildingservices.com
e-mail: dave@cornerstonebuildingservices.com
Additional Information: Specializing in fine custom home building, Cornerstone Building
has built its success upon experience, craftsmanship and professionalism – the three traits
needed in providing a quality product.

132

COUNTRY CLUB HOMES, INC. ....**(203) 966-5550**
505 Country Club Rd. W, New Canaan   Fax: (203) 972-5889
See Ad on Page: 152,153
Principal/Owner: Walter B. Cromwell
Website: www.countryclubhomesinc.com e-mail: countryclubhomes@yahoo.com
Additional Information: Nationally recognized high-end residential home builders. Family owned
and operated since 1955.

DAVENPORT CONTRACTING, INC. ....**(203) 324-6308**
78 Harvard Avenue, Stamford   Fax: (203) 967-9912
See Ad on Page: 158
Additional Information: Custom home builders/renovators for over 20 years in Westchester and
Connecticut. Professional staff employing detailed tracking systems for following your project.
Each project has continuous focus to "Delight Customers!"

E.M. ROSE BUILDERS, INC. ....**(203) 481-4550**
9 Business Park Drive, Branford   Fax: (203) 481-1927
See Ad on Page: 168,169
Principal/Owner: Eric M. Rose
e-mail: erose@emrose.net

GIROUARD ASSOCIATES, INC. ....**(203) 972-6580**
62 Main Street, New Canaan   Fax: (203) 972-5850
See Ad on Page: 103,104,170
Principal/Owner: Richard Girouard
Website: www.girouardassociates.com e-mail: info@girouardassociates.com
Additional Information: With 25 years of luxury home building experience and numerous awards
for their work, Girouard Associates, Inc. handles all aspects of the building process to create a
truly magnificent home that exceeds buyers' dreams and expectations.

GRAYSON CONSTRUCTION CO. INC. ....**(203) 221-7426**
965 Post Road East, Westport   Fax: (203) 221-0924
See Ad on Page: 154, 206
Principal/Owner: Anne Leepson
e-mail: grayson2000@aol.com
Additional Information: High-end design/build firm specializing in new construction, renovations
and additions. Known for innovative solutions, custom finish work and attention to the smallest
detail.

continued on page **142**

Experience the Difference ...

Our construction management team is ready to work with client, architect, or designer on any project being planned, whether it's a custom home, or remodeling.

We believe in presenting all the options to make informed decisions. We handle the budgets, bidding, contracts, site supervision, building department, schedule, insurance and warranty. We build by process.

You can focus on the realization of your project, with the integrity you expect.

CONSTRUCTION MANAGEMENT + GENERAL CONTRACTING

CUSTOM RESIDENCE AND REMODELING

A.P. Savino LLC

building
by process

3 West End Avenue   P.O. Box 49   Old Greenwich, CT 06870

office   203 698 1147   service   800 879 0783
fax   860 663 2912   e-mail   apsavinollc@aol.com

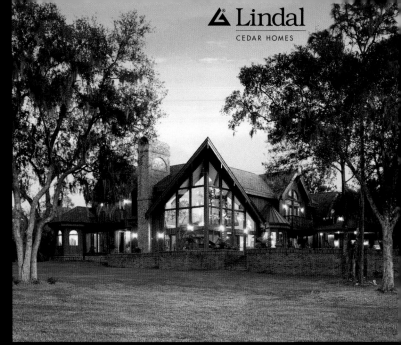

△ Lindal
CEDAR HOMES

Nothing Matches
The Quality of Our Homes.
(Except Our Sunrooms)

Dreaming of a new home? Planning to remodel? Nobody will bring it to
life more beautifully than Lindal. Whether you prefer our trademark open
and airy post & beam interiors, or something quite different, we'll
customize our plans to fit your dreams perfectly.

Independently distributed by:

Post Road Homes
www.LindalConnecticut.com
335 Post Road West • Westport, CT 06880 • (203)227-0479 or (800)246-4063

CONSTRUCTION CONCEPTS CORP.™

The award winning Design/Build team

Construction Concepts Corp. of Stamford, CT has recently won first place in three categories of the
Home Building Association of Connecticut's
HOBI awards, the most prestigious award present in Connecticut.
The three winning categories are:
Best Kitchen Renovation in CT, Best Accessory Building CT, and Best Home Office in CT.
Construction Concepts Corp. is a full service residential Design/Build firm serving
Fairfield County, CT and Westchester County, NY.
The firms winning portfolio may be seen and an appointment made for a free
consultation by calling (203) 325-8102.

Contact-Jeffrey R. Glass, GMB/CGR/CGB
tel 203.325.8102   fax 203.357.1984   email: ccc@constconceptscorp.com
CT #535858-WC #3332 H90
www.constconceptscorp.com

KARP ASSOCIATES...

AWARD-WINNING BUILDERS AND REMODELERS OF EXCELLENCE FOR OVER TWENTY YEARS

KARP
ASSOCIATES, INC.
80 MAIN STREET
NEW CANAAN, CT 06840
TEL: 203 972-3366
www.karpassoc.com

Brenner Builders is one of the most highly respected
residential construction firms in Westchester and
Fairfield Counties. In existence since 1984,
Brenner Builders maintains a staff of 50 employees, and
each project has a full-time onsite job supervisor to
oversee Brenner Builders' skilled carpenters,
craftspeople, artisans, and laborers.

Brenner Builders & Associates, Inc.
18 Ebenezer Lane, Pound Ridge, New York 10576

"Home and family are top priorities for everyone. When someone entrusts me to build or to renovate their home, I take that responsibility very seriously."

Kevin Brenner

www.brennerbuilders.com
(914)763-0035

Clarke Builders Inc.

Clarke Builders, Inc. has been building custom homes in the Greenwich, Connecticut, Fairfield County and Westchester County, New York for over 35 years. Scores of highly satisfied homeowners live in these magnificent homes. Architects, realtors and lending institutions have also come to know us as a leader in new home construction. On time, on budget, Clarke Builders, Inc. is your source for prompt, professional service.

Clarke Builders, Inc. is an award winning, licensed Scholz Design builder. We have hundreds of Scholz Design plans to choose from, all of which are readily customized to meet your desires.

P.O. Box 187 • Riverside, CT. 06878
203.637.4135 • 203.637.8126

BRINDISI & YAROSCAK
CUSTOM BUILDERS INC.

39 Leroy Avenue ▪ Darien, CT 06820
Tel: 203-656-1948 ▪ Fax: 203-656-2511

Custom
Homebuilders

HOBBS INCORPORATED..**(203) 966-0726**
27 Grove Street, New Canaan   Fax: (203) 966-3252
See Ad on Page: 147
Principal/Owner: Ian Hobbs

HOME BUILDERS ASSOCIATION OF FAIRFIELD COUNTY ....**(203) 268-7008**
324 Elm Street, Unit 102B, Monroe   Fax: (203) 268-7141
See Ad on Page: 155
Principal/Owner: Laura Sharp
Website: www.fairfieldcountyhba.com e-mail: info@fairfieldcountyhba.com
Additional Information: A non-profit organization affiliated with the National Association of
Homebuilders. Our builder and associate members are committed to better housing and our
code of ethics is delivering to our customers the best job possible.

I.K. BUILDERS LLC...**(203) 367-5521**
P.O. Box 6351, Bridgeport   Fax: (203) 209-3782
See Ad on Page: 164,165
Principal/Owner: Mark Iuraduri

KARP ASSOCIATES, INC. ....**(203) 972-3366**
80 Main Street, New Canaan   Fax: (203) 966-0455
See Ad on Page: 136,137
Principal/Owner: Arnold M. Karp
Website: www.karpassoc.com e-mail: karpassociates@yahoo.com
Additional Information: A high-end residential building and remodeling design firm with a repu-
tation for distinctive, quality speculative and custom homes with attention to detail,
giving particular consideration to each client's desires.

KLING BROTHERS BUILDERS INC. ....**(203) 866-7820**
6 Lawrence Street, Norwalk   Fax: (203) 831-8783
See Ad on Page: 144,145
Principal/Owner: Keith J. Kling & Kevin Kling
e-mail: KlingBrothers@erols.com
Additional Information: Kling Brothers Builders Incorporated is a general contracting and construction management company, working with old family values building in a new era of architecturally designed projects, in the commercial and custom residential markets.

LOPARCO ASSOCIATES, INC. ....**(203) 531-0200**
245 Mill Street, Greenwich   Fax: (203) 531-2992
See Ad on Page: 160,161
Principal/Owner: Steven LoParco
Website: Loparco.com e-mail: steve@loparco.com
Additional Information: LoParco Associates specializes in the construction, renovation and
expansion of distinctive homes in Fairfield and Westchester Counties as well as New York City.
Our management team focuses on our clients' every need, ensuring a positive and stress-free
experience.

MAYFAIR CONSTRUCTION ....**(203) 622-1070**
100 Northfield Street, Greenwich   Fax: (203) 622-1604
See Ad on Page: 162,163
Principal/Owner: Timothy Ryan/John Leone
Website: www.mayfairconstruction.com e-mail: tryan@mayfairconstruction.com
Additional Information: Custom home builder specializing in classical architecture. Offices in
Greenwich and Long Island.

MEINKE ASSOCIATES INC. ....**(860) 434-7629**
P.O. Box 4151, 100 Halls Rd., Old Lyme   Fax: (860) 434-7649
See Ad on Page: 159
Principal/Owner: Jeffrey R. Meinke
Website: www.maiconstruction.com e-mail: jeff@maiconstruction.com
Additional Information: General contractors specializing in architect designed custom residential
projects. Your construction solution.

142

continued on page **156**

BARRINGTON

──LUXURY HOME BUILDER──

BUILDING COMPANY

Barrington Building Company is a two time winner of the prestigious HOBI award for design. Featured in several magazine and newspaper articles over the years, this company has come to be known for it's intricate sense and pursuit of detail as well as superior reliability, both in terms of construction time and budget.

Barrington Building Co, LLC
250 Post Road East, Suite 108 • Westport, CT 06880
Tel: 203.227.5862 • Fax: 203.227.6430
Email: Barringtonbldg@aol.com

KLING BROTHERS BULIDERS INC.

RESIDENTIAL • COMMERCIAL

6 Lawrence St Norwalk CT. 06854 • 203.866.7820

RB BENSON & COMPANY, INC.

Building Exceptional New Homes for a Better Community
Since 1981

Specializing in Custom New Homes and
Construction Management with Exquisite detailing
and craftsmanship. Each home is built as if we were
going to live in it ourselves. Customer service beyond
your expectations.

Photos by Kim Cooper

RB Benson & Company, Inc   Office: 203-255-1428
1465 Post Road East   Fax: 203-259-1854
Westport, CT 06880   e-mail: BEN3RB@aol.com

SIMPLY THE BEST

HOBBS, INCORPORATED

27 GROVE STREET   VILLAGE GREEN
NEW CANAAN, CT   BEDFORD, NY

203-966-0726
www.hobbsinc.com

NEW HOMES • ADDITIONS • ALTERATIONS

T

R.C.TORRE
CONSTRUCTION CORP. INC.
Commercial & Residential

---

213 Railroad Avenue
Bedford Hills, NY 10507
Tel (914) 666-6993
Fax (914) 666-8420

TURNKEY
ASSOCIATES
INC.
203-938-8336
DESIGN/BUILD

Architectural Design   Custom & Spec Homes

Renovations   TIMBERPEG   Custom Millwork

REALIZE
YOUR DREAM

P.O. Box 491
Redding Ridge, CT 06876
fax (203) 938 -8337
www.turnkeycustombuilders.com

CONTINUING THE TRADITION OF BUILDING EXCELLENCE SINCE 1955

 COUNTRY CLUB HOMES, INC.

CUSTOM DESIGNED HOMES

505 COUNTRY CLUB ROAD NEW CANAAN, CT 06840 T 203 966 5550 F 203 972 5889

www.countryclubhomesinc.com

Renovate

Build

Design

Grayson

Architectural Design • Construction • Interior Design
Anne Leepson – Principal

965 Post Road East, Westport, CT 06880
Phone (203)221-7426 • Fax (203)221-0924 E-MAIL: GraysonCo2000@aol.com

HOME BUILDERS & REMODELERS ASSOC.
OF FAIRFIELD COUNTY INC.

www.fairfiledcountyhba.com

YOUR FIRST STOP IN FINDING A QUALITY BUILDER OR REMODELER

MISSION STATEMENT

The Home Builders & Remodelers Association of Fairfield County is a non-profit organization with the National Association of Home Builders and the Home Builders Association of Connecticut. HRA of Fairfield County is committed to providing education, information, representation and benefits to our membership, our community, and the home building industry. Quality of life for our citizens is achieved through better housing and the economic prosperity home building generates.

Choosing a qualified, reputable, professional builder or remodeler is of paramount importance when making one of the most important decisions of a lifetime – transforming your building plans into reality. Whether it's simply adding a room or building the home of your dreams, HBRA is committed to helping consumers avoid becoming the victims of unscrupulous contractors, and instead enables you to enjoy the excitement and fulfillment of the entire building experience.

Builders & Remodelers focus on creating homes suitable for a lifetime of enjoyable living, with features and amenities designed – all with education in mind. HBRA members are committed to consumer education. This education provides you with the knowledge necessary to empower you to make qualified decisions when selecting building professionals.

WHEN YOU CHOOSE HBRA MEMBERS – YOU'RE CHOOSING THE BEST!

MEMBER CODE OF ETHICS

❖ Members shall constantly seek to provide better values for the customers they serve.
❖ Members shall at all times share their knowledge with fellow members and the public which they serve.
❖ Members all comply, both in spirit and letter, with the rules and regulations prescribed by law and government agencies for which would tend to reflect poorly on, or bring into disrepute any part of the industry served by the association.

COMMUNITY SERVICE

HBRA members are proud of the work they do individually and collectively – making Connecticut be a better place to live. Our members give their time, money and talent to countless charities. They build playscapes and handicap accessibility ramps, contribute expertise and labor toward the construction of Habitat for Humanities homes, hold benefit auctions, dances and golf outings for all kinds of worthy causes, and serve on many civic organizations.

For more information on the Home Builders & Remodelers Association visit us at
info@fairfiledcountyhba.com

NAHB   324 Elm St. Unit 102 B • Monroe, CT 06468
Phone 203/268-7008 • Fax 203/268-7141

Custom
Homebuilders

OLSON DEBERADINIS DEVELOPMENT, LLC...**(860) 529-2730**
902 France Street, Rocky Hill   Fax: (860) 202-2336
See Ad on Page: 172
Principal/Owner: Gail Olson
e-mail: OlsonDeBeradinis@aol.com
Additional Information: Custom home building and renovations. CT Contractor's
Lic - 561018

PERDIKARIS - CONSTANTINE DEVELOPERS, INC. ....**(914) 251-1346**
2300 Westchester Avenue, Purchase   Fax: (914) 251-1347
See Ad on Page: 130, 131
Principal/Owner: Robin Constantine
e-mail: robin@westnet.com
Additional Information: Residential custom builder. "Legacy and Lifestyle."

POST ROAD HOMES ....**(203) 227-0479**
335 Post Road West, Westport   Fax: (203) 222-0190
See Ad on Page: 134
Principal/Owner: Finn Olander
Website: www.LindalConnecticut.com e-mail: postrdhome@discovernet.net
Additional Information: Designers and distributors of Lindal cedar homes and sunrooms, cus-
tom designed post and beam constructed homes.

R.B. BENSON & CO. ....**(203) 255-1428**
1465 Post Road East, Westport   Fax: (203) 259-1854
See Ad on Page: 146
Principal/Owner: Rick Benson
Website: e-mail: ben3rb@aol.com
Additional Information: R.B. Benson & Company has built exceptional residences in all sizes and
price ranges since 1981. We have built our reputation on fine design, great value for your budget, customer service beyond your expectations, and significant involvement in the Westport
community. We look forward to satisfying your new home dreams.

R.C. TORRE CONSTRUCTION CORP. ....**(914) 666-6993**
213 Railroad Avenue, Bedford Hills   Fax: (914) 666-8420
See Ad on Page: 148, 149
Principal/Owner: Robert C. Torre
e-mail: RCTBuild@aol.com

ROSE ADAMS CABINETRY ....**(203) 222-4944**
17 Kings Highway North, Westport   Fax: (203) 227-9995
See Ad on Page: 306
Principal/Owner: Rose Adams
Website: homeportfolio.com e-mail: roseadams2000@aol.com
Additional Information: Designers of fine custom cabinetry for all rooms of the house. Expertly
crafted, solid wood cabinetry inspired by classic English tradition for the discerning homeowner.

TURNKEY ASSOCIATES ....**(203) 938-8336**
P.O. Box 491, Redding Ridge   Fax: (203) 938-8337
See Ad on Page: 150, 151
Principal/Owner: Karin Williams
Website: www.turneykeycustombuilders.com e-mail: turnkey@optonline.com
Additional Information: Turnkey Associates is a complete design/build firm. We have a fine rep-
utation for bringing our customers dreams into reality - all under one roof.

WRIGHT BROTHERS BUILDERS INC...**(203) 227-8215**
325 Post Road West, Westport   Fax: (203) 227-0408
See Ad on Page: 112, 113
Principal/Owner: Kelly M. Wright
Website: www.wrightbuild.com e-mail: wbb@wrightbuild.com
Additional Information: Since 1985 Wright Brothers Builders has built a reputation as the area's
premier builder of fine custom homes. We delivery quality and superior customer service in the
building and renovation of residential properties.

BOURKE & MATTHEWS COMPANIES

Builders of Extraordinary Custom Homes
203-622-0100

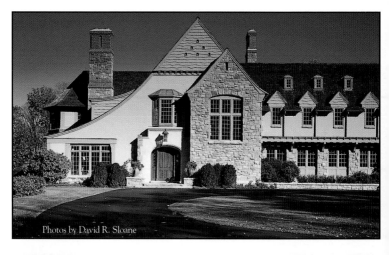

Photos by David R. Sloane

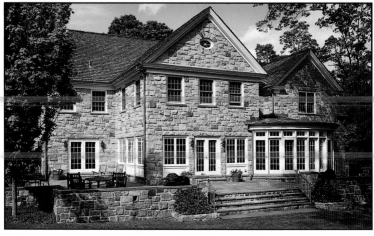

"Delighting Our Customers"

Davenport Contracting, Inc.

78 Harvard Avenue, Stamford, CT 06902   203.324.6308

MEINKE
ASSOCIATES
INC.

Construction Solutions

Specializing in custom projects
throughout Fairfield County for over 30 years.

Visit us at *www.maiconstruction.com*

Meinke Associates, Inc., PO Box 4151, Old Lyme, CT 06371
(860) 434-0056

LoParco
ASSOCIATES, INC

The Art of Home Building...

Fine Homes & Alterations

245 Mill Street Greenwich, CT 06830
203.531.0200 • fax 531.2992
loparco.com

Mayfair Construction

100 Northfield Street, Greenwich, Connecticut 06830
(203) 622-1070 • (516) 739-2244
e-mail tryan@mayfairconstruction.com

Tim Lee Photography

IK BUILDERS LLC
BUILDING & REMODELING

WESTPORT, CT
203.367.5521
IKBUILDERS@AOL.COM

AMERICAN DEVELOPMENT CORPORATION

Voice: 845.621.1521 • Fax: 845.621.2843

www.americandevelopmentcorp.com

Exquisite Home Construction and Premium Carpentry

AMERICAN DEVELOPMENT CORPORATION

Voice: 845.621.1521 • Fax: 845.621.2843

www.americandevelopmentcorp.com

Exquisite Home Construction and Premium Carpentry

Photography by: Olson Photographic

EMR

Architect: Dean Telfer, AIA
Photo by: Patrick Vigno Photography

Architect: Sean O'Keane, AIA
Photo by: Olson Photographic, LLC

Architect: Arbomes King Vlock
Photo by: Olson Photographic, LLC

Only your architect can create your dream house.

E.M. Rose Builders will make it turn out

the way you expected.

E.M. ROSE BUILDERS, INC.

9 Business Park Drive, Suite 12
Branford, CT 06405
tel 203.481.4550   fax 203.481.1927

GIROUARD ASSOCIATES, INC.

C U S T O M   H O M E   B U I L D E R

62 Main Street, New Canaan, CT 06840   P 203.972.6580   F 203.972.5850
www.girouardassociates.com

Remodeling
Specialists

A & G CONTRACTING INC. ....**(203) 469-5098**
662 Coe Ave #3, East Haven Fax: (203) 469-5098
See Ad on Page: 174
Principal/Owner: Anthony J. Bianco Jr. and Gerard
Additional Information: High quality construction with superior craftsmanship. Specializing in custom interior millwork. Dedicated to detail and committed to customer satisfaction.

BAMMAN BUILDING...**(203) 226-1234**
10 Kettlewood Lane, Weston Fax: (203) 454-1819
See Ad on Page: 171
Website: www.bammanbuilding.com e-mail: info@bammanbuilding.com
Additional Information: A full-service residential building company known for its distinctive kitchens, baths, additions and remodels.

BENCHMARK BUILDERS, LLC..**(203) 544-7162**
96 Old Mill Road, Wilton Fax: (203) 544-7162
See Ad on Page: 173
Principal/Owner: Andrew and Laura Payne
Website: www.remodelct.com e-mail: bbllc@optonline.net
Additional Information: Established in 1987, Benchmark Builders is a mid-sized company providing meticulous craftsmanship and general contracting services for residential additions, renovations, and antique restoration. We are a husband and wife team with a focus on superb professionalism and customer service.

CONSTRUCTION CONCEPTS CORP. ....**(203) 325-8102**
87 Brookhollow Lane, Stamford Fax: (203) 357-1984
See Ad on Page: 135, 199, 289
Principal/Owner: Jeffrey Glass
Website: www.constconceptscorp.com e-mail: ccc@constconceptscorp.com
Additional Information: A full-service custom home & remodeling design/build company.

171

HOFFMAN CONTRACTING LLC ....**(203) 966-1919**
32 Cross Street, New Canaan Fax: (203) 972-8756
See Ad on Page: 175
Principal/Owner: Ned Hoffman
Website: www.hoffmancontractingllc.com
Additional Information: Established in 1978, Hoffman Contracting, LLC specializes in Interior/Exterior restoration.

OLSON DEBERADINIS DEVELOPMENT, LLC..**(203) 227-8080**
902 France St., Rocky Hill Fax: (203) 529-2730
See Ad on Page: 172
Principal/Owner: Gail Olson
e-mail: olsondeberadinis@aol.com
Additional Information: Custom home building and renovations. CT Contractor's Lic - 561018

TDS HOME LINE DESIGNING & BUILDING SERVICES ....**(203) 866-3777**
39 Fort Point Street, Norwalk Fax: (203) 853-7700
See Ad on Page: 170
Principal/Owner: Donald Freitag
Website: www.tdshomeline.com
Additional Information: Our Handyman Services Division was established based upon a realization that a serious void exists in response to minor household fix-up problems. For this reason we have created a quick-response team - just dial 1-866-ITS-FIXD to schedule an appointment.

Electrical
Contractor

CHRIS CARLO ELECTRICAL CONTRACTORS, INC. ....**(203) 637-5802**
P.O. Box 565, Greenwich Fax: (203) 969-0891
See Ad on Pages: 174a-174h
Principal/Owner: Chris Carlo
e-mail: Christopher.Carlo@snet.net
Additional Information: Chris Carlo Electrical Contractors "for everything electrical".

Olson • DeBeradinis

Custom Home Building & Renovations
Tel: 203.227.8080
Email: olsondeberadinis@aol.com
Connecticut contractors License
561018

BENCHMARK BUILDERS, LLC

Additions and Alterations • Fine Craftsmanship

Proudly serving discerning homeowners since 1987
Phone: 203.544.7162   Fax: 419.715.3419
E-mail: bbllc@optonline.net

www.remodelct.com

A&G
Contracting, Inc

662 Coe Avenue, Unit 3
East Haven, CT 06512
Tel/Fax: 203.469.5098

Building a **Custom** House

Interview and Select an Architect and Builder

This is the time to test the fit between what you want, what you need and what you can spend. It is advisable to interview two or three architects and builders and check their references before making a firm decision.

Site Selection

If you don't already own the land, meet with a realtor of your choice to describe the parameters of your future house. Also discuss future sites with your architect and builder.

Interview and Select an Interior Designer

A skilled designer will collaborate with the architect on matters such as windows and door location, appropriate room size and lighting plans.

Breaking Ground

What a joy to see that construction of your new home is underway!

Foundation Work

This will include footings and dampproofing. The cement will need a few days to solidify.

Framing Begins

Rough framing of the house begins. At the end of this phase the structure will be in place, and you'll be able to see the rooms as they're going to look. This phase will take two to three months.

Roofing Begins

Since the time you broke ground until the time you get to this stage, probably four months have lapsed. With the exterior framing of the house completed, the contractor can start working on the interior (mechanical elements).

| MONTH 1 | MONTH 4 | MONTH 5 | MONTH 6 | MONTH 9 |

Design/Build Firms

A design/build firm is a company that employs architects, builders, estimators and sometimes interior designers and realtors. Read more about them in the Architects section.

• **Your architect and builder must work together.** The architect and contractor must be continually matching their budget and timelines. The architect converts the vision into buildable drawings. The contractor uses the drawings to make the plan work.

• **Final decisions:** Once you've received the initial drawings for the front, back and both sides of your house plus floor plans, you must make final decisions. You must decide on the exact footage of every level of your house and decide what unique elements you may want to include. For example, do you want your own home theater and entertainment center? Home automation and lighting?

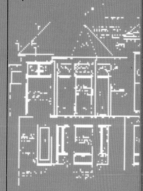

Inspecting the Progress

At various times throughout the process, there will be building/municipal inspections to make sure the house meets all city codes and zoning issues. Often, a builder will insist on a six-month, follow-up courtesy inspection.

• **Choosing a contractor**: The builder is usually considered the general contractor for the job. The general contractor will line up the subcontractors and enter into an agreement with the vendors. The general contractor will be solely responsible for construction methods, techniques, schedules and procedures. The key is that teams need to be in place.

• **Seasonal costs**: The builder will keep in mind that different times of the year require different costs. The cost of lumber, for example, traditionally goes up in late spring to mid-summer. Good builders might also be able to figure when there will be occasional shortages in such items as drywall and brick. They might also know when to buy certain items in bulk to decrease your overall costs.

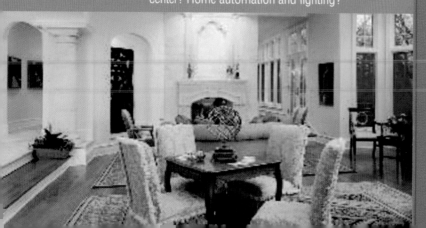

Building Your Dream Home

This timetable is included to support you in transforming your dream into reality. The sections of this book include specific categories to help you find the best quality craftsmanship available. This timeline will help you to understand the process from start to finish. How long might it take for you from designing the house to making it your own home? It could take from one year to a year and a half. Eighteen months is not unusual for a completely custom-built home. It can take four to six months to receive design approval and city permits alone. So be patient and plan ahead. Often delays occur because of a lack of communication. Take the initiative to keep in touch with all parties necessary. We hope this timeline will help give you an indication of how that dream home of yours will become a reality!

No Substitute For
Superior Quality Workmanship

Fine Home Building ~ Painting ~ Restoration
Masonry ~ Carpentry ~ New Construction ~ Roofing ~ Remodeling

Hoffman Contracting. LLC
32 Cross Street, New Canaan, CT 06840

(203) 966-1919   HOFFMANCONTRACTINGLLC.COM   HOFFMANCONTRACT@AOL.COM

PLEASE CONTACT NED HOFFMAN FOR MORE INFORMATION @ 203•219•8388

The TDS Homeline Handyman Super Hardware Store on Wheels

handymanservices

**HOUSE
FIX-UP
PROBLEMS**?
one call does it all!
1-866-ITS-FIXD

our custom quality
SPECIALTY DIVISIONS

designing&**building
millworking
painting**&**decorating**

licensed / insured / since 1978

Bamman **B**uilding

An Uncommon Company

Kitchens · Baths · Additions

Bamman Building, Inc.

Weston, CT   203.226.1234

www.bammanbuilding.com

Roofing
Specialists

ADVANCED ROOFING INC. ....**(203) 762-1002**
6 Salem Road, Wilton
See Ad on Page: 179
<u>Principal/Owner</u>: David Hand

Fax: (203) 762-0177

CT Lic. #554261
Westchester Lic. #11504H01

David J. Hand
President

Advanced
Roofing Co., Inc.

CUSTOM ROOFING & COPPER

Specializing in Detailed Roof Installations for Fairfield and Westchester Counties Finest Homes...

Connecticut **203.762.1002**
203.531.7098 | *Westchester* **914.939.0949**

Location,
Location,
Location!

What better LOCATION for your
advertisement than the
CONNECTICUT/WESTCHESTER
COUNTY HOME BOOK!

Just as our readers realize how important
location is when choosing a home, we realize
that it's just as important to you when
allocating your advertising dollars.
That's why we have successfully positioned the
CONNECTICUT/WESTCHESTER COUNTY
HOME BOOK to reach
the high-end consumers you want as clients.

**Call 203-323-7400 to find out about our
unique marketing programs and
advertising opportunities.**

Published by
The Ashley Group
1234 Summer St., Stamford, CT, 06905
203-323-7400 fax 203-326-5177
E-mail: ashleybooksales@ReedBusiness.com

Mechanical Work Begins

This includes the rough plumbing, HVAC, electrical and low-voltage work. Allow two to three weeks each for the mechanical steps.

Interior Work Begins

Once the rough mechanical work is completed, the insulation and drywall can be installed. The hardwood floors and tile can be worked on concurrently. Next up are the stairs and the cabinets. Then the millwork (trim around the doors and windows) takes shape. The painting of trim, walls and ceilings follows. Then the mechanical work can be finalized.

Finishing the Work

Final sanding, sealing, carpeting and closet shelving complete the job. Allow three to four months for the interior work and final items to take place.

MONTH 10   MONTH 11   MONTH 15   MONTH 16

Final Inspection

Independent appraisals take place at this time.

Final Close

Representatives for both the builder and the client will attend, along with a staff person from the closing company.

Releasing the contractor

The client does a walk-through inspection and provides a "punch list" — a list of miscellaneous items the contractor needs to do to finish the work.

• **Environmental and energy concerns:** Of course, you will want to save on energy consumption, so make sure the builder doesn't forget these issues. Consider the selection of furnaces and water heaters. Ask your builder what their standard efficiency ratings are. Your initial investment might be more, but you could reap the benefit of lower energy costs in the long run. Where the sun rises and sets may seem inconsequential. But you'll want to make sure some key rooms allow natural light at particular times (for example, the greenhouse effect).

Also, as you build your house, you may want to ask your builder about different ways to protect the outside of the house using some sort of protective covering or wrap. That helps address your concerns about water intrusion.

Keeping on Schedule

Make sure the builder provides you with a schedule and completion date. The duration of the project should be clearly defined in the contract. However, you can almost depend on the schedule changing due to unforeseen delays such as weather-related items. But the homeowner can also affect the schedule by making late selections and desiring personal changes.

• **There are certain laws that protect the client.** Experts other than independent appraisers may be called upon to ensure that all agreements and building codes have been met. The client can, of course, make notes and have miscellaneous details taken care of.

• **Warranty:** Most states provide warranty protection for the client. The builder's warranty is typically one year for construction. Specific manufacturer warranties can last as long as five to 10 years.

Additional Information

For more information, contact the National Association of Home Builders (NAHB) 1201 15th St. NW Washington, DC 20005-2800 202-266-8111.

SPONSORED BY:

Chris Carlo

ELECTRICAL CONTRACTORS

P.O. Box 565, Greenwich, CT 06830
Phone: (203)637-5802 • Fax: (203)969-0891
Email: Christopher.Carlo@snet.net

"for everything electrical"

Project Description

Building an upscale, one-acre property, single-family home. This work includes planning the project (selecting an architect and builder), executing the project (the steps from breaking the ground to finishing the interior work) and finishing the project (closing on your new home).

In Conclusion

Your new house started as a dream with a piece of land. Now your custom-designed home has become a reality. It's time to start living in the special place you've created. Enjoy!

Special thanks to Orren Pickell Designers and Builders, Bannockburn, IL, and Centurian Development, Scottsdale, AZ, for their contributions to this article.

Produced by The Ashley Group
847.390.2882
www.theashleygroup.com

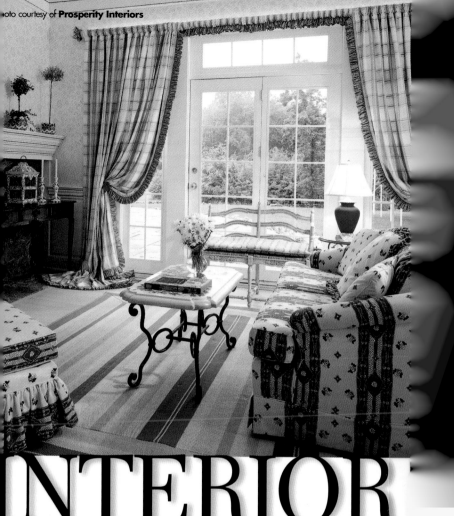

Photo courtesy of **Prosperity Interiors**

INTERIOR
DESIGNERS

181
**Inner Expressions
of Self**

187
**Interior
Designers**

210
**Interior Design
Spotlight**

LIGHT

TEXTURE

Audrey Morgan Interiors, Inc.
INTERIOR DESIGN AS ART

19 POST ROAD WEST, WESTPORT, CT 06880
PHN: 203.227.1344 FAX: 203.454.2392
AUDREYMORGAN@MINDSPRING.COM

Audrey Morgan Interiors, Inc.

INTERIOR DESIGN AS ART

OLSON PHOTOGRAPHIC, LLC

| COLOR | SPACE | TEXTURE | LIGHT | FORM |

Exceptional Design. Exceptional Service.
Exceptional Clients.

19 POST ROAD WEST, WESTPORT, CT 06880
PHN (203) 227-1344 FAX (203) 454-2392
AUDREYMORGAN@MINDSPRING.COM

Inner Expressions of Self

You know that something has to be done about your home's interior. You know what styles you like and what styles you couldn't possibly live with. You may even have your mind on a certain furnishing or piece of art that you want to be a central part of a particular room. But beyond that, you haven't the foggiest idea of how to bring everything together. That's where an interior designer comes in.

There are many good reasons to work with an interior designer, not the least of which is you will most likely save time and money. It's so easy to get bogged down in the many small details of home decorating, and lose track of the big picture. An interior designer has the training and experience to help you define your style, and keep your project focused, minimizing costly decorating mistakes. With their years of professional experience and the tools that they have at their fingertips, designers can orchestrate, layer by layer, design elements that compose an inviting and harmonious décor. Best of all, designers often have access to the best decorating resources in the area, from furniture showrooms to the most coveted interior painter. They'll handle the myriad details while you enjoy the results.

Photo courtesy of **Hampton Court Interiors**

WHERE STRUCTURE MEETS INSPIRATION

A great interior designer, like a great architect or builder, sees space creatively, applying years of education and experience to deliver a distinguished residence at the highest level of quality in an organized, professional manner. Intensely visual, these talented individuals imprint a home with the spirit and personality of the family living there.

A top quality interior designer who is licensed by the state is educated in the field of interior design, usually holding a bachelor's or master's degree in the subject. In addition to creating interiors, your interior designer also handles the "nuts and bolts" business end of the project. With skill and experience in placing and tracking orders, scheduling shipping, delivery and installation, the designer can bring your project to its perfect conclusion.

AN INTERIOR DESIGNER IS A TEAM MEMBER

Choose an interior designer when you select your architect, builder, and landscape architect. A skilled designer can collaborate with the architect on matters such as window and door location, appropriate room size, and practical and accent lighting plans. In new construction and remodeling, try to make your floor plan and furniture choices simultaneously, to avoid common design problems, such as traffic corridors running through a formal space or awkward locations of electrical outlets.

CREATE THE BEST CLIENT-DESIGNER RELATIONSHIP

Talk to the best interior designers in the area and they'll tell you how exciting and gratifying it is for them when a client is involved in the process. This is happening as more homeowners turn their attention to hearth and home, dedicating their time and resources to achieve a style they love.

Define your needs, in terms of service and the end result. Have an interior designer involved during the architectural drawing phase of a new or renovation project, and get the process started early. Be clear about how much help you want from a designer. Some homeowners have a strong sense of what they want and simply need a consultant-type relationship. Others want significant guidance from a professional who will oversee the entire process.

Set up a relationship that encourages an open exchange of ideas. In pursuit of personal style, you need to trust a professional designer to interpret your

---

FIVE
THINGS YOU
SHOULD
KNOW

1. Know what level of guidance you want: a person to handle every detail, someone to collaborate with you or simply an occasional consultation.
2. Know what you're trying to achieve. Start an Idea Notebook, filling it with pictures of rooms you like and don't like. This will help you define your style and stay true to your goal.
3. Know your budget. Prices of high-end furnishings know no upper limit. Adopt a "master plan" to phase in design elements if your tastes are outpacing your pocketbook.
4. Know what's going on. Always ask; don't assume. Design is not a mystical process.
5. Know yourself. Don't get blinded by beauty. Stay focused on what makes you feel "at home," and you'll be successful.

thoughts and needs. You must be comfortable saying, "No, I don't like that," and receptive to hearing, "I don't think that's a good idea."

Be forthcoming about your budget. Not all interiors are guided by a budget, but the majority are. Your designer must know and respect your financial parameters and priorities. If a gorgeous dining room table is a top priority, objets d' art can be added later as you find them. Prices of exquisite furniture, custom-carved cabinets, and other high-end furnishings know no upper limit. Be realistic about what you will spend and what you expect to achieve. Do some research in furniture stores and specialty shops, starting with those showcased in this book.

Be inquisitive as the design unfolds. This is a creative effort on your behalf, so let yourself enjoy it, understand it and be stimulated by it.

START THINKING VISUALLY: STOP, LOOK AND CLIP

Before you start scheduling initial interviews with interior designers, start compiling an Idea Notebook – it's the best tool for developing an awareness of your personal style. Spend a weekend or two with a pair of scissors, a notebook, and a stack of magazines, (or add a section to the Idea Notebook you made to inspire your architecture and building plans). Make this a record of your personal style. Include pictures of your favorite rooms, noting colors, fabrics, tile, carpet, fixtures, the way light filters through a curtain, anything that strikes your fancy. On those pictures, circle the design elements that you'd like to incorporate into your own home décor and make comments regarding those elements you don't care for. Think hard about what you love and loathe in your current residence. Start to look at the entire environment as a rich source of design ideas. Movies, billboards, architecture, clothing – all are fascinating sources for visual stimulation.

Then, when you hold that initial meeting, you, too, will have a book of ideas to share. Although a smart designer will be able to coax this information from you, it's tremendously more reliable to have visual representations than to depend on a verbal description. It also saves a tremendous amount of time.

THE INTERIOR DESIGN PROCESS: GETTING TO KNOW YOU

Give yourself time to interview at least two interior designers. Invite them to your home for a tour of your current residence and a look at items you wish to use in the new environment. If you're building

TIME TO REDESIGN

The example below gives a general estimate of the costs involved in redesigning a 15 x 22 sq. ft. living room in a mid-scale price range.
Initial consultation: $500
Cost per hour (5 hour minimum): $100/hr
New rug (oriental or custom): $8,000
Furniture:
Transitional (contemporary upholstery, traditional wood pieces)
Sofa, $3,000
Chairs (2) $1,000 ea.
Coffee table, $2,000
End tables (2), $1,000 ea.
Sofa table, $2,000
French Be'rgre chair, $3,000
Lamps (1 bronze, 2 porcelain): $1,200
Lighted wall sconces: $1,000
Artwork: $2,000
New paint (labor and paint): $1,500
Accessories: $3,000

Total: $31,700

183

or remodeling, an interior designer can be helpful with your overall plans when he or she is given the opportunity to get involved early in the building process.

During the initial meeting, count on your intuition to guide you toward the best designer for you. Decorating a home is an intimate and very personal experience, so a comfortable relationship with a high degree of trust is absolutely necessary for a good result. You may adore what a designer did for a friend, but if you can't easily express your ideas, or if you feel he or she isn't interested in your point of view, don't pursue the relationship. Unless you can imagine yourself working with a designer two or three homes from now, keep interviewing.

You may wish to hire a designer for one room before making a commitment to do the whole house.

Some designers maintain a high degree of confidentiality regarding their clients, but if possible, get references and contact them, especially clients with whom they've worked on more than one home. Be sure to ask about the quality of follow-up service.

Be prepared to talk in specific terms about your project, and to honestly assess your lifestyle. For a home or a room to work well, function must be considered along with the evolving style. Designers ask many questions; some of them may be:

• What function should each room serve? Will a living room double as a study? Will a guest room also be an exercise area?

• What kind of relationship do you want to establish between the interior and the landscape?

• Style: Formal, casual or a bit of both?

• Are you comfortable with color?

• Are you naturally organized or disorganized?

• What kind of art do you like? Do you own art that needs to be highlighted or displayed in a certain way? Do you need space for a growing collection?

• Do you feel at home in a dog-eared, low maintenance family room or do you soothe your soul in an opulent leather chair, surrounded by rich cabinetry and Oriental rugs?

• What kind of furniture do you like? Queen Anne, Contemporary, American Arts and Crafts, casual wicker, or eclectic mixing of styles?

• What words describe the feeling you want to achieve? Cheerful, cozy, tranquil, elegant, classic?

PROFESSIONAL DESIGNATIONS

ASID (American Society of Interior Designers/ Connecticut
169 Hotchkiss Grove Rd.
Branford, CT 06405
800.505.ASID

IIDA (International Interior Design Association)
International Headquarters
998 Merchandise Mart
Chicago, IL 60654
312.467.1950
www.iida.org
email:
IIDAhq@iida.org
Offers referrals to area homeowners.

Designers who add ASID or IIDA after their names are certified members of the organization.

184

COMPUTING THE INTERIOR DESIGN FEE

Designers use individual contracts, standard contracts drawn up by the American Society of Interior Designers (ASID), or letters of agreements as legal documents. The ASID contract outlines seven project phases – programming, schematic, design development, contract documents, contract administration, project representation beyond basic services, and additional services. It outlines the designer's special responsibilities, the owner's responsibilities, the fees agreed upon, and the method of payments to the designer, including reimbursement of expenses.

Payment deadlines vary. Payments may be due at the completion of each project phase, on a monthly or quarterly basis, or as orders are made. You can usually expect to pay a retainer or a 50 percent deposit on goods as they are ordered, 40 percent upon the start of installation, and the balance when the job is completed.

Design fees, which may be based on "current market rate," are also computed in various ways. They may be charged on a flat fee or hourly basis, or may be tied to retail costs. Expect fees of approximately $100 an hour, varying by experience, reputation and workload. A designer's fee may also be commission-based, which is when a percentage of the cost of the project is added to compensate the designer. When charging by the fixed or hourly fee methods, designers may also add commission to items they purchase for the project. A designer's fees may also be based on the square footage of the area to be designed or decorated. Make sure you understand your fee structure early on.

If you work with a designer at a retail store, a design service fee ranging from $100 to $500 may be charged and applied against purchases.

FROM THE MIND'S EYE TO REALITY

Once you've found a designer who you like and trust, and have signed a clear, specific agreement, you're ready to embark on the adventure.

A good designer knows his or her way around the masses of products and possibilities. Such a person will guide you through upscale retail outlets and to craftspeople known only to a fortunate few in the trade. You can be a "kid in a candy store."

Just as you've allowed time to carefully consider and reconsider architectural blueprints, temper your enthusiasm to rush into decisions regarding your interiors. Leave fabric swatches where you see them day after day. Look at paint samples in daylight,

IMMERSE YOURSELF

The more exposure you have to good design, the easier it becomes to develop your own style.
• Haunt the bookstores that have large selections of shelter magazines and stacks of books on decorating, design and architecture.
• Attend show houses, especially the Designer Showcase homes presented twice annually by ASID, and visit model homes, apartments or lofts.

185

EMBRACE THE MASTER PLAN

Gone are the days when area home-owners felt the need to move into a "finished" interior. They take their time now, letting the flow of their evolving lifestyle and needs guide them along the way.

evening light and artificial light. If possible, have everyone in the family "test sit" a kitchen chair for a week before ordering the whole set, and play with furniture placement. This small investment of time will pay handsomely in the end.

Be prepared to wait for your interiors to be installed. It's realistic to allow eight months to complete a room, and eight to 12 months to decorate an entire home.

Decide if you want your interiors to be installed piecemeal or all at once. Many designers recommend waiting for one installation, if you have the patience. Homeowners tend to rethink their original decisions when pieces are brought in as they arrive. By waiting for one installation, they treat themselves to a stunning visual and emotional thrill. ■

Interior Designers

ALEXA WHEELER INTERIORS ....**(203) 256-1704**
79 Gorhman Road, Fairfield   Fax: (203) 256-9544
See Ad on Page: 195
Principal/Owner: Alexa Wheeler
e-mail: alexaw@optonline.com
Additional Information: Complete interior design services from project conception to completion.

ARCHITREASURES INTERIORS..**(914) 666-4242**
215 Railroad Park, Bedford Hills   Fax: (914) 666-3092
See Ad on Page: 200
Principal/Owner: Renee Jordan
e-mail: architreasures@aol.com
Additional Information: At Architreasures Interiors our commitment to our clients needs
and vision, paired with our commitment to excellence, enables us to create spaces of beauty,
warmth and personality.

AUDREY MORGAN INTERIORS ....**(203) 227-1344**
19 Post Road West, Westport   Fax: (203) 454-2392
See Ad on Page: 181-183
Principal/Owner: Audrey Morgan & Joyce G. Clear
Website: www.audreymorgan.com e-mail: audreymorgan@mindspring.com
Additional Information: Exceptional design. Exceptional Service. Exceptional Clients.

BANKS DESIGN ASSOCIATES, LTD..**(203) 259-8899**
368 Center Street, Southport   Fax: (203) 259-1703
See Ad on Page: 57
Principal/Owner: Cheryl Dixon
Website: www.banksdesigassociates.com e-mail: :
Additional Information: Since 1984, Banks Design Associates has been creating beautiful archi-
tecture and interiors for families who appreciate tradition, quality and creativity.

BEAUTIFUL HOME ....**(203) 422-2777**
103 Greenwich Avenue, Greenwich   Fax: (203) 422-2315
See Ad on Page: 191
Principal/Owner: Nancy Almeida
Additional Information: Exclusive custom designs in furniture, doors, libraries and mantels.
Complete interior design service.

BUDD & ALLARDYCE INTERIORS LLC ....**(203) 762-1235**
84 Keelers Ridge Road, Wilton   Fax: (203) 762-2859
See Ad on Page: 188, 189
Principal/Owner: Nancy Budd
Additional Information: Budd & Allardyce Interiors specializes in custom interior design for the
discriminating homeowner. They combine principals of good design with each client's own personality and style.

CHAMPA INTERIORS..**(203) 255-9902**
1160 Catamount Road, Fairfield   Fax: (203) 254-6545
See Ad on Page: 201
Principal/Owner: Debora P. Champa
Additional Information: Interior Design is a collaborative effort. The interiors I do are a reflection
of my clients, not me. I'm just an interpreter.

187

continued on page **198**

Budd & Allardyce Interiors

NANCY BUDD

Budd & Allardyce Interiors

NANCY BUDD

Elegant, Creative, Timeless Design

84 Keelers Ridge Road   (203) 762-1235 P
Wilton, Connecticut 06897   (203) 762-2859 F

INTERIOR DESIGN

CUSTOM WORKROOM

FURNITURE

CARPETS

WALLPAPER

ACCESSORIES

DÉCOR
of Greenwich, Inc

164 MASON STREET, GREENWICH   203-869-710

Beautiful Home

GREENWICH'S CUSTOM SHOP

Exclusive Custom Furniture, Doors and Libraries

Elegant Wood Mantels

Custom Window Treatments

Fine European Fabrics

Handpainted Lamps and Speciality Shades

Decorative Accessories

Complete Interior Design Service

103 Greenwich Avenue, Greenwich, CT
203.422.2777
(Next to CVS in the rear parking area)

DAVENPORT & CO.
DESIGN
RESOURCE

JANE GLEASON
ISABELLE VANNECK
DAVENPORT & CO. DESIGN RESOURCE

79 East Putnam Avenue, Greenwich, CT 06830
Tel: 203-629-9181 • Fax: 203-629-1090
davnportco@aol.com

DIANA SAWICKI
INTERIOR DESIGN INC.
14 WARNOCK DRIVE
WESTPORT, CT 06880
TEL 203•454•5890
FAC 203•454•5869
DSAWIGOR@AOL.COM

DIANA SAWICKI ASID

Alexa Wheeler Interiors

Interior Design

79 Gorham Road
Fairfield, CT 06430
Phone (203) 256-1704   Fax (203) 256-9544

Sheridan Furniture Barn

Discounted Major Brands

Immediate Delivery

Sheridan Interiors

Full Service Design Firm

Designing Fairfield's Best for 28 Years

198 Danbury Road, Wilton, CT 06897
Barn 203.762.7985 • Sheridan Interiors 203.762.2888
Fax 203.762.9878

Interior Designers

CHRISTMAN STUART INTERIORS ....**(203) 431-4752**
381 Main Street, Ridgefield   Fax: (203) 431-8236
See Ad on Page: 205
Principal/Owner: Debbie Christman

CONSTRUCTION CONCEPTS CORP. ....**(203) 325-8102**
87 Brookhollow Lane, Stamford   Fax: (203) 357-1984
See Ad on Page: 135,199,289
Principal/Owner: Jeffrey Glass
Website: www.constconceptscorp.com e-mail: ccc@constconceptscorp.com
Additional Information: A full-service custom home & remodeling design/build company.

COUNTRY DESIGN, INC. ....**(203) 966-9131**
88 Elm Street, New Canaan   Fax: (203) 966-9890
See Ad on Page: 207
Principal/Owner: Fiona Sigg
Additional Information: Country Design is represented by 2 stores and 7 designers. Our
furniture store, Country Design II showcases most major high-end llines of furniture. Our
design store has every fabric and accessory source. We have been established for 25 years and
shop weekly for our clients in New York and bi-annually in High Point and Europe.

DAVENPORT & CO. ....**(203) 629-9181**
79 East Putnam Avenue, Greenwich   Fax: (203) 629-1090
See Ad on Page: 192, 193
Principal/Owner: Jane Gleason/Isabelle Vanneck

DÉCOR OF GREENWICH ....**(203) 869-7100**
164 Mason Street, Greenwich   Fax: (203) 869-8363
See Ad on Page: 190
Principal/Owner: Wende Kamnitzer

DIANA SAWICKI INTERIOR DESIGN, INC. ....**(203) 454-5890**
14 Warnock Drive, Westport   Fax: (203) 454-5869
See Ad on Page: 194
Principal/Owner: Diana Sawicki ASID
e-mail: dsawigor@aol.com
Additional Information: High-end interior design firm that offers personal attention and excellent
customer service, creating warm, sophisticated interiors in a timeless style.

DUJARDIN DESIGN ASSOCIATES ....**(203) 622-8882**
112 Mason Street, Greenwich   Fax: (203) 622-0134
See Ad on Page: 204
Principal/Owner: Trudy Dujardin/ F. Price Connors
Website: www.dujardindesign.com e-mail: info@dujardindesign.com

EDELMANN KITCHEN, BATH & INTERIOR DESIGN ....**(203) 730-1144**
128 Greenwood Avenue, Bethel   Fax: (203) 744-6029
See Ad on Page: 209, 297
Principal/Owner: Joseph Edelmann

GRAYSON CONSTRUCTION CO. INC. ....**(203) 221-7426**
965 Post Road East, Westport   Fax: (203) 221-0924
See Ad on Page: 154, 206
Principal/Owner: Anne Leepson
e-mail: grayson2000@aol.com
Additional Information: High-end residential and commercial interiors.

continued on page **226**

CONSTRUCTION
CONCEPTS
CORP.™

CATHY GLASS INTERIORS

87 Brookhollow Lane
Stamford, CT 06902
(203) 325-8102
Email: ccc@constconceptscorp.com
www.constconceptscorp.com

ARCHITREASURES
Interiors
Renee Jordan

215 Railroad Avenue ✦ Bedford Hills, NY 10507
Phone (914) 666-4242 ✦ Fax (914) 666-3092

Champa Interiors

1160 Catamount Road
Fairfield, CT 06430
Tel: 203-255-9902 Fax: 203-254-6545

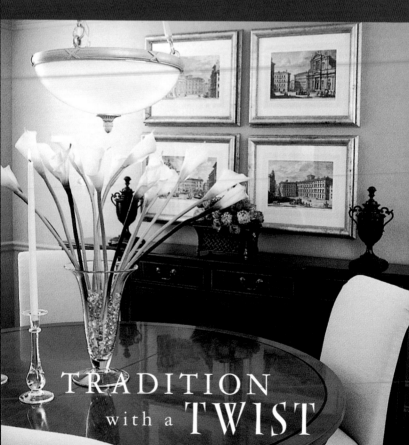

TRADITION
with a TWIST

WESTO
CAPITA
Management, L

implicity **&** *Style*

Photography by Bob Capazzo

ROBIN McGARRY & ASSOCIATES
INTERIOR DESIGN

Professional Member, A.S.I.D.

WESTON | CT | 203.454.1825

DUJARDIN DESIGN ASSOCIATES INC.

Interior Design & Architecture / Environmental Consulting

GREENWICH, CT   ph 203-622-8882   /   NANTUCKET, MA   ph 508-228-1120

DEBBIE CHRISTMAN STUART, ASID

IMAGINATIVE.

INVENTIVE.

INSPIRED.

CHRISTMAN STUART INTERIORS

381 MAIN STREET, RIDGEFIELD, CT 06877
203-431-4752

Architectural Design • Construction • Interior Design

Anne Leepson - Principal

965 Post Road East
Westport, CT 06880
Phone (203) 221.7426 • Fax (203) 221.0924
GraysonCo2000@aol.com

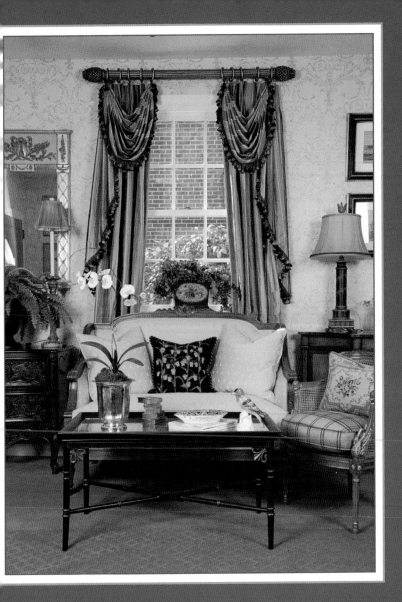

Beautiful Reproduction Furniture • Decorative Accessories • Fine Unique Prints & Oils • Custom Upholstery • Full Interior Design Services

COUNTRY DESIGN, INC.

Tel 203-966-9131 • Fax 203-966-9890
88 Elm Street • New Canaan, CT 06840

COUNTRY DESIGN II

Tel 203-966-2949
150 Elm Street • New Canaan, CT 06840

"You feel extremely welcome and relaxed in the dining room of this wonderful Norman Style Tudor home. The period furniture and accessories comfort you as the meal is served. The family is content, my job is complete."

GREGORY ALLAN CRAMER & COMPANY

Interior Design and Decoration
New Rochelle, New York
914.636.4393

EDELMANN llc
KITCHEN · BATH & Interior Design

128 Greenwood Avenue
Bethel, CT 06801
203.730.1144
Fax 203.744.6029

Photo by **David R. Sloane**

210

PROSPERITY INTERIORS, INC.

Susan Marcus Lamy, ASID: "The clients wanted their family room to have the understated elegance of a European country home. We used a palette of blues, soft yellows and whites with a myriad of pattern blending on window treatments and upholstery. A neutral tone of wheat on the faux-finished walls and on the area rug completes the room."

Desi

DUJARDIN DESIGN ASSOCIATES, INC.

Trudy Dujardin/F. Price Connors: "For this Massachusetts summer home the vision was to create a 1920s Sconset cottage, combining an Atlantic coast ambiance with the client's personal antique collection from Europe. The open floor plan makes rooms flow into each other, so the textiles and accessories reappear in different locations in the house. Stars on the exterior light fixtures adorn the front door, opening to starry carpet descending the stairs, then carried along the hallway toward the French doors opening to the sea."

Photo by Terry Pommett

ROBIN MC GARRY & ASSOCIATES

Photo by **Bob Capazzo**

Robin McGarry, ASID: "Children's bedrooms have become havens where a child can dream of fairytales in their own storybook room. This room was created for a little girl. The girl's room was based on the book *The Secret Garden*, depicting an English garden scene with stone walls, a pond, bird bath and much more. The girl loves flowers and gardens, so the theme was a natural inspiration for me. Accessories such as the weeping cherry blossom tree that hangs from the corner add a nice three-dimensional touch."

ners

AUDREY MORGAN INTERIORS, INC.

Audrey Morgan: "This early English 19th century dining table is graced by the simplicity of antique chairs and complemented by soft colors against amber woods. The Caucasian rug tones – aquas, ochres, siennas and warm creams – fill the room with luminosity. The starkness of

Photo by **Olson Photographic**

contemporary black and white photos, framed with large white mats, contrast the antique mirror, console and early ballast jars. Shirred silk panels on wood poles soar into the upper space, and the crystal chandelier adds sparkle to this dining room."

HAMPTON COURT INTERIORS

Linda Maine: "This casual 'nautical library' was designed as a library and home office for a sailing enthusiast. It provides a place for trophies, photographs and nautical memorabilia to be proudly displayed. Custom color nautical blueprint fabric is used for draperies, and upholstery furniture acts as the backdrop for mahogany tables and desk. Vintage fabrics cover the pillows, and the room is completed by mercury glass and mid-20th century accessories."

Desi

Photo by **Rosemarie Stiller**

CONSTRUCTION CONCEPTS CORP.

Cathy Glass: "When designing any room in the home, we use colors that have an immediate impact. These rich, full colors give the room warmth and excitement, as well as being a dramatic backdrop for patterned fabrics and rugs. Antique furnishings and collectibles, which give any room its character, are enhanced when shown against bold color."

Photo by **William Kildow**

BANKS DESIGN ASSOCIATES, LTD.

Linda Banks: "Simplicity and a timeless spirit were the design objectives for this active family. They requested a distinctly nautical and American style throughout for their new Connecticut home on the water. We selected relaxed, comfortable furnishings for the primary seating in this living room. The bold graphic quality of the vintage American flag defined the color palette and set the precedent for a clean, fresh interior."

iners

GRAYSON CONSTRUCTION CO.

Susan McKeon: "Our client, a busy professional woman, wanted her bedroom to be a warm, comfortable retreat to which she could retire at the end of the day. A European hand-woven carpet was laid over existing wall-to-wall carpeting to set the rich palette of the room. In order to make the ceiling appear higher we hung brown velvet draperies from custom-made iron rods that were mounted from the ceiling. The soft toile sheers cover the old windows, but allow light to filter into the room. French antiques were selected to complement the scale of the room, and the old ceiling light fixture was replaced with a lovely French chandelier. The cozy but quietly elegant feeling offers just the reprieve our client was hoping for."

GREGORY ALLAN CRAMER & CO.

Gregory Allan Cramer: "'Antique, mid-century Modern and numerous other wonderful art works create a gallery feeling in this upscale loft apartment in New Rochelle, Westchester County. The hardwood floors, tin ceiling and gallery lighting showcase the couple's love of eclectic personal objects."

Photo by **Dawn Glover**

Desi

COUNTRY DESIGN, INC.

Fiona Sigg: "This room illustrates the collected look. Armless loveseats provide an ideal setting to incorporate two seating areas and also maintain a flow essential for social gatherings and holidays. The use of different fabrics, solids, florals, stripes and patterns with the correct scale and proportions balances the dimensions of the room. Faux painted walls and under-mantel incorporate color tones to evoke an inviting feeling.

Small details such as tassels and trim set a formal tone and create a balance in the design layout. Recessed panel molding gives the fireplace significance in the center of the room, and offers the seating area a focal point."

BEAUTIFUL HOME

Nancy Almeida: "In this large and stately home, my clients wanted the dining room to be a focal point of the house because it is the first room one sees when one enters. I placed emphasis on the window because it overlooks a beautiful garden area. The window treatments frame the window without enclosing it, so as to block the view. The custom-made mahogany dining table has hand-carved gold leaf detailing around the apron. Because my clients had only four dining chairs, the remaining chairs were reproduced exactly the same—so much so that no one can tell which are the originals and which are the copies. Light rose tone-

Photo by **Sandy Reicino**

on-tone wallpaper grace the walls, along with a faux finish under the chair rail. To give balance to the room, custom mahogany corner cabinets were designed and made. The end result is a classic and elegant dining room that welcomes guests to dine in style."

ners

CONNECTICUT DESIGN CENTER

Martin L. Abbatiello: "Our clients wanted us to create a room in their New York loft that was comfortable, with simplicity and functionality. It needed to be contemporary with a touch of Zen! They wanted it contemporary but not modern, not over-accessorized. Swaim upholstery and an ebony-colored cocktail table were our primary pieces to achieve the result. The table was made of a wormy maple. The wood was left in its natural state, with worm holes in it, in order to achieve this feeling of softness, the yin and yang of Zen. We chose an earthy, pale green for the sofa, and a rock water fountain provided another calming touch, filling the room with the constant, peaceful sound of trickling water."

PALLADIO INTERIOR DESIGN

Carolyn Coffman: "This library was created in the former 1920s weekend residence of Helena Rubinstein. The Mediterranean-style home was the perfect setting for rich, luxurious textures and colors. Each element of the room, however, was chosen for its comfort and function, as well as aesthetic appeal. What was once one of the truly wasted spaces of the

home has been turned into a warm and inviting room. Comfort, function and luxury work together harmoniously here in creating a beautiful library/ living room, which has now become a vital part of the home."

Photo by **Walter Putrycz**

BUDD & ALLARDYCE INTERIORS, LLC

Nancy Budd: "Before designing any space, we take our cues from the client and the architecture. This space is a family room, meant for casual living. The built-ins house a television behind the cabinets, brick fireplace, and wood pass-through. Warm colors and soft, rich fabrics establish an inviting palette for this room, which complements the client's lifestyle and projects a feeling of comfort and timelessness."

ners

RADCLIFF INTERIORS, INC.

Ann Radcliff Munigle:
"A small space and a limited budget made for a challenging task. In this master bathroom, we eliminated the one sink, small tub, a wall dividing the toilet from the tub and all of the brown tile. We installed custom cabinetry with two sinks, new tile and wallpaper and a seamless glass shower stall. We also added recessed lighting to the existing ceiling light and exhaust. The master bathroom was transformed into a bright, inviting, functional space."

Photo by **Nick Saraco**

CHRISTMAN STUART INTERIORS

Susan Leggitt: "In this Colonial Williamsburg living room, the hand-blocked English linen print on the draperies is repeated on the camelback sofa, while the various tones of the Pakistani rug enhance the hue of the wainscoting. The Chippendale bench and Sheraton loveseat near the fireplace make a cozy conversational grouping."

218

Desi

DIANA SAWICKI INTERIOR DESIGN, INC.

Diana Sawick, ASID: "The project: to create an inviting space where family can gather...a warm, intimate place to share a family's special moments. By selecting leather, corduroy and chenille in natural colors, I related the indoors to the outside wooded surroundings. The accessories emphasized the family's love of handmade and collected objects. The room is at once casual and inviting, providing an atmosphere of happiness and relaxation."

ALEXA WHEELER INTERIORS

Alexa Wheeler: "Long gone are the days of stiff, unapproachable formal living rooms. This living room balances formality and comfort, creating an inviting setting. The custom-built upholstery, in cozy velvet and soft paisley jacquard, has extra deep poly/down seats for comfort, but still maintains the clean and formal lines appropriate to the room. These fabric choices fulfill the dual need of a formal look with durability and comfort

for daily use. Further, the fabrics complement the fine antiques and artwork, creating a feel of subtle elegance. Marble lamps stand atop bamboo-carved British khaki teak end tables with cane shelving, and a 19th century Chinese serving table is used as a coffee table. Light is brought in through French doors leading to a sunroom with skylights. Recessed lights are combined with the softness of ambient lighting, contributing to the comfortable formality of the room."

ners

HAMPTON COU

390 Main Street
Ridgefield, CT 06877

RT INTERIORS

Tel 203.438.6300
Fax 203.438.7637

All Interiors: Ken Hockin, ASID

Kent Pruzan Interiors, LLC

Interior Decoration And Design

Kent Pruzan & Linda Yepez, ASID

At The Mill

328 Pemberwick Road Greenwich, CT 06831
Tel 203 531-5959   Fax 203 531-1270

Karen Houghton

INTERIORS

41 N. Broadway, Nyack, NY 10960   845-358-0133

Maggie Cole

Lowenthal PARTNERS
interior design

Dianne Lowenthal · ASID
Lynda Saraceni · ASID

2 Park Street
Norwalk, CT 06851

T/203.846.1329
F/203.847.5162

info@lowenthalpartners.com

VI
VANDAMM INTERIORS

VICTORIA VANDAMM

375 GREENWICH AVENUE

GREENWICH CONNECTICUT

203-622-9070

Interior **Designers**

GREGORY ALLAN CRAMER & COMPANY ....(914) 636-4393
50 Webster Avenue, New Rochelle   Fax: (914) 636-6716
See Ad on Page: 208
Principal/Owner: Gregory Allan Cramer
e-mail: gacramer@aol.com
Additional Information: Full service interior design for residential and commercial with retail
store at 43 Lawton Street Design, 43 Lawton Street, New Rochelle10801 914-637-7500

HAMPTON COURT INTERIORS...(203) 438-6300
390 Main Street, Ridgefield   Fax: (203) 438-7637
See Ad on Page: 220, 221
Principal/Owner: Linda Maine ASID/James F. Tulles
e-mail: lmaine@aolcom
Additional Information: Interior design with a retail showroom of fine furniture and accessories.

KAREN HOUGHTON INTERIORS...(845) 358-0133
41 North Broadway, Nyack   Fax: (845) 358-0405
See Ad on Page: 223
Principal/Owner: Karen Houghton
e-mail: khi@spyral.net   Additional Information: Karen Houghton Interiors has a reputation for
creating elegant, comfortable interiors. We work closely with our clients to design homes which
reflect their personality and lifestyle.

KATHERINE COWDIN, INC., INTERIOR DESIGN.......................................(203) 661-4844
33 East Elm, Greenwich   Fax: (203) 661-6237
See Ad on Page: 227
Principal/Owner: Dotsie Doran

KENT PRUZAN INTERIORS, LLC ....(203) 531-5959
328 Pemberwick Road, Greenwich   Fax: (203) 531-1270
See Ad on Page: 222
Principal/Owner: Kent Pruzan
Additional Information: Residential interior design firm specializing in a variety of high end interiors noted for individuality and service. Our mission is to provide you with interior design services that not only fulfill your requirements, but exceed your expectations.

LOWENTHAL PARTNERS INTERIOR DESIGN ....(203) 846-1329
2 Park Street, Norwalk   Fax: (203) 847-5162
See Ad on Page: 224
Principal/Owner: Dianne Lowenthal, ASID/Lynda
Website: www.lowenthalpartners.com e-mail: info@lowenthalpartners.com
Additional Information: LPid is an established high-end design firm whose city and country interiors have been featured in several Fairfield County showhouses and national publications. We
specialize in the thoughtful design and decoration of interiors and pre-construction planning of
new homes and renovations.

PALLADIO INTERIOR DESIGN ....(914) 238-1408
108 Campfire Road, Chappaqua   Fax: (914) 238-1407
See Ad on Page: 228
Principal/Owner: Carolyn Coffman
Additional Information: Interior design and architectural services available for residential and
commercial projects. Catering to the functional requirements and personal style of each individual client with a reputation for creating distinctive yet timeless interiors.

continued on page **234**

Katherine Cowdin, Inc.

INTERIOR DESIGN

DOTSIE DORAN
AMY ANDREWS
DAPHNE DEMAS
NANCY ELSBERRY
RANDI FILOON
NICOLE LIMBOCKER

33 EAST ELM STREET, GREENWICH
(203) 661-4844 (212) 371-3350

PALLADIO

INTERIOR DESIGN

108 Campfire Road
Chappaqua, New York 10514
Tel 914 238-1408 • Fax 914 238-1407

Prosperity
INTERIORS, INC.

When you're ready for the best!

Understated elegance is our trademark.

1330 Post Road East, Westport, CT 06880
230-255-2734
www.prosperityinteriors.com
By chance or by appointment

V.W. INTERIORS, LLC

25 HALSEY DRIVE
OLD GREENWICH, CT 06870
(2 0 3)   6 3 7 - 3 3 4 8
W W W . V W I N T E R I O R . C O M
V W I N T @ O P T O N L I N E . N E T
M E M B E R   A S I D

The A
Grou

THE ASHLEY GROUF

The Ashley Group is the largest publisher of visual
designing, building and decorating information and
For more on the many products of **The Ashle**
Reed Business Information (www.ReedBusiness.com
U.S. provider of business information to 1
and retail. Reed's rich content portfoli
Publishers Weekly, Design News and 152 othe

shley

RESOURCE COLLECTION

...home resource images. It provides the highest quality
...resources available to upscale consumers and professionals.
Group, visit our website at www.theashleygroup.com.
...a member of the Reed Elsevier plc group, is a leading
...vertical markets, including entertainment, manufacturing
...encompasses more than 140 Web sites as well as *Variety*,
...market-leading business-to-business magazines

Interior Designers

PROSPERITY INTERIORS, INC. ....**(203) 255-2734**
1330 Post Road East, Westport   Fax: (203) 255-6131
See Ad on Page: 229
Principal/Owner: Susan Marcus Lamy
Website: www.prosperityinteriors.com e-mail: lamydesign@aol.com
Additional Information: A full service interior design firm offering sophisticated high-end design
and home furnishings in a variety of classic and eclectic styles. Designer Susan Lamy is
renowned for understated elegance, her wonderful use of color, fabulous fabric selection, and
for creating rooms that are beautiful, comfortable and reflect the client's dreams, taken to the
highest levels of realization. Ms. Lamy is a member of ASID and
writes a design column for the Minuteman Newspapers and for Home Resource & Design
Magazine.

RADCLIFF INTERIORS, INC. ....**(203) 698-0788**
1465 East Putnam Ave., No. 109, Old Greewich   Fax: (203) 698-2174
See Ad on Page: 230
Principal/Owner: Ann Radcliff Munigle

ROBIN MCGARRY & ASSOCIATES ....**(203) 454-1825**
11 Riverfield Drive, Weston   Fax: (203) 454-9999
See Ad on Page: 202,203
Principal/Owner: Robin McGarry ASID
Additional Information: Full service interior design, new construction (providing full specifications for contractors), renovation, budget analysis, custom-designed window treatments, all
interior furnishings and finishes.

SHERIDAN INTERIORS ....**(203) 762-2888**
198 Danbury Road, Wilton,CT   Fax: (203) 762-9878
See Ad on Page: 196, 197
Principal/Owner: Thomas Sheridan/Kerry Sheridan
Additional Information: A leading Fairfield County design firm for 27 years with a brand new
barn showcasing their lines of upholstery and case goods.

V. W. INTERIORS LLC ....**(206) 373-3348**
25 Halsey Drive, Old Greenwich
See Ad on Page: 231
Principal/Owner: Veronica Whitlock

VANDAMM INTERIORS OF GREENWICH ....**(203) 622-9070**
375 Greenwich Avenue, Greenwich   Fax: (203) 622-3112
See Ad on Page: 225
Principal/Owner: Victoria Vandamm
e-mail: VVDVI@aol.com
Additional Information: Landscaping

234

photo courtesy of **Alfredo LDC**

LANDSCAPING

235
Natural Selection

242
**Landscape
Architects**

248
**Landscape
Contractors**

252a
**Timeline:
Landscaping Your
Dream Home**

256
**Hardscape,
Masonry, Water
Gardens**

262
**Swimming Pools,
Spas & Sport**

268
**Decks &
Architectural
Elements**

273
Landscape Lighting

278
Automatic Gates

The Professional Services of Alfredo LDC

Alfredo LDC has all the materials and capabilities required for the completion of any landscape design project, from luxury home landscaping to large property maintenance. Although one of the largest and most successful landscape companies in the tri-state area, Alfredo LDC has been offering its customers the hands-on attention of a family business for two generations.

Please call for a free consultation

Alfredo LDC

The Landscape Specialists

Armonk, New York 10504•Phone 914-666-3950

Alfredo LDC

The Landscape Specialists

Alfredo LDC approaches your landscape with vision. Committed to environmental integrity, the company can bring out all the natural beauty of your property. Alfredo LDC's landscape professionals will complete the project on schedule, while maintaining the highest level of quality.

Armonk, New York 10504•Phone 914-666-3950

Natural
Selection

Landscaping is the only design area that is, by nature, intended to evolve over time. The philosophy behind landscape design has evolved as well. There are various styles for your unique landscape design statement. These include traditional European formality, the naturalism of Prairie Style or the simplicity and order of Far Eastern influences.

More and more people are blurring the divisions between inside and outside environments, with expanses of windows, patios designed to act as "outdoor rooms," and various types of glass and screened enclosures to enjoy the outdoors whatever the weather. Landscape becomes almost an architectural element at times, creating an interplay and synthesis of indoors and outdoors.

Water gardens are growing in popularity as people learn that these are ecosystems in their own right, requiring little additional time or attention once they are established. Think of it: the soothing splash of a waterfall or babbling brook right in your own backyard!

Photo courtesy of **SGDA, LLC**

GETTING BACK TO THE GARDEN

Think of the land as a canvas for a work of environmental art. Think of the landscape professional as an artist who uses nature to translate your needs and desires into a living, breathing reality. A formal English garden or seemingly artless arrangements of native plantings, a winding cobblestone walkway leading from a hand-laid brick driveway – these are the kinds of possibilities you can explore. When you work with a professional who is personally committed to superior work and service, designing a landscape is full of creativity, new ideas and satisfying results.

GETTING A LANDSCAPE STARTED

Selecting a landscape professional to create and maintain a distinctive landscape is one of the most important decisions you'll make as a homeowner. In making your decision, consider these questions:

• Do you want to hire a landscape architect or a landscape designer? Landscape architects have met the criteria to be registered by the state. Many hold university degrees in landscape architecture. A landscape designer generally has had training and/or experience in horticulture and landscaping and may also have a background in art.

• Do you want full service? If you want to work with one source, from design to installation to maintenance, only consider those who offer comprehensive service.

Allow approximately one month to interview at least two professionals before making a decision. Start even earlier if you plan to install a swimming pool, which should be dug the same time as the foundation of a new home.

Invite the professional to your home to acquaint him or her with your tastes and personality. Be prepared to answer questions like:

• Do you prefer a formal or informal feel? The formality of symmetrical plantings or the informal look of a natural area?

• Is there a place or feeling you'd like to recreate? Summers spent at the cottage? Your childhood home?

• What colors do you like? Your answer may impact the flowers chosen for your gardens.

• Are you a gardener? Would you like to be? If you're fond of flower, herb or vegetable gardening, your landscape professional will plan and build the appropriate garden.

THE VISION

First you choose your views, then you build your home. To create a harmonious balance between your home and its surroundings, your architect should be invited to visit the site of your new home, and to meet with your landscape architect. The site can often serve as a catalyst, inspiring a design that responds to the uniqueness of the site. When all the team members are included, important details can be discussed and settled, leading to the best results for you and your family.

A PARTY OF GARDENS

As gardening attracts more devotees, people are rediscovering the satisfaction of creating imaginative gardens. Some ideas: butterfly gardens, fragrance gardens, moonlight gardens and Japanese gardens.

• How will you use the space? Will children use the backyard for recreation? Will you entertain outdoors? If so, will it be during the day or at night? Do you envision a pool, spa, gazebo or tennis courts there?

• Are you fond of lawn statuary, fountains or other ornamental embellishments?

• What architectural features must be considered? A wrap-around porch, large picture windows? Brick or stone exteriors?

• To what extent will you be involved in the process? Most landscape architects and designers are happy to encourage your involvement in this labor of love. There is a great deal of pleasure to be derived from expressing your personality through the land. A lifelong hobby can take root from this experience. Landscapers say their clients often join garden clubs after the completion of their project, and that many of their rehabbing jobs are done for clients who are already avid gardeners.

Landscape professionals expect that you will want to see a portfolio and inquire about their styles and experience. You may wish to request permission to visit sites of their installed landscapes. If you have special concerns, such as environmental issues, ask if the landscape professional has any experience in such areas.

COMPUTING LANDSCAPE FEES

It's easy to be caught off guard when you get a landscape proposal – it is a significant investment. Therefore, be sure you create a workable budget with your landscape professional before the project begins.

To give the outside of your home the appropriate priority status, plan to invest 10 to 25 percent of the cost of a new home and property in the landscaping. Although landscape elements can be phased in year after year, expect that the majority of the cost will be incurred in the first year. Maintenance costs must also be considered.

Billing practices vary among professionals and depend on the extent of the services you desire. Some charge a one-time fee for a contract that includes everything, some charge a flat design fee up front, others charge a design fee which is waived if you select them to complete the project, and still others build a design fee into the installation and/or maintenance cost.

THE PRICE OF BEING GREEN

What might it cost to create a new paver patio and walk, retaining wall and 600 sq. ft. of new planting beds along the front foundation?
Design contract fees - $500
Cut Lanonstone retaining wall (85 face sq. ft.) - $4,130
Concrete paver patio and walkway (480 sq. ft.) - $7,785
Planting development - 600 sq. ft. ($9,000) Includes shrubs, four mid-size trees, perennials, annual beds and sod.
Landscape management of one-half acre site for one season - $3,648
Weekly mowing, trimming and disposal; monthly pavement edging; monthly cultivation of open beds; preventative weed control; granular fertilization of beds; pruning; weekly dead heading of faded flowers, groundcover maintenance, turf fertilization.

Total - $25,063

237

A PROFESSIONAL DEVELOPS AN ENVIRONMENT

While you're busy imagining glorious gardens, your landscaper will be assessing practical issues like grading and drainage, the location of sewers, utility lines and existing trees, where and when the sun hits the land and the quality of the soil.

This important first step, the site analysis, should take place before construction has even begun, in the case of a new house. Site work helps ensure that the blueprints for your house won't make your landscape dreams impossible to achieve, and vice versa. If you've told your builder you want a breakfast nook, you'll probably get one regardless of the fact that it requires taking out a tree you value.

If you're considering installing a custom driveway or sidewalk, this early stage is the time to inform your builder. Ask your builder not to do construction outside the building envelope. You and your landscape professionals should design and build your driveway and walkways.

Expect the design process to take at least six weeks. During this time, the designer is developing a plan for the hardscape, which includes all of the man-made elements of your outdoor environment, and the many layers of softscape, which are the actual plantings. You can expect to be presented with a plan view that is workable and in harmony with your home, as well as your budget.

Hardscape elements, like irrigation systems and pavements, will be installed first, before a new house is completely finished. Softscape will go in later.

At the end of the first phase of your project, do not be surprised if the land does not look "complete." A landscape should be given time in the hands of nature to mature: three years for perennials, five years for shrubs and 15 years for trees.

LUXURY LIVING WITH A CUSTOM-DESIGNED POOL

The beauty and value of a custom-designed swimming pool are unmatched. A welcome design element to the landscape, a pool adds to the overall property value of the residence and creates greater use and enjoyment of the yard. As area families spend more of their leisure time at home, a pool answers their dreams of living well at home.

Deciding to build a swimming pool is best done as a new home is being designed so the pool can enhance the home and landscape architecture. By integrating the pool into the overall scheme, you'll be able to establish a realistic budget. One of the biggest mistakes homeowners make when purchasing

LIGHTING YOUR LOT

"Less is more" is the best philosophy when designing an outdoor lighting system. Today's beautiful, functional fixtures are themselves worthy of admiration, but their purpose is to highlight the beauty of your home while providing safe access to your property. Well-established lighting companies and specialty companies offer extensive landscape lighting product lines.

238

THE FINAL EVALUATION

When the landscape is installed, conduct a final, on-site evaluation. You should evaluate the finished design, find out what elements will be installed later and learn more about how the plan will evolve over time. You, the landscape designer or architect, project manager, and maintenance manager should be involved.

a pool is not initially getting all the features they want. It's difficult and costly to add features later.

The design process is time consuming. You may have four or more meetings with your pool professional before finalizing the design. Pool projects can be started at almost any time of year, so avoid getting caught in the busy season, spring to summer. Start getting approvals in January if you want to be enjoying your pool in the summer. The building process takes about two months, after obtaining permits. You should plan to have your pool dug at the same time as the home foundation. Pools are often accompanied by surrounding decks, so make sure your landscape architect, pool builder and hardscape contractor are coordinating efforts to construct both.

OUTDOOR LIVING

Today's homeowners, having invested the time and resources to create a spectacular environment, are ready to "have it all" in their own backyards.

Popular features of today's upscale homes include outdoor living rooms, screened rooms, gazebos and custom-made jungle gyms that will grow with your children. The extended living space perfectly suits our "cocooning" lifestyle, offering more alternatives for entertaining, relaxation and family time at home. Many new homes tout outdoor living space as a most tantalizing feature.

Multi-level terraces and decks offer extra living space and are functional enough to host almost any occasion. With thoughtful and proper design, they fulfill our dreams of an outdoor getaway spot. A multi-level deck built up and around mature trees can feel like a tree house. A spa built into a cedar deck, hidden under a trellis, can give you the feel of being in a far-off paradise.

Landscaping features that will compliment your outdoor living space include Koi ponds and imaginative theme gardens, such as moonlight, Zen, butterfly, fragrance, two-color and native plant gardens.

With so many options available, outdoor living provides a unique opportunity for homeowners to give their creativity free rein. However, consult with your landscape architect and contractor before deciding on these outdoor features. Some outdoor living space and garden options will function better than others, depending on what area of the country you reside in.

THINKING ABOUT OUTDOOR LIVING

If you're interested in pursuing any of the ideas mentioned above, then the first step is to arrange an on-site meeting with a landscape architect or a

EVERY KID'S FANTASY

In a yard with plenty of flat area: A wood construction expandable play system with: several slides, bridges to connect structures, a tic-tac-toe play panel, three to four swings, climbing ropes, fire pole, gymnastics equipment (trapeze, turning bar), sandbox pit, and a built-in picnic table with benches. Price Tag: around $26,000

In a smaller yard: a wood construction expandable play system with: a small fort, three swings, climbing ropes and two slides. Price Tag: around $6,500

GARDENER'S EDENS

Visit these artistic gardens for ideas and inspiration.

239

licensed contractor who is an expert in landscape building. An experienced professional will guide you through the conceptualization by asking questions like these:

• Why are you building the structure or specialty garden? For business entertaining, family gatherings, child or teen parties, private time?

• Do you envision a secluded covered area, a wide open expanse or both?

• Do you want a single level or two or more levels (the best option for simultaneous activities)?

• Will it tie in with current or future plans?

• How do you want to landscape the perimeter?

• Do you want a chiminea to be included in your outdoor living room, a certain variety of sand for your Zen garden or specific wood used in creating your gazebo?

Don't let obstacles block your thinking. Your gas grill can be moved. Decks are often built around trees and can convert steep slopes into usable space.

Once a design has been settled upon, expect at least three to four weeks to pass before a gazebo or other living space is completed. In the busy spring and summer months, it most likely will take longer. The time required to get a building permit (usually two to four weeks) must also be considered.

If you're landscaping during this time, be sure to coordinate the two projects well in advance. Building can wreck havoc on new plantings and your lawn will be stressed during construction.

A TYPICAL LANDSCAPE DESIGN TIMETABLE

• **One to two weeks to get the project on the boards**

+

• **One to two weeks to do the actual site and design work and prepare plans**

+

• **One week to coordinate calendars and schedule presentation meeting**

+

• **One to two weeks to leave the plans with the client and get their feedback**

+

• **One week to incorporate changes, create and get approval on a final design**

=

FIVE TO EIGHT WEEKS

DISTINCTIVE OUTDOOR SURFACES

Driveways, walkways, patios and hardscape features were once relegated to "last minute" status, with a budget to match. Today they are being given the full and careful attention they deserve. A brick paver driveway can be made to blend beautifully with the color of the brick used on the house. Natural brick stairways and stoops laid by master crafters add distinctive detail and value. Custom-cut curved bluestone steps, hand selected by an experienced paving contractor, provide years of pride and pleasure.

Hardscape installation doesn't begin until your new home is nearly complete, but for your own budgeting purposes, have decisions made no later than home mid-construction phase.

To interview a paving or hardscape contractor, set up an on-site meeting so you can discuss the nature of the project and express your ideas. Be ready to answer questions like:

• Will the driveway be used by two or three cars, or more? Do you need it to be wide enough so cars can pass? Will you require extra parking? Would you like a circular driveway? A basketball court?

• Will the patio be used for entertaining? Will it be a family or adult area, or both? How much furniture will you use? Should it be accessible from a particular part of the house?

• Do you have existing or future landscaping that needs to be considered?

• Would you like to incorporate special touches, like a retaining wall or a stone archway?

    If you're working with a full service landscape professional, and hardscape is part of the landscape design, be certain a hardscape expert will do the installation. A specialist's engineering expertise and product knowledge are vital to the top quality result you want. ■

WHY YOU NEED AN ARBORIST

It's not just your kids, dogs and the neighborhood squirrels trampling through your yard during construction. Excavation equipment, heavy trucks and work crews can spell disaster for your trees. Call an arborist before any equipment is scheduled to arrive and let him develop a plan that will protect the trees, or remove them if necessary.

Landscape
Architects

ALFREDO LDC...**(914) 666-3950**
P.O. Box 250, Armonk   Fax: (914) 666-2813
See Ad on Page: 235-237
Additional Information: Offers complete property care from luxury home landscaping to large property maintenance. Free consultation.

BEDFORD STONE & MASONRY ....**(914) 666-6404**
284 Adams Street, Bedford Hills   Fax: (914) 666-2526
See Ad on Page: 252-259
Principal/Owner: Daryl Burbank-Wear
Additional Information: Suppliers of quality masonry and landscape supplies since 1925.

D.L.T.C., INC. ....**(203) 866-1303**
205 Wilson Avenue, South Norwalk   Fax: (203) 866-3506
See Ad on Page: 246
Principal/Owner: Jon Sweeney
Website: www.dltcusa.com   e-mail: jon@dltcusa.com
Additional Information: Lawn installation and renovation & foundation, privacy plantings, athletic fields, sports turf, excavating, grading and drainage, stone walls, patios and walks.

KENT GREENHOUSE & GARDENS..**(860) 927-4436**
30 South Main Street, P.O. Box , Kent   Fax: (860) 927-4340
See Ad on Page: 244,245
Principal/Owner: Bruce & Debby Bennett
Website: www.kentgreenhouse.com   e-mail: infoatthegreenhouse@earthlink.net
Additional Information: Premiere design-build firm for complete site planning, landscape construction, project management.

RICHARD F. HEIN...**(914) 834-1414**
138 Larchmont Avenue, Larchmont   Fax: (914) 833-9569
See Ad on Page: 247
Principal/Owner: Richard F. Hein

SGDA ....**(203) 221-7848**
256 Post Road East, Westport   Fax: (203) 221-0582
See Ad on Page: 243
Principal/Owner: Shaun Grover
Website: sgda.net   e-mail: sgrover@sgda.net
Additional Information: Landscape design/build, pool design/build, gardens.

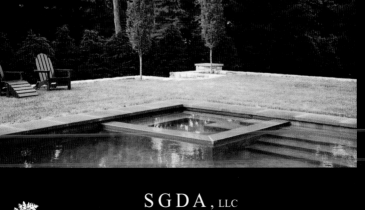

SGDA, LLC
SHAUN GROVER DESIGN ASSOCIATES

256 POST ROAD EAST • WESTPORT, CT 06820
TEL: 203.221.7848

Kent Greenhouse & Gardens
30 South Main Street Kent, CT. 06757
860-927-4436
www.kentgreenhouse.com

Design-Build
Services

~adding practical construction
solutions to design ingenuity~

Landscape Installations & Maintenance
Lawn Renovations Seed & Sod
Shade Trees & Ornamental Plantings
Privacy Plantings

DLTC
Darien Lawn & Tree Care, Inc.

www.dltcusa.com   203-866-1303

RICHARD F. HEIN
A R C H I T E C T S
ARCHITECTURE/LANDSCAPE

*"We see the garden in the architecture,
we see the architecture in the garden"*

138 Larchmont Avenue • Suite 4
Larchmont • NY 10538
t: 914.834.1414 • f: 914.833.9569
rfhdesign@hotmail.com

Landscape
Contractors

ALFREDO LDC..**(914) 666-3950**
Mount Kisco   Fax: (914) 666-2813
See Ad on Page: 235-237
Principal/Owner: Tom Alfredo
e-mail: alfredoldc13@hotmail.com
Additional Information: Offers complete property care from luxury home landscaping to large property maintenance. Free consultation.

B. HIRSCH LANDWORKS, LLC..**(203) 857-0087**
52 Day Street, Norwalk   Fax: (203) 854-1778
See Ad on Page: 249, 257
Principal/Owner: Brian Hirsch
e-mail: hirschlandworks@aol.com
Additional Information: At B. Hirsch Landworks we pride ourselves in personalized service as well as quality workmanship and craftmanship in all facets of landscape construction and masonry.

BARCHELLA CONTRACTING COMPANY, INC. ....**(914) 937-6521**
27 Eldredge Street, Port Chester   Fax: (914) 937-5758
See Ad on Page: 250, 251
Principal/Owner: Frank A. Barchella
Website: www.barchella.com e-mail: barchella@aol.com
Additional Information: In our 22 years of business we have developed an excellent reputation for dealing with our customers on a personal level.

D.L.T.C., INC. ....**(203) 866-1303**
205 Wilson Avenue, South Norwalk   Fax: (203) 866-3506
See Ad on Page: 246
Principal/Owner: Jon Sweeney
Website: www.dltcusa.com e-mail: jon@dltcusa.com
Additional Information: Lawn installation and renovation & foundation, privacy plantings, athletic fields, sports turf, excavating, grading and drainage, stone walls, patios and walks.

continued on page **252**

B. Hirsch Landworks. LLC

52 Day Street ■ Norwalk, CT 06854
203.857.0087 fax 203.854.1778

DESIGN

The following design books represent the premier works of selected designers, luxury homebuilders and architects.

This book is divided into 10 chapters, starting with design guidelines in regards to color, personality and collections. In these chapters, interior designer Perla Lichi presents beautiful, four-color photographs of the design commissions she has undertaken for clients accompanied by informative editorial on the investment value of professional interior design.

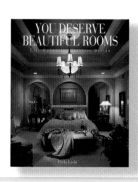

YOU DESERVE BEAUTIFUL ROOMS
120 pages, 9.75" x 14"
Home Design, Architecture
1-58862-016-6 $39.95   Hardcover

Orren Pickell is renowned as one of the nation's finest builders of custom homes. In this collection of more than 80 beautiful four-color photos and drawings, Pickell shows off some of his finest creations to give homeowners unique ideas on building a new home or adding to an existing one.

LUXURY HOMES & LIFESTYLES
120 pages, 9.75" x 14"
Architecture, Home Design
0-9642057-4-2 $39.95   Hardcover

Designer Susan Fredman has spent 25 years creating interiors, which, in one way or another, have been inspired by nature. In this book, she takes readers through rooms which reflect elements of our surroundings as they are displayed throughout the year.

AT HOME WITH NATURE
136 pages, 11.25" x 11.25"
Home Design, Architecture
1-58862-043-3 $39.95 Hardcover

The Ashley Group is proud to present these spec

CALL TO ORDE

BOOKS

Michigan-based architect Dominick Tringali uses the skill and knowledge that has brought him over 20 industry awards to share strategies on building the ultimate dream house. By combining unique concepts with innovative techniques and materials, Dominick's portfolio displays an array of homes noted for their timeless appeal. This $45 million collection of elite, custom homes contains the residences of notable CEOs, lawyers, doctors and sports celebrities including Chuck O'Brien, Joe Dumars, Tom Wilson, Larry Wisne and Michael Andretti.

RESIDENTIAL ARCHITECTURE:
LIVING PLACES
May 2002.
144 pages.
9" x 12"
Art & Architecture
1-58862-088-3
$39.95   Hardcover

Top rug dealers throughout the country are profiled to provide helpful hints to successfully choose a rug that best suits a buyer's needs. Readers will also gain an understanding of the key elements to consider when purchasing an Oriental rug. Over 100 images will help a potential buyer get a feel for the styles and patterns available through each dealer. Additionally, this book provides a solid directory of vendors who hold invaluable expertise in this arena.

PORTFOLIO SERIES:
ORIENTAL RUGS
November 2002.
150 pages.
10" x 10"
Home Design
1-58862-987-2
$29.95   Hardcover

s on luxury home style, design and architecture
888.458.1750

Landscape
Contractors

FEMIA LANDSCAPING, INC. ....**(203) 943-7332**
P.O. Box 815, Lewisboro   Fax: (203) 357-1850
See Ad on Page: 253
Principal/Owner: Anthony Fermia
Additional Information: From conceptual design to completion, we perform all aspects of land-
scape installation, unique stone designs and site development as well as the maintenance of the
above.

H.J. LUCIANO ....**(203) 838-9366**
7 Sherry Street, Norwalk
See Ad on Page: 254
Principal/Owner: Henry J. Luciano
Additional Information: Specializing in stone walls, walks, patios, fireplaces, chimneys, drive-
ways, driveway aprons and foundations.

PERFECT PLANTINGS ....**(203) 852-1687**
8 Melbourne Road, Norwalk   Fax: (203) 852-1687
See Ad on Page: 255
Principal/Owner: Jason S. Minoff
Additional Information: Creative gardening, landscape design and maintenance.z

Landscaping a **Custom** House

Develop Your Vision
You will have to spend a large part of your planning stage deciding what will be most flattering to your home, what plants will work best in the climate you live in, what aspects will require the most upkeep and what is most cost effective. Plan on spending at least two to three months developing ideas for your landscape project.

Research Landscapers
You may find the architect, designer or developer who can create your dreams, but plan on spending at least one month looking for that perfect fit. At this point, if you want to be fully involved with the overall process, it would be best to inform landscapers.

Choosing Subcontractors
The landscaper usually chooses the subcontractors who will assist on the project, but there are situations in which the client will choose. This process should take approximately one month.

WK 1 **WK8** **WK12**

Inspecting the Progress
Throughout the construction process, keep an eye on the progress. Be checking for items listed on your contract. When you are completely involved with the process, you will be able to be vocal about it.

Inspection
Your landscaper will first have to inspect, evaluate and map out your site. He or she will take site measurements, which may include extensive grading details. The process should take about one to two weeks to complete.

Designing
If all goes smoothly, the landscape architect or designer will be able to complete the final designs of your project within a week. Keep in mind that modifications will likely have to be made, so you will need to leave time for negotiation.

Ordering Materials
Once you've had the pleasure of choosing the plants and hardscape you desire, let your landscaper order them. This way, the responsibility for any problems is theirs alone.

WK16 **WK18** **WK19**

Design/Build Landscapers
A design/build landscaping firm offers its clients both the design of the project and the services to construct it. It differs from firms that may offer just design or construction services.

• **Who does what?** A landscape architect and a landscape designer perform similar tasks for projects, including surveying the land, discussing ideas with clients and drawing up plans. Due to an architect's more technical education, however, he or she is more eligible to handle the complicated projects. A landscape contractor installs the plants, trees, shrubs and hardscape of the project.

• **Who chooses the subcontractors?** This is a tedious process, because subcontractors are on other job sites and the new job has to be explained to each one. If you feel more comfortable meeting those who will potentially be working on your project, talk to your landscaper about being present at the interviews.

Garden Styling
Imaginative theme gardens are becoming popular. Some ideas: a garden of native plants, a one-or two-color garden, a fragrance garden, a Zen garden, a moonlight garden. Don't forget to consider including arbors, sculpture, benches or water features.

• **Pretty Pathways:** Depending on where and how it's quarried, natural stone can vary in color, and brick can vary as well. To be certain that your bricks, cobbles or specialty stones perfectly match, have your contractor buy them from the same lot. There's nothing quite as disconcerting as a pathway where the bricks or stones are slightly different colors.

Landscaping Your **Dream** Home

An important part of your dream home will be your outside surroundings, so, of course, you will want a beautiful landscape to complement your home. A great deal of thought will need to go into your landscaping project – this type of project does not solely consist of planting gorgeous flowers or deciding where to place trellises. The following guide will give you an idea of the steps and time that go into landscaping an upscale residential project.

Project Description

Landscaping an upscale, one-acre property, single family home. This project includes the installation of a swimming pool, masonry walls, fence, lighting, brick paving, a patio, and an assortment of shade trees and plants.

The Pool

The installation of your swimming pool should take about five to six weeks. However, a pool with bar stools, an elevated spa or special water features may take longer.

Hardscape

The materials used for hardscape, such as brick paver paths, patios and retaining walls, will dictate the time needed to create them: brick or cobblestone paths take more time than flagstone stepping paths, and mortarless flagstone patios take more time than those joined with mortar.

WK22

Softscape

Softscape includes all your plantings and sodding. Once the hardscape is finished, the softscaping can begin. Depending on the amount of detail in your plan, a one-acre area may take from six days to two weeks. Water features and lighting are not considered part of the softscape; they are added last.

WK28

Lighting

After the major aspects of your landscaping project are complete, the installation of lighting will begin. The overall process of lighting installation is fairly straightforward and will take a few days at the most to complete. Keep in mind, though, that setbacks do arise.

WK29

Final Inspection

Take an initial walk-through and get an overall sense of the finished project. Let your surroundings soak in and then take a second inspection. Bring your landscape architect along so you can let him or her know immediately if something just isn't right.

WK30

Payment

When it comes to making the final payment of your landscaping bill, be sure to review the charges carefully. Additions, rare plants and specialty products all add on to the final cost of your project. An estimated price for the landscape project described here is around $200,000.

Bumps in the Road: There are many reasons why your project may be delayed: materials are scarce or not in season, your new plants may not transplant well, or the specialty stones for your masonry walls are not available. Various problems can arise in the construction of a pool. And there will be numerous subcontractors working on your construction, who also work on other projects at the same time. For example, if the concrete layers are delayed two days and the electrician has other jobs scheduled, the added time could be significant. These setbacks are not pleasant, but they are realistic. Being emotionally prepared for such setbacks helps.

Types of Lighting

There are many ways to illuminate your garden. Do you entertain often? Try torches or tiki lights. Will you have a moonlight garden? Chinese hanging lanterns, floating candles in a glass bowl and lamp posts complement it well. Solar-powered lights are also popular now.

Grows on You: Keep in mind that some aspects of your completed landscape project may not be at their fullest potential when first implemented. Although good planning alleviates many surprises, it often takes one to three years for a landscape to mature. So if the flowers or shrubbery don't complement the walkway as you thought they would, give them some time. The flowers you want may not be available for another year, but you can always add a different variety. Larger, more permanent aspects of the landscape project, such as the swimming pool or a greenhouse, are, of course, much harder to change or alter, but can be done.

A Work in Progress

Landscapers expect their clients to freshen their landscaping every few years. So if you'd like to add more color or even move plants, don't be shy about giving your landscape professional a call.

SPONSORED BY:

BEDFORD STONE
&
MASONRY
SUPPLY CORP

P.O. BOX 475, 284 Adams Street
Bedford Hills, New York 10507
914-666-6404

In
Conclusion

The actual completion of a landscaping project varies greatly — a small project could take as little as one week and a large project can take as long as one year. There is no definite timeframe for a project like this. Talk to your landscaper in the initial interviewing and hiring process about timeframes. Ask if you can speak with past clients to find out how long their projects took to complete. This is not a small aspect of the overall completion of your dream home. Therefore, plan on dedicating a significant amount of time to the landscaping of your home. Eventually you will have a finished product that you can be proud of for years to come!

Special thanks to the American Society of Landscape Architects and Van Zelst Inc., Wadsworth, Illinois, for their contribution to this timeline and to Linda Oyama Bryan for her photography.

Produced by The Ashley Group
847.390.2882
www.theashleygroup.com

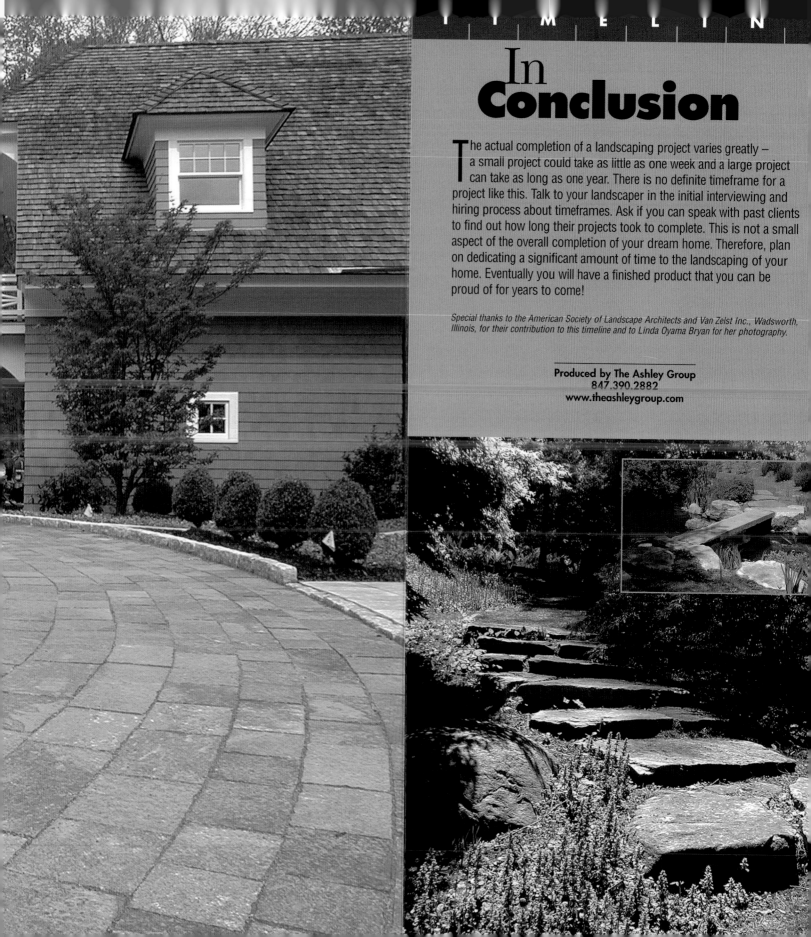

Experience our expertise, knowledge and professionalism. Dedicated to design and develop your dream property from concept to completion.

From conceptual design to completion, we perform all aspects of landscape installation, unique stone designs and site development, as well as the maintenance of the above.

FEMIA
LANDSCAPING
AND SITE DEVELOPMENT
INC ™

(914) 533-6333 • (203) 357-7689

H.J.Luciano

paving · Mason Contractor

Stone Walls, Walks and Patios
Brick Flagstone Fieldstone, Belgium Block
Fireplace / Chimneys
Fieldstone, Brick, Stucco
Driveways / Driveway Aprons
Asphalt, Native Stone, Belgium Block, Paving Stone, Cobblestone
Foundation
Concrete, Block, Stone/ Veneer
Serving Fairfield Country
Free Estimates • Fully Insured • One call does it all
7 Sherry Street • Norwalk, CT 06851 • (203) 838-9366

- Landscapes Design
- Garden Maintenance
- Complete Masonry Services
- Specialty Gardens
- Container Gardens
- Extensive Bulb Plantings
- Seasonal Planting
- Trees, Shrubs, Perennials
- Complete Property Maintenance
- Winter Holiday Decorating

*P*erfect *P*lantings, LLC

Let us design, install and maintain your *P*erfect garden.

We invite you to be part of our blooming success

203.852.1687

Hardscape
Contractors

ALFREDO LDC..**(914) 666-3950**
P.O. Box 250, Armonk   Fax: (914) 666-2813
See Ad on Page: 235-237
Principal/Owner: Tom Alfredo
e-mail: AlfredoLDC13@hotmail.com
Additional Information: Alfredo LDC offers complete property care from luxury home landscaping to large property maintenance. Free consultation.

B. HIRSCH LANDWORKS, LLC...**(203) 857-0087**
52 Day Street, Norwalk   Fax: (203) 854-1778
See Ad on Page: 249, 257
Additional Information: At B. Hirsch Landworks we pride ourselves in personalized service as well as quality workmanship and craftmanship in all facets of landscape construction and masonry.

CONNECTICUT BOMANITE SYSTEMS, INC. ....**(203) 778-5719**
17A Trowbridge Drive, Bethel   Fax: (203) 778-5242
See Ad on Page: 261
Principal/Owner: Tom Lockwood
e-mail: ct.bomanite@snet.net
Additional Information: Specialty architectural concrete paving systems for creative flooring and pavements, exterior and interior since 1984.

COPPOLA & SONS CONSTRUCTION CO. INC. ....**(203) 359-1625**
74 Old Mill Lane, Stamford   Fax:
See Ad on Page: 258
Principal/Owner: Joe Coppola

D.L.T.C., INC. ....**(203) 866-1303**
205 Wilson Avenue, South Norwalk   Fax: (203) 866-3506
See Ad on Page: 246
Principal/Owner: Jon Sweeney
Website: www.dltcusa.com   e-mail: jon@dltcusa.com
Additional Information: Lawn installation and renovation & foundation, privacy plantings, athletic fields, sports turf, excavating, grading and drainage, stone walls, patios and walks.

JASON ROBERTS, INC. ....**(203) 876-1204**
69 Eastern Steel Road, Milford   Fax: (203) 410-2666
See Ad on Page: 259
Principal/Owner: Robert Hartman Sr.

SUMMER RAIN ....**(203) 629-8050**
288 Valley Road, Cos Cob   Fax:
See Ad on Page: 260
Principal/Owner: Bill Gallagher

Let one of our well-trained knowledgeable landscape construction, masonry and/or maintenance team's help enhance your property to the fullest potential.

B. Hirsch Landworks, LLC

52 Day Street
Norwalk,CT 06854
203-857-0087 • Fax: 203-854-1778
Toll Free: 877-977-0087
hirschlandworks@aol.com

ELEGANT FORMS OF MASONRY AND BEYOND

OPPOLA & SONS
ONSTRUCTION
OMPANY INC.

Greenwich: (203) 869-9600 Stamford: (203) 359-1625

Web site: www.gccoppola.com E-mail: gccoppola@aol.com

BBB
MEMBER
CONNECTICUT

Any concrete surface can be transformed to look like Bluestone, Brick, Tile and much more!

After

Before

Salt, Oil,
Freeze/Thaw,
Water and Skid
RESISTANT
Plus Low Maintenance

 ## Jason Robert's Inc.®
Concrete Restoration & Resurfacing Specialists

69 Eastern Steel Road, Milford, CT 06460
1-800-801-7587 • 203-876-1152

www.jasonrobertsinc.net

Selected as one of the top 100 irrigation contractors
in the USA by the Irrigation Association.

$\mathcal{D}$esign and installation of quality turf and shrub irrigation systems
for more than 20 years. Prompt, courteous and professional service you can rely o*
Serving Fairfield and Westchester Counties.

Summer Rain

SPRINKLER SYSTEMS, INC.
TURF & SHRUB IRRIGATION

Bill Gallagher, President   Michael Hyland, Vice President
288 Valley Road, Cos Cob, Connecticut 06807   Telephone 203-629-8050 CT. J3 Lic. No. 2086*

www.summerrainsprinklers.com

Beautiful Hardscapes Inspired by Nature

CONNECTICUT
Bomanite
SYSTEMS INC.

Bomanite, the original cast-in-place architectural
concrete paving system offers a virtually limitless
palette of colors, textures and patterns.

Visit our showroom for creative designs & ideas.
Call for an appointment

17A Trowbridge Drive, Bethel, CT (off Rt. 53)
Ph. 203.778.5719 800.253.9097

Landscaping

Swimming
Pools & Spas

ALL AMERICAN CUSTOM POOL & SPAS, INC. ....**(203) 847-2704**
10 Vantassel Court, Norwalk   Fax: (203) 846-9852
See Ad on Page: 266, 267
<u>Principal/Owner</u>: Johnny Romano

ANTHONY & SYLVAN POOLS ....**(203) 655-4040**
528 Post Road, Darien   Fax:
See Ad on Page: 264
<u>Principal/Owner</u>: Cindy Mulholland

CARDILLO POOLS & SPAS LLC ....**(203) 325-8069**
114 Grove Street, Stamford   Fax: (203) 325-0576
See Ad on Page: 265
<u>Principal/Owner</u>: Luigi Casale
<u>Website</u>: cardillopools.com   <u>e-mail</u>: cardpools@aol.com
<u>Additional Information</u>: We specialize in building in-ground concrete custom pools, spas, waterfalls, spray fountains, patios and decks.

LANG POOLS, INC. ....**(203) 846-3943**
169 Westport Avenue, Norwalk   Fax: (203) 846-9347
See Ad on Page: 263
<u>Principal/Owner</u>: Christopher Lang
<u>Website</u>: www.langpools.com   <u>e-mail</u>: chris@langpools.com

🦢 *Lang Pools, Inc.*
"We Build Swimming Pools and Relationships!"

Come Visit Our Outdoor Show Pool!

169 Westport Avenue
Norwalk, CT

(203) 846-3943

www.Langpools.com

Lic#556566

Being home
has never been better.

What better way to welcome your family and friends to your home. From a tropical oasis with rock waterfall to a more contemporary design ideal for swimming laps or relaxing in your own spa, the choice is yours. Add beauty, tranquility and a special sanctuary to your life. With more than 50 years pool building experience, why trust any one else to build your dream pool.

ANTHONY & SYLVAN

Where America Swims℠

877-SAY-SWIM
www.anthonysylvan.com

Est. 1946 | NASDAQ: SWIM | 350,000 pools built nationwide
Computerized design | 100% financing available

CARDILLO POOLS & SPAS LLC

114 Grove St. • Stamford, CT 06901
203.325.8069 • 203.325.0576

The pleasure is all yours.
The quality is all ours.

*A*ll American Pools is the complete resource for the pool of your dreams. From design, through construction to service, our in-house departments can transform beautiful design concepts into your everyday reality. By using construction techniques and specifications perfected from over 25 years of pool building, we are able to give a lifetime warranty on the shell of your pool.

There is a reason why we are Connecticut and Westchester county's most highly awarded pool company. Since 1977, we've mastered the blending of old world quality craftsmanship with the latest technology available.

ALL AMERICAN
CUSTOM POOLS & SPAS, INC.

8-10 VAN TASSEL COURT, NORWALK, CT 06851
800-ALL-POOL
www.allamericanpools.com

Architectural Elements

CONNECTICUT FENCEMEN, INC, THE ....**(203) 377-1008**
541 Honeyspot Road, Stratford   Fax: (203) 377-0338
See Ad on Page: 272
Website: www.ctfencemen.com
Additional Information: Manufacturers and installers of high quality fences and gates, etc., serving the people of Connecticut for over 50 years.

COLONIAL COLLECTIONS OF NEW ENGLAND, INC. ....**(203) 254-4495**
1476 Post Road, Fairfield   Fax: (203) 254-4496
See Ad on Page: 418
Principal/Owner: Len & Renee D'Andrea
Website: www.colonialcollection.com
Additional Information: The store for your "finishing touches". Colonial Collections specializes in decorative accessories such as upscale address markers, mailboxesand post systems, handcrafted weathervanes and cupolas, as well as handcrafted copper & brass lighting fixtures. Although many of our products fit well with a colonial design home, we have designs for most homes.

FISHE BROS., MERCHANTS OF INTEREST...**(203) 840-1345**
625 Main Avenue, Route 7, Norwalk   Fax: (203) 849-8775
See Ad on Page: 269
Principal/Owner: Peggy Ann White
Website: Sculpturedgardens.com e-mail: Fishebro@optonline.com
Additional Information: Fishe Bros. offers Fairfield County's most unique selection of garden ornaments from across the states and Europe, including Vicenza, limestone, cast iron, granite and fine estate statuary.

WALPOLE WOODWORKERS ....**(508) 668-2800**
767 East Street, Walpole, MA   Fax: (508) 668-7301
See Ad on Page: 270, 271
Principal/Owner: Sue Donahue

FISHE BROS.
Merchants of Interest, LLC

Fountains • Birdbaths
Urns & Planters
Cast Stone
Fiberglass • Granite
Terra Cotta
Sundials & Armillaries
Quality Reproductions & Estate Items

625 Main Avenue, Rte. 7
Norwalk, CT 06851
203.840.1345   203.845.8775 fax
fishebro@optonline.net

Farmington, CT • 1079 Farmington Ave., (Rt 4) • 860-677-9690
Westport, CT • 1835 Post Road East • 203-255-9010

Make your great outdoors greater.

Walpole is full of fresh ideas for your outdoors. Like hand crafted garden furniture, arbors, trellis, mailbox and lantern posts, weathervanes, window boxes, birdhouses, flagpoles and much more. Visit our store nearest you or call for our FREE Selections brochure.

Walpole Woodworkers

Quality Fence Since 1933

Ridgefield, CT • 424 Ethan Allen Hwy., (US Rt. 7) • 203-438-3134 • 203-869-6190
www.walpolewoodworkers.com

THE CONNECTICUT FENCEMEN INC.

The Craftsmen of the Industry

For over 50 years serving the people of CT
with the highest quality products & service.

Office • Showroom • Yard
541 Honey Spot Rd Stratford CT 06615
Tel. (203) 377-1008 • Fax (203) 377-0338
Toll free in CT only 1-800-942-3362

Visit our Other Division in Your Area
Frankson Fence Co. North haven Ct (203) 288-2588
Perfection Fence Co. Waterbury Ct (203) 756-8991

Landscape
Lighting

CUSTOM LANDSCAPE & LIGHTING, LLC...**(203) 255-6935**
P.O. Box 578, Fairfield
See Ad on Page: 274, 275
<u>Principal/Owner</u>: Craig Boland
<u>Website</u>: CustomLandscapeLighting.com
<u>Additional Information</u>: Installers of low voltage landscape lighting for over 15 years.

DESIGN LIGHTING BY MARKS ....**(914) 747-7777**
70 Sarles Lane, Pleasentville   Fax: (914) 747-5234
See Ad on Page: 276, 277
<u>Principal/Owner</u>: Mark Mosello

CUSTOM LANDSCAPE LIGHTING, LLC ™

(866) UP-LIGHT   *CALL FOR QUALITY*

Servicing Westchester county, Fairfield county, and the entire Connecticut shoreline.

P.O. Box 578 Fairfield   Connecticut   06430

Member of the Low Voltage Lighting Institute of America

**By using a variety of
low voltage techniques you can
enjoy your home & landscape
long into the evening**

Since 1986, Craig Boland, owner of Custom Landscape Lighting, has been installing low voltage landscape lighting in high-end residential landscape settings. When designing lighting systems uniquely suited to each client and their environment, CLL considers the lighting effects rather than just the appearance of the fixtures themselves. Whenever possible, CLL prefers to use copper and brass fixtures for their longevity. However, we also use powder-coated fixtures, available in a number of colors, that carry the industry's highest guarantee on the finish.

Custom Landscape Lighting uses only the highest quality fixtures, not necessarily the highest priced in every installation.
Call today for a free consultation & estimate
www.customlandscapelighting.com

GO

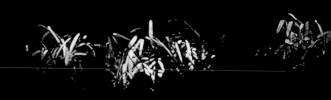

Landscape lighting is the creation of a lighting effect.
not the display of lighting fixtures. Lighting can have many
purposes ranging from aesthetics to safety and security.
The illumination of gardens, trees, shrubbery and ground
cover extends the beauty of nature into the nighttime
and enhances your environment and property

LIGHT?

DESIGN
LIGHTING
BY MARKS

914-747-7777 • 516-374-1888
203-967-4777 • 201-343-9266
www.designlightingbymarks.com
e.l.c. 103278

Automated
Gates

GARON FENCE COMPANY INC. ....**(914) 666-5596**
323 Railroad Avenue, Bedford Hills   Fax: (914) 666-6604
See Ad on Page: 279
<u>Principal/Owner</u>: Gary Prato
<u>Additional Information</u>: Custom designed wood and iron fencing, automated entry systems, gazebos, pergolas, perimeter security, deer control fences, iron railings and pool fences. All fabrication done on premises.

GARON FENCE COMPANY

Bedford Iron works

- Custom
  wood gates

- Custom
  iron gates

- Automated
  gate system

- Telephone
  communications
  systems

- Camera systems

323 Railroad Ave • Bedford Hills, NY 10507
phone: 914.666.5596 • fax: 914.666.6604

The Ashley Group Luxury Home Resource Collection

The **Ashley Group (www.theashleygroup.com)** is pleased to offer as your final destination when searching for home improvement and luxury resources the following **Home Books** in your local market. Available now: *Chicago, Washington D.C., South Florida, Los Angeles, Dallas/Fort Worth, Detroit, Colorado, New York, Atlanta, Arizona, Philadelphia, San Diego, North Carolina, Boston, Houston* and *Las Vegas*. These comprehensive, hands-on guides to building, remodeling, decorating, furnishing, and landscaping a luxury home, are required reading for the serious and selective homeowner. With over 500 full-color, beautiful pages, the **Home Book** series in each market covers all aspects of the building and remodeling process, including listings of hundreds of local industry professionals, accompanied by informative and valuable editorial discussing the most recent trends.

Order your copies today and make your dream come true!

THE ASHLEY GROUP LUXURY HOME RESOURCE COLLECTION

Yes! Please send me the following Home Books! At $39.95 for each, plus $4.00 Shipping & Handling and Tax per book.

☐ Dallas/Fort Worth Home Book *Premier Ed.* ___ # of Copies	☐ Detroit Home Book *Premier Ed.* ___ # of Copies
☐ New York Home Book *Premier Ed.* ___ # of Copies	☐ Colorado Home Book *Premier Ed.* ___ # of Copies
☐ Chicago Home Book *6th Ed.* ___ # of Copies	☐ Los Angeles Home Book *2nd Ed.* ___ # of Copies
☐ Washington DC Home Book *2nd Ed.* ___ # of Copies	☐ South Florida Home Book *2nd Ed.* ___ # of Copies
☐ North Carolina Home Book *Premier Ed.* ___ # of Copies	☐ Las Vegas Home Book *Premier Ed.* ___ # of Copies
☐ San Diego Home Book *Premier Ed.* ___ # of Copies	☐ Philadelphia Home Book *Premier Ed.* ___ # of Copies
☐ Arizona Home Book *Premier Ed.* ___ # of Copies	☐ Atlanta Home Book *Premier Ed.* ___ # of Copies
☐ Boston Home Book *Premier Ed.* ___ # of Copies	☐ Houston Home Book *Premier Ed.* ___ # of Copies

I ordered (# Of Books) _____ X $43.95 = $ _____   Total amount enclosed: $ _____

Please charge my: _____Visa _____Mastercard _____American Express

Credit Card #: _____   Exp. Date: _____

Name: _____ Phone: _____

Signature: _____

Address: _____ Email: _____

City: _____ State: _____ Zip Code: _____

Send order to: Attn: Book Sales–Marketing, The Ashley Group–Reed, 2000 Clearwater Drive, Oak Brook, Illinois 60523
Or Call Toll Free at: 1-888-458-1750 • Or E-mail ashleybooksales@ReedBusiness.com • Visit us on-line at www.theashleygroup.com

All orders must be accompanied by check, money order or credit card # for full amount.

Photo courtesy of **Studio Snaidero Greenwich**

KITCHEN & BATH

281
Places to Unwind

288
Kitchen & Bath Designers

312a
Timeline: Building Your Dream Kitchen & Bath

314
New in the Showroom

316
Fixtures & Hardware

320
Appliances

KITCHEN AND BATH CENTER

Benson

297 DANBURY ROAD, WILTON, CONNECTICUT 06897
(203) 834-0880 FAX (203) 834-1782
MEMBER NATIONAL KITCHEN & BATH ASSOCIATION

LIFETIME
WOOD-MODE
Limited
WARRANTY

Wood·Mode
FINE CUSTOM CABINETRY

SERVING FAIRFIELD AND WESTCHESTER
COUNTIES FOR 32 YEARS

297 DANBURY ROAD

WILTON, CONNECTICUT 06897

(203) 834-0880

FAX: (203) 834-1782

Places to Unwind

Ever notice that when there's a social gathering in a home, people congregate in the kitchen? Today, the kitchen serves not only as a place for preparing food, but also as a place where the party begins and ends, where couples relax over coffee in a cozy breakfast nook, or where delicious buffets await family and guests alike.

Kitchen islands now function as self-serve appetizer stations, fully equipped with range tops, warming bins and microwaves. Open architectural floor plans call for kitchens to flow into areas to gather for conversation or entertainment. Without a doubt, today's larger kitchen is the real family room, the heart and soul of the home.

The bath has evolved into a truly multipurpose "cocooning" area as well. Sufficient room for exercise equipment, spacious master closets and spa features are in high demand, resulting in master suites to allow one to escape from the world. The emphasis on quality fixtures and luxury finishes remains, whatever the size of the room.

Photo courtesy of **Rose Adams Cabinetry**

DEFINING THE WAY WE LIVE

Homeowners building a new home, or remodeling an existing one, demand flexible and efficient spaces, custom designed to fill their needs. Reaching that goal is more challenging than ever. As new products and technologies race to keep up with the creative design explosion, the need for talented, experienced kitchen and bath designers continues to grow.

The kitchen/bath designer will be a member of your homebuilding team, which also includes the architect, contractor, interior designer and, in new home construction, the landscape architect.

Professional kitchen and bath designers, many of whom are also degreed interior designers, possess the education and experience in space planning particular to kitchens and baths. They can deliver a functional design perfectly suited to your family, while respecting your budget and your wishes. Their understanding of ergonomics, the relationship between people and their working environments, and a familiarity with current products and applications will be invaluable to you as you plan.

SEARCH OUT DESIGN EXCELLENCE

Designing a kitchen or bath is an intimate undertaking, filled with many decisions based on personal habits and family lifestyles. Before you select the kitchen/bath professional who will lead you through the project, make a personal commitment to be an involved and interested client. Since the success of these rooms is so important to the daily lives of you and those around you, it's a worthwhile investment of your time and energy.

Choose a designer whose work shows creativity and a good sense of planning. As in any relationship, trust and communication are the foundations for success. Is the designer open to your ideas, and does he or she offer information on how you can achieve your vision? If you can't express your ideas freely, don't enter into a contractual relationship, no matter how much you admire this person's work. If these rooms aren't conceived to fulfill your wishes, your time and resources will be wasted.

What also is true, however, is that professional designers should be given a comfortable degree of latitude to execute your wishes as best as they know how. Accomplished designers earned their reputation by creating beautiful rooms that work, so give their ideas serious consideration for the best overall result.

Many homeowners contact a kitchen or bath designer a year before a project is scheduled to begin. Some come with a full set of complete drawings they simply want to have priced out. Some take full

---

INGREDIENTS OF A NEW KITCHEN

What might it cost to design and install a 16 ft. x 33 ft. kitchen?
• Cabinetry: kitchen, island, pantry, desk, 36-42 in. high wall cabinets, maple, modified Shaker styling, custom solid wood construction: $44,000
• Stained glass doors, glass shelves: $3,500
• Granite countertop & tumbled marble backsplash with mosaic: $14,500
• Two electric ovens, 36 in. gas cooktop with hood, 48 in. built-in refrigerator, two dishwashers, under counter refrigerator, warming drawer, microwave, disposal, hot water dispenser: $20,000
• Plumbing fixtures: $2,900
• Porcelain tile flooring: $4,000
• Lighting: low voltage, halogen and xenon: $2,500
• Labor: $7,000

Total: $98,400

advantage of the designer's expertise and contract for plans drawn from scratch. And some want something in between. Be sure a designer offers the level of services you want – from 'soup to nuts' or strictly countertops and cabinetry.

Designers charge a design fee, which often will be used as a deposit if you choose to hire them. If you expect very detailed sets of drawings, including floor plans, elevations, and pages of intricate detail, such as the support systems of kitchen islands, the toe kick and crown molding detail, be specific about your requirements. All contracts should be written, detailed, and reviewed by your attorney.

TURNING DREAMS INTO DESIGNS – GET YOUR NOTEBOOK OUT

The first step toward getting your ideas organized is to put them on paper. Jot down notes, tape photos into an Idea Notebook, mark pages of your Home Book. The second step is defining your lifestyle. Pay close attention to how you use the kitchen and bath. For example, if you have a four-burner stove, how often do you cook with all four burners? Do you need a cook surface with more burners, or could you get by with less, freeing up space for a special wok cooking module or more counter space? How often do you use your bathtub? Many upper-end homeowners are forgoing the tub in favor of the multi-head shower surround and using bathtub space for a dressing or exercise area or mini-kitchen. As you evaluate your lifestyle, try to answer questions like these:

THINKING ABOUT KITCHEN DESIGN

• What feeling do you want to create in the kitchen? Traditional feel of hearth and home? The clean, uncluttered lines of contemporary design?

• Is meal preparation the main function of the kitchen? Gourmet cooks and gardeners want a different level of functionality than do homeowners who eat out often or want to be in and out of the kitchen quickly.

• How does the family use the kitchen? How will their needs change your requirements over the next ten years? (If you can't imagine the answer to this question, ask friends who are a few years ahead of you in terms of family life.)

• Do you want easy access to the backyard, dining room, garage?

• Is there a special view you want preserved or established?

APPLIANCES NOW

New appliances in the kitchen are fun and user-friendly.
• Prep sinks and cooktops located conveniently in the island
• Refrigerators with titanium finishes that don't leave fingerprints
• Monitors that can be built-in or mounted under a cabinet.
• Wireless water-proof keyboards for surfing the Internet while bathing or cooking
• Refrigerator touch screens for pulling up favorite recipes
• Dishwashers with a full-size, flat third rack for broiler pans, cookie sheets and other hard-to-wash items
• Recessed lighting and task lighting fixtures, such as sleek pendant lamps
• Built-in coffeemakers with electrical lift systems that hide them within a cabinet after the lattes and espressos have been served.

283

WHAT DESIGNERS OFFER YOU

1. Access to the newest products: With their considerable knowledge of products and solutions, your remodeling or budget limitations can be more easily addressed.

2. Ergonomic design for a custom fit: Designers consider all the measurements - not just floor plan space - but also how counter and cabinet height and depth measure up to the needs of the individual family members.

3. A safe environment: Safety is the highest priority. As kitchens and baths serve more functions, managing traffic for safety's sake becomes more crucial.

4. Orderly floor plans: When an open refrigerator door blocks the path from the kitchen to the breakfast room, or you're bumping elbows in the bathroom, poor space planning is the culprit.

5. Smart storage: Ample storage in close proximity to appropriate spaces is essential.

• Do you want family and friends to be involved and close to the action in the kitchen?

• What appliances and amenities must be included? Warming drawers, refrigeration zones, wine coolers, ultra-quiet dishwashers that sense how dirty the dishes are, cooktops with interchangeable cooking modules, and convection ovens with electronic touchpad controls are all available.

• What are your storage needs? If you own a lot of kitchen items, have a relatively small kitchen, or wan personally tailored storage space, ask your kitchen designer to take a detailed inventory of your possessions. Top quality cabinets can be customizec to fit your needs. Kitchen designers, custom cabinetmakers, or space organization experts can guide you. Consider custom options such as:
  • Slotted storage for serving trays
  • Pull-out recycling bins
  • Plate racks and wine racks
  • Cutlery dividers
  • Angled storage drawer for spices
  • Pivoting shelving systems
  • Pull-out or elevator shelves for food processors, mixers, televisions or computers

• Is the kitchen also a work area or home office? Do you need a location for a computerized home management or intercom system?

THINKING ABOUT BATH DESIGN

• What look are you trying to create? Victorian, Colonial, Contemporary, whimsical?

• What functions must it fill? Exercise area, sitting room, dressing or make-up area?

• Who will use the bath? Children, teens, guests (and how many)?

• What is the traffic pattern? How do people move in and around a bathroom? (Set up your video camera in the corner one morning to get a realistic view.)

• What amenities are desired? Luxury shower systems, whirlpool tub, ceiling heat lamps, spa, heated tile floors, audio and telephone systems

• What are your storage needs? Linen or clothes closets? Stereo and CD storage? Professionals will customize spaces for your needs.

• Do you want hooks for towels or bathrobes? Heated towel bars or rings?

THE SKY'S THE LIMIT

New high-end kitchen budgets can easily reach the $100,000 range, so it's important to identify your specific needs and wishes. The sky's the limit when designing and installing a luxury kitchen or bath in the 2000s, so don't get caught by surprise by the cost of high quality cabinetry, appliances and fixtures. Know what you're willing to spend and make sure your designer is aware of your budget. Projects have a way of growing along the way. If you've established a realistic budget, you have a solid way to keep the project moving forward and prioritizing your wishes. Think in terms of this general breakdown of expenses:

Cabinets	40%
Appliances	15%
Faucets and Fixtures	8%
Flooring	7%
Windows	7%
Countertops	8%
Labor	15%

TODAY'S KITCHEN-ANTIQUE OR SLEEK, IT'S YOUR CHOICE

Whether your tastes run to classical and traditional European designs, or you prefer contemporary looks, today's imperative is custom. You determine what you want. Gorgeous imported natural stone countertops and floors, and luxury options like dedicated wine coolers, stem glass holders, and plate racks are ever popular and can be accommodated in any style.

Today's refrigerators can now serve as home automation control centers. Plasma screens built into refrigerator doors can serve as touch-screen home automation control centers, running everything from ovens and entertainment centers to security systems. In other modes, they function as TV screens, even Internet portals. Check your e-mail while you're peeling the potatoes – why not!

With advances in refrigeration technology, homeowners now have separate integrated refrigerators and freezer drawers installed near the appropriate work zone – a refrigerated vegetable drawer near the sink, a freezer drawer by the microwave, dedicated refrigerators to keep grains or cooking oils at their perfect temperatures. Ultra-quiet dishwashers with push-button controls hidden on top of the door for a sleek appearance, instant hot water dispensers, roll-out warming drawers and cooktops that can boil water in seconds are just some of the products that meet the demands of today's luxury lifestyle.

"WHAT ABOUT RESALE?"

This is a question designers hear when homeowners individualize their kitchens and baths. It's only prudent to consider the practical ramifications of any significant investment, including investing in a new custom kitchen and bath.

Beautiful upscale kitchens and baths will only enhance the value of your home. Indeed, these two rooms are consistently credited with recouping more than their original cost, estimates range from an increase in value of 10% to 50% over what was spent. The greatest return, however, is in the present, in the enjoyment of the space.

A STEP UP

Custom counter height is an idea whose time has arrived in new and remodeled homes. Multiple heights, appropriate to the task or the people using the particular area, are common. When one permanent height doesn't work as a solution to a problem, consider asking for a step to be built in to the toe kick panel of the cabinetry.

GET TWO DISHWASHERS

Homeowners today are installing extra dishwashers:
1. To make cleanup after a party a one-night affair.
2. To serve as a storage cabinet for that extra set of dishes.
They're also installing dishwashers at a more friendly height to eliminate unnecessary bending.

TODAY'S BATH – BRINGING THE SPA EXPERIENCE HOME

Imagine it's a Thursday night at the end of a very busy week. You come home, have a great work out while listening to your favorite CDs over the loudspeakers in your private exercise room, then jump into an invigorating shower where multiple shower heads rejuvenate your tired muscles, and a steaming, cascading waterfall pulls all the stress from your body. You wrap yourself in a big fluffy bath sheet, toasty from the brass towel warmer as you step onto the ceramic tile floor that's been warmed by an underfloor radiant heating unit. You grab something comfortable from your lighted, walk-in closet, and then head out of your luxurious bathroom to the kitchen to help with dinner.

Today's master baths are indeed at-home spas. They are a place to de-stress from hectic and active lifestyles, and new designs seek to accomplish this through simplicity, softness of textures and surfaces and the use of water's soothing nature itself. You've heard about aromatherapy, now there's Chromatherapy-colored lights located in the bathtub. The system cycles through eights hues, and if you like a particular color, you can settle on that one by pushing a button.

For the utmost in minimalist faucet design, how about eliminating the faucet altogether? New faucet designs have the water flowing directly out of the wall. Used with porcelain hand basins, these wet surface lavatories are formulated for a comforting, almost Zen-like washing experience. Water flows onto a raised plateau, with an overflow perimeter reminiscent of disappearing edge pools that catches the water and sends it down the drain. The open-bottom hand basin creates a seal with the lavatory's surface when filled with water, enabling you to use it as a wash basin and then release the contents by simply lifting it. Perfect for those who want the experience of washing in a fountain instead of an ordinary sink.

For those seeking a mega-experience, spa tubs can provide the bathing equivalent of the Jumbotron Watch a 48-inch color plasma TV screen as you pop in a video and soak to your heart's content (though soaking through a 3-hour movie like Lord of the Rings might be a bit much.)

THE REALITY OF REMODELING

Dollar-smart homeowners know that in cost versus value surveys, kitchen renovations and bath additions or renovations yield a very high return on the original investment. These homeowners rarely embark on such remodeling projects with resale in mind. However, knowing their investment is a wise one gives them the freedom to fully realize their dreams of the ultimate sybaritic bath or the friendliest family kitchen that accommodates them now and well into the future.

For more information on remodeling, see "The Second Time's The Charm" in the Custom Home Builders and Remodelers section.

A REMODELING CONTINGENCY FUND

Kitchen and bath remodeling projects are well known for unexpected, unforeseen expenses, so put a contingency fund in your budget from the beginning. This fund can cover anything from structural changes to your sudden desire to install skylights in the kitchen.

THE BEAUTY OF TOP QUALITY SURFACES

Luxury surfaces continue to add astonishing beauty to kitchens and baths in new and remodeled homes throughout the area. Solid surfaces now are available in an ever-widening range of colors, including a granite look, with high degrees of translucence and depth. Granite and stone add a beautiful, natural look, with an abundance of choices and finishes. Tile, stainless steel, laminates, and wood – even concrete – are other possibilities. Each surface has its benefits, beyond the inherent beauty it can add to your design.

Your kitchen designer will advise you on the best choices for your project, based on overall design and budget. Use the professionals showcased in these pages to find the best quality materials and craftsmanship. ∎

ELECTRIC VS. GAS

An age-old debate, yes, but today's electric ranges have come a long way. Sleek, scratch-resistant glass cooktops feature simmer settings that hold sauces and stews below the boiling point. And controls can be locked for child-safety. Today's gas ranges feature grates that are dishwasher safe and sealed burners that make cleanup easy. Dual-stacked burners offer greater low-end control for melting or simmering. Electric, gas or both; the choice is yours.

287

Kitchen & Bath
Designers

A MATTER OF STYLE ....**(203) 272-1337**
714 South Main Street, Cheshire   Fax: (203) 272-9414
See Ad on Page: 309
Principal/Owner: Robbin Ricci
Additional Information: A unique design studio which elevates design, craftsmanship and installation to a fine
art. Fine custom cabinetry for kitchens, baths & other creative interior locations throughout a home. We
compliment this process with a design-build team to coordinate projects from concept through completion.

BILOTTA HOME CENTER..**(914) 347-3635**
33 West Main, Suite, 408, Elmsford   Fax: (914) 347-3862
See Ad on Page: 301
Principal/Owner: Mary Conner

CONNECTICUT KITCHEN & BATH..**(203) 743-2095**
87 Mill Hill Road, Danbury   Fax: (203) 743-2148
See Ad on Page: 312-319
Principal/Owner: Phyllis Boughton

CONSTRUCTION CONCEPTS CORP. ....**(203) 325-8102**
87 Brookhollow Lane, Stamford   Fax: (203) 357-1984
See Ad on Page: 135, 199, 289
Principal/Owner: Jeffrey Glass
Website: www.constconceptscorp.com e-mail: ccc@consconceptscorp.com
Additional Information: A full-service custom home & remodeling design/build company.

COUNTRY KITCHENS, LLC ....**(203) 834-0295**
300 Danbury Road, Suite 410, Wilton   Fax: (203) 834-0296
See Ad on Page: 313
Principal/Owner: Jeffrey A. Titus
Website: www.titusbuiltllc.com e-mail: jtitus@titusbuiltllc.com
Additional Information: Custom cabinetry for every room in your home including libraries, bathroom
vanities, entertainment cneters and much more. Enjoy personalized one-on-one design services.

CUSTOM KITCHENS & BATHS ....**(203) 438-0066**
6 Prospect Street, Ridgefield   Fax: (203) 438-9966
See Ad on Page: 304
Principal/Owner: Thomas H. Senf
Additional Information: Full service kitchen & bath design and contracting firm.

EDELMANN KITCHEN, BATH & INTERIOR DESIGN ....**(203) 730-1144**
128 Greenwood Avenue, Bethel   Fax: (203) 744-6029
See Ad on Page: 209, 297
Principal/Owner: Joseph Edelmann

EMPIRE KITCHENS...**(914) 242-9011**
193 Main Street, Mt. Kisco   Fax: (914) 242-4603
See Ad on Page: 310, 311, 352, 353
Principal/Owner: John Mansor

FRENCH COUNTRY LIVING ....**(203) 869-9559**
34 East Putnam Avenue, Greenwich   Fax: (203) 869-9790
See Ad on Page: 406, 407

GALLERY OF KITCHENS ....**(203) 226-7550**
1027 Post Road East, Westport   Fax: (203) 226-6848
See Ad on Page: 290, 291
Principal/Owner: Matt Cowan
e-mail: gallokitch@aol.com

HOFFMAN CONTRACTING, LLC ....**(203) 966-1919**
32 Cross Street, New Canaan   Fax: (203) 972-8756
See Ad on Page: 175
Principal/Owner: Ned Hoffman
Website: www.hoffmancontractingllc.com e-mail: hoffmancontract@aol.com
Additional Information: Established in 1978, Hoffman Contracting, LLC specializes in
Interior/Exterior restoration.

KITCHEN & BATH CENTER..**(203) 834-0880**
297 Danbury Road, Wilton   Fax: (203) 834-1782
See Ad on Page: 281-283
Principal/Owner: Joe Benson
e-mail: kitchensbybenson@hotmail.com

288

Winning Concept

Winning Concept, HOBI Awards, Best Kitchen Renovation in CT   Photo by Rosemarie Stiller

The award winning Design/Build team

Construction Concepts Corp. of Stamford, CT has recently won first place in three categories of the Home Building Association of Connecticut's HOBI awards, the most prestigious awards presented in Connecticut.

The three winning categories are:
Best Kitchen Renovation in CT, Best Accessory Building in CT, and Best Office in CT. Construction Concepts Corp. is a full service residential Design/Build firm serving Fairfield County, CT and Westchester County, NY.

The firm's winning portfolio may be seen and an appointment made for a free consultation by calling (203) 325-8102.

CONSTRUCTION
CONCEPTS
CORP.

Contact-Jeffrey R.Glass, CGR/GMB/CGB
Construction Concepts Corp. / Tel: 203.325.8102 • Fax: 203.357.1984
E-mail: ccc@constconceptscorp.com / www.constconceptscorp.com
CT #535858•WC #3332H90

HANDCRAFTED ENGLISH & TRADITIONAL CUPBOARDS
PROFESSIONAL DESIGN & INSTALLATION
1027 ROAD EAST • WESTPORT • (203) 226-7550

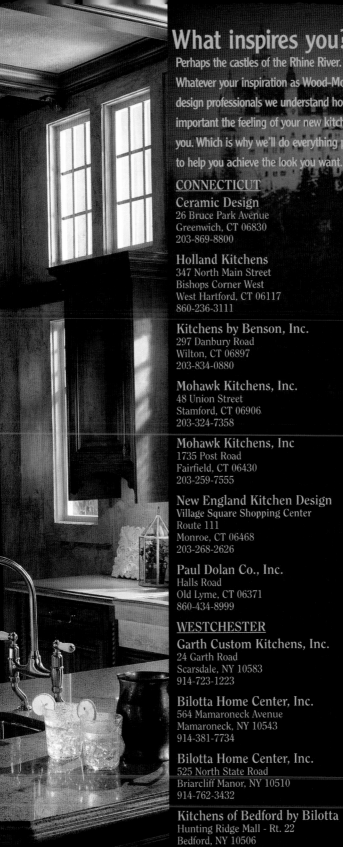

What inspires you?

Perhaps the castles of the Rhine River. Whatever your inspiration as Wood-Mode design professionals we understand how important the feeling of your new kitchen is to you. Which is why we'll do everything possible to help you achieve the look you want.

CONNECTICUT

Ceramic Design
26 Bruce Park Avenue
Greenwich, CT 06830
203-869-8800

Holland Kitchens
347 North Main Street
Bishops Corner West
West Hartford, CT 06117
860-236-3111

Kitchens by Benson, Inc.
297 Danbury Road
Wilton, CT 06897
203-834-0880

Mohawk Kitchens, Inc.
48 Union Street
Stamford, CT 06906
203-324-7358

Mohawk Kitchens, Inc
1735 Post Road
Fairfield, CT 06430
203-259-7555

New England Kitchen Design
Village Square Shopping Center
Route 111
Monroe, CT 06468
203-268-2626

Paul Dolan Co., Inc.
Halls Road
Old Lyme, CT 06371
860-434-8999

WESTCHESTER

Garth Custom Kitchens, Inc.
24 Garth Road
Scarsdale, NY 10583
914-723-1223

Bilotta Home Center, Inc.
564 Mamaroneck Avenue
Mamaroneck, NY 10543
914-381-7734

Bilotta Home Center, Inc.
525 North State Road
Briarcliff Manor, NY 10510
914-762-3432

Kitchens of Bedford by Bilotta
Hunting Ridge Mall - Rt. 22
Bedford, NY 10506
914-234-2121

Wood·Mode®
FINE CUSTOM CABINETRY

www.wood-mode.com

©2002 Wood-Mode, Inc.

Defining moments...
defining styles...

**Clerestory row above cabinets for delft collection;
Rear potting area; Pass through pantry with bar;**

Photography by David Sloane Photography

**Antique replica china closet for teapot collection
(not shown); Antiqued delft back splash; Limestone
countertops to resemble soap stone.**

when the details
are important.

**American Black Cherry cabinets and columns;
Venetian light fixtures; Custom hammered hardware;
Tumbled limestone floor.**

Photography by Peter Leach Photography

SBD Kitchens, LLC New Canaan, CT. 203-972-8341
Sarah A Blank, CKD

Over 160 clients in Westchester and Fairfield Counties & Beyond
KITCHENS, LIBRARIES, BATHS, FAMILY ROOMS <www.SBDkitchens.com

Photo by Olson Photographic, L.L.

THE KITCHEN FACTOR

Local 203.469.76(
Toll Free 1.800.927.92(
Fax 203.469.519

193 SILVER SANDS ROAD
EAST HAVEN, CONNECTICUT 06512

a division of East Haven Builders Supply, Inc.

www.ehbuilders.com/kitchenfactor

Photo by Olson Photographic, L.L.

128 Greenwood Avenue
Bethel, CT 06801
203.730.1144
Fax 203.744.6029

PLATO

KITCHEN & BATH CREATIONS LLC

630 Main St.
(Route 25)
Monroe, CT 06468
203-445-2991
203-445-2992

278 Post Rd.
(Route 1)
Orange, CT 06477
203-779-0587
203-799-0721

From creation to completion
we can service all of your needs.

When it's a kitchen by Deane it's your kitchen.

A "serious cooks" kitchen placed 2nd nationally in the Sub-Zero/Wolf 2000/01 Kitchen Design Contest.

Kitchens by Deane combined "smart design, the highest quality materials and service" to place first in the nation in the annual Kitchen & Bath Design News Leadership Awards, competing with the leading kitchen design firms from all across the country.

And this year we are featuring over 30 distinctive design personalities in our new 2002 Design Show at our Stamford showroom. Stop by and find yours.

1267 East Main Street, Stamford (203) 327-7008
89 Elm Street, New Canaan (203) 972-8836
www.kitchensbydeane.com

Kitchen & Bath
Designers

KITCHEN & BATH CREATIONS, LLC...**(203) 799-0587**
278 Boston Post Road, Orange   Fax: (203) 799-0721
See Ad on Page: 298
Principal/Owner: David Brown & David Vrabel
Additional Information: A full service remodeling company with 2 large, well appointed show-rooms.

KITCHEN COMPANY, THE...**(203) 288-3866**
370 Sackett Point Road, North Haven   Fax: (203) 248-5219
See Ad on Page: 302,303
Principal/Owner: John Fecke & Gail Bowling
Website: www.thekitchencompany.com e-mail: the.kitchen@snet.net
Additional Information: Service oriented company designing and installing beautiful kitchens since 1953.

KITCHEN FACTOR, THE ....**(203) 469-7601**
193 Silver Sands Road, East Haven   Fax: (203) 469-5193
See Ad on Page: 296
Principal/Owner: Siobhan Daggett
Website: www.ehbuilders.com/kitchenfactor Additional Information: A division of East Haven Builders Supply, Inc., serving all of Connecticut and Westchester County

KITCHENS BY BENSON ....**(203) 834-0880**
297 Danbury Road, Wilton   Fax: (203) 834-1782
See Ad on Page: 281-283
Principal/Owner: W. Joseph Benson
e-mail: kitchensbybenson@hotmail.com
Additional Information: Specializing in working with builders and architects and their clients.

KITCHENS BY DEANE ....**(203) 327-7008**
1267 East Main Street, Stamford   Fax: (203) 975-1949
See Ad on Page: 299
Principal/Owner: Carrie and Peter Deane
Website: www.kitchensbydeane.com e-mail: pmdeane@kitchensbydeane.com
Additional Information: Design and install high-end kitchens, baths, family rooms and libraries.

MASTERWORKS CABINETRY, INC. ....**(203) 791-2034**
17 Diamond Avenue, Bethel   Fax: (203) 791-2473
See Ad on Page: 348, 349
Principal/Owner: Raymond P. Menard, President
Website: www.masterworkscabinetry.com

NEW CANAAN MARBLE & TILE...**(203) 966-7339**
3 Morse Court, New Canaan   Fax: (203) 966-1346
See Ad on Page: 388, 389
Principal/Owner: Kevin Pezeshkian

NEW ENGLAND KITCHEN DESIGN CENTER.................................**(203) 268-2626**
Route 111 Village Square Shopping , Monroe   Fax: (203) 452-7490
See Ad on Page: 305
Principal/Owner: F. Scott & Nancy Johnson
Website: www.newenglandkitchen.com e-mail: info@newenglandkitchen.com
Additional Information: Making houses homes since 1972. Specializing in kitchen and bath design. Wood-Mode Cabinetry top dealer for over 25 years. Full service from design concept to installation. Visit our showroom - open Monday through Saturday.

PAUL DOLAN COMPANY, INC...**(860) 434-8999**
19 Halls Road, Old Lyme   Fax: (860) 434-3440
See Ad on Page: 308
Principal/Owner: George D. Crane CKD
Website: www.pauldolancompany.com e-mail: info@pauldolancompany.com
Additional Information: Kitchen design featuring Wood-Mode Brookhaven and Birchcraft cabinets.

PUTNAM KITCHENS INC...**(203) 661-2270**
406 East Putname Avenue, Cos Cob   Fax: (203) 661-6637
See Ad on Page: 300-303
Principal/Owner: Peter Genovese/ Vincent Cappello
Additional Information: Custom cabinetry for any room in your home with infinite selections of finishes, woods and stylings. Highly regarded in the area as the premier design boutique in custom kitchens and cabinetry.

RINGS END LUMBER..**(203) 656-7515**
181 West Avenue, Darien   Fax: (203) 656-7586
See Ad on Page: 366
Principal/Owner: Craig Sinclair

PUTNAM
KITCHENS

406 East Putnam Ave. • Cos Cob, CT 06807
203 661-2270 • FAX 203 661-6637

Timeless...

Country Elegance...

PUTNAM KITCHENS

406 East Putnam Ave. • Cos Cob, CT 06807
203 661-2270 • FAX 203 661-6637

PUTNAM KITCHENS

406 East Putnam Ave. • Cos Cob, CT 06807
203 661-2270 • FAX 203 661-6637

MADE IN ENGLAND

Clive Christian

LONDON · PARIS · NEW YORK

0 EAST PUTNAM AVENUE, GREENWICH, CONNECTICUT (203) 629-9417

RUTT

houldn't you have a
itchen that cooks
ven if you're eating
ake-out?

ome to Bilotta, where making kitchens
s as much an art as using them.

BILOTTA
KITCHENS · BATHS · WINDOWS

Mamaroneck   Bedford Village
Briarcliff Manor   New York City

914 381 7734

The Kitchen Company

www.thekitchencompany.com

RUTT
HANDCRAFTED
CABINETRY

370 Sackett Point Rd.
North Haven, CT 06473

203.288.3866

CRYSTAL
a fine name in cabinetry

Custom Kitchens & Baths

HORST-SEN

6 Prospect Street, Ridgefield, Connecticut 06877
Tel. 203.438.0066 • Fax. 203.438.9966

Making Houses Homes Since 1972

NEW ENGLAND
NEKDC
KITCHEN DESIGN CENTER, INC.

Wood·Mode®
FINE CUSTOM CABINETRY

BROOKHAVEN
CABINETRY

CORIAN®
SOLID SURFACES
DUPONT

Route 111
Village Square Shopping Center
Monroe, CT 06468
Tel: (203) 268-2626   Fax: (203) 452-7490
www.newenglandkitchen.com

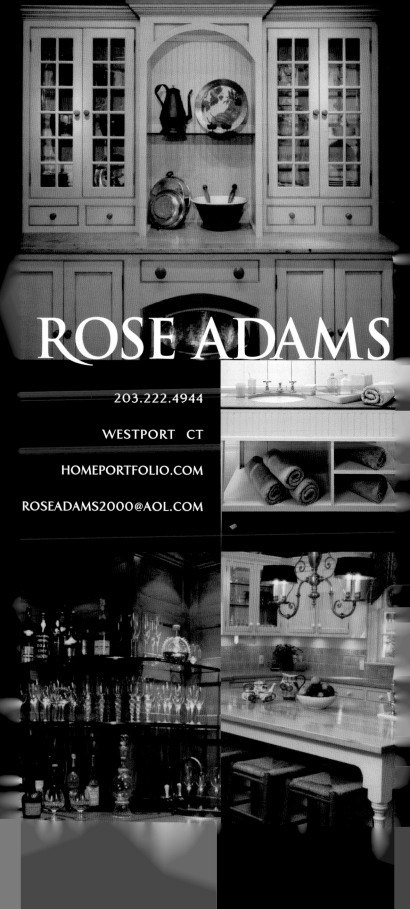

ROSE ADAMS

203.222.4944

WESTPORT CT

HOMEPORTFOLIO.COM

ROSEADAMS2000@AOL.COM

Form Follows Life

Ola 2000 by Pininfarina

snaidero
KITCHENS + DESIGN

For a location nearest you, call toll free: 1-877-SNAIDERO
or visit our web site at www.snaidero-usa.com

STUDIO SNAIDERO GREENWICH
384 W. Putnam Ave.
Greenwich, CT 06830
Tel: 203.869.7448
www.studiosnaidero.com

OLD LYME, CT 06371
(860) 434-8999
www.pauldolancompany.com

A Matter of Style
KITCHENS & BATHS

714 South Main Street

Cheshire, CT 06410

Phone: (203) 272-1337

www.covoda.com/ams

W D C

Empire Kitchens

The Westchester Design Center

Empire Kitchens of Greenwich

193 Main Street, Mount Kisco, New York 10549
Telephone (914) 242-9011   Fax (914) 242-4603

95 Putnam Avenue, Putnam, CT 06830
Telephone (203) 863-9690

Get The Selection You Deserve
We Set The Standard
For Superior Craftsmanship!

Let us be your complete one stop shop
for all your bathroom & kitchen renovation needs!
Manufacturing & installation of fine wood work
and all other renovation needs

• Customized & Install • Kitchen • Bathrooms • Fine Cabinetry • Licensed &
Insured • Granite & Supply Tiles • Custom Made Borders From Granite Marble

Top Drawer Custom Cabinetry Corp.

FREE Delivery & Estimates

11 Lincoln Avenue
New Rochelle, NY 10801
Tel. (914) 632-4222 Fax (914) 637-0843

Lic #
WC-09724-H98

Building Your **Dream** Kitchen and Bath

Examine your Options
Contact three to five remodelers. Make appointments to discuss ideas and begin the basis for a cost estimate.

Narrow the Field
Hold initial meetings with the remodelers. These visits to the house include a walking inspection with measurements taken of specific rooms, etc.

Select Your Partner
Choose a designer/remodeler and blueprints will be created. Expect that it will take three weeks for a project of this size. A retainer will probably be required.

Review Designs
Meet with your remodeler to review the designs. Establish a budget per design.

Approve Drawings
Finalize and sign off on drawings and hold a "rough budget" meeting.

Approve budget and sign the contract.

Demolition
Walls, flooring, etc. are torn up and removed. Generally takes three days.

Framing
Rough framing and room modifications are completed.

Mechanical Work & Whirlpool Bath
All electrical, plumbing, heating, ventilating and air conditioning work is finished. Low-voltage work is completed and whirlpool bath is installed.

Interior Work
Drywall is installed, walls are taped and primed.

Flooring
Floors are completed. Depending on the complexity of the materials used, this may take up to three more days than anticipated.

WK 1	WK5	WK9	WK12	WK13	WK14	WK15	WK16

Your Vision
The first appointment is the time to discuss your vision and the remodeler's suggestions for potential layout of the rooms, such as how to squeeze more features into an existing space, etc.

• **In some cases, designers and remodelers** are employed by the same firm; in other cases, they could be separate firms. There are advantages to going to a company that has both services under one roof, but you are not obligated to hire a design/build firm for both services. Many firms are willing to do one or the other.

• **To prevent ending up with an addition that doesn't fit** the style of your home, look at pictures of a company's work and make certain to visit homes that it has remodeled.

Windows
Attempt to keep existing window locations during any remodeling project. Moving windows is not a cost-saving endeavor.

• **Whenever you are adding on** new space to a home, have a heating contractor determine whether your existing heating system can accommodate and heat the extra space. You don't want to overwork and thereby damage your existing equipment and be forced to replace the entire unit.

• **Consider your cabinet options carefully.** Those choices will drive the overall price. You can add some options at a later date to defray some of the initial cost. Some that are easy to add include tilt front doors, spice racks and slide-out wire baskets. However, if you decide to wait, make certain that the option you want will be available and can be added after installation.

Building Your **Dream** Kitchen and Bath

Y ou may live in a house you love, in a neighborhood that suits you perfectly. However, your home may not fit your changing lifestyle or desires. The following timeline shows the steps involved in planning, executing, and finishing the major remodeling of a kitchen and full bath. It will help you to see the major tasks involved, and give you helpful information to make this process go more smoothly.

Project Description

T he remodeling of a kitchen and full bath. For the kitchen, the cabinets will be replaced, an island added, new flooring installed, and a breakfast nook with a bay window constructed. For the bath, a whirlpool will be installed, new flooring and new countertops will replace the old, and a closet will be carved out of the existing space.

Countertops, Plumbing & Back Splash

It only takes a day to install countertops but you must wait two weeks after the cabinetry is installed before you can begin. If, during the wait, you change your mind and order different countertops, this will delay installation by three extra weeks. All plumbing is hooked up.

Depending on the materials used, it can take from one to four days to complete the back splash.

Cabinetry and Kitchen Island

Kitchen island and all cabinetry are installed. Complicated cabinetry may take up to three more days than anticipated.

● All painting is completed.

Project Completed!

After the final clean-up, be sure to make a final inspection to ensure that everything is done to your satisfaction.

WK17   WK19   WK20   WK21

• If you are going to add a **large jetted tub** to your project, consider adding a water heater dedicated to that tub. A large jetted tub can hold up to an average of 75 gallons or more, which can easily overextend your existing water heater and cause problems down the road.

Gaining Space

Examine how you are utilizing space. You may be able to steal some space from a neighboring room or closet. If your bathroom space is limited, purchase a jetted tub and shower combination or install a pedestal lavatory instead of a vanity cabinet with a sink.

• While most states provide warranty protection for the client, the remodeler will include a warranty as well. This may last as long as five years for general items and as long as 10 years for manufacturing products. Certain laws also protect the client. Experts may be called upon to ensure that all agreements and building codes have been made.

Additional Information

For more information, contact the National Association of the Remodeling Industry (NARI), 780 Lee Street, Suite 200 Des Plaines, IL 60016 847-298-9200.

SPONSORED BY:

Connecticut
KITCHEN
& Bath

87 Mill Plain Road, Danbury, CT 06811
203.743.2095   203.743.2148 FAX

487 Federal Road, Brookfield, CT 06804
203.740.7542   203.740.7720 FAX

www.ctkitchen.com

In
Conclusion

The process of remodeling a kitchen and bath can be somewhat mysterious, sometimes perplexing, and often frustrating. At the end of the process, however, will be two of the most beautiful, comfortable, and enjoyable rooms of your home well into the future!

Produced by The Ashley Group
847.390.2882
www.theashleygroup.com

Do you dream in black & white or stainless?

dacor®

The life of the kitchen™

For a dealer or brochure call **800.772.7778** or visit **www.dacor.com**

VENTILATION · MICROWAVES · OUTDOOR GRILLS

Design
your kitchen around
Our Appliances.

Make your dream kitchen a reality with the finest in
professional style and built-in appliances from
Stamford's Premiere Appliance Store...
County TV and Appliance.

• Viking • Sub-Zero • Thermador • Jenn-Air • Daco
• Gaggenau • Asko • Vent-A-Hood • Maytag • GE
• Marvel • Wolf • Amana • Whirlpool

Serving Fairfield and Westchester Counties for 46 Years.

COUNTY
TV • APPLIANCES • AUDIO

2770 Summer St. • Stamford, Conn. 06905
Phone: 203-327-2630
Mon. & Thurs. 9AM-9PM, Tues., Wed., Fri., Sat. 9AM-6PM, Sun. 11AM-5P

We won't sell you a thing...only inspire & educate.

While you will find a feast for the eyes at Clarke, the one thing you will never find is pressure to purchase, as we actually cannot sell you a thing. As New England's most acclaimed appliance distributor, we sell through a select network of appliance dealers and kitchen designers. We can help you locate the one nearest you and arm you with all of the information you will need to speak their language, but only they can quote prices and delivery on the appliances you wish to purchase. The wonderful thing about this is that it allows our consultants to concentrate on answering your questions and making your showroom experience absolutely delicious.

Our success is no longer a secret.

Over the past decade, Clarke has been featured on HGTV, *This Old House* and various other television programs. The company has also garnered distinctions such as *Boston Magazine's* **Best of Boston**, the **Industry Leadership Award** from *Kitchen & Bath Design News*, numerous builder association awards in both Massachusetts and Connecticut and Ernst & Young's **Entrepreneur of the Year.**

Call for your appointment...

As the premier luxury kitchen resource in the Northeast, Clarke invites you to one of their exciting appliance showrooms.

Hopkinton, MA
800-842-5275

South Norwalk, CT
866-838-9385

CLARKE.

New England's Premier Luxury Kitchen Resource

Sub-Zero • Wolf • Asko • Best • Independent

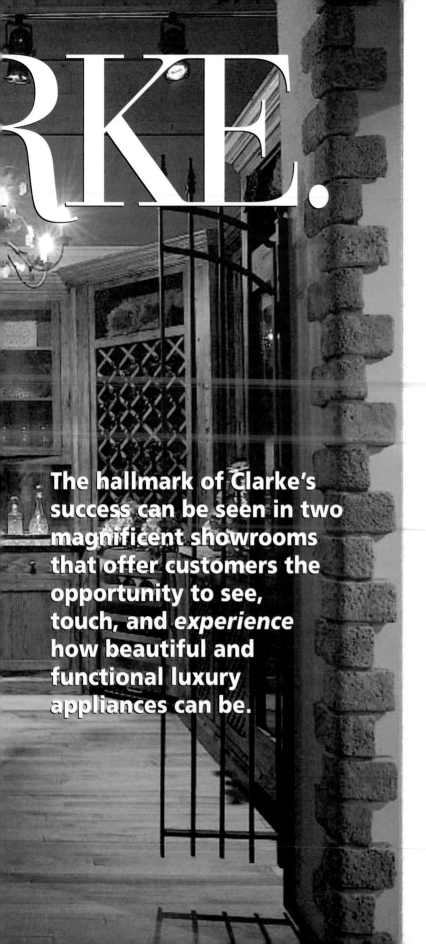

RKE.

The hallmark of Clarke's success can be seen in two magnificent showrooms that offer customers the opportunity to see, touch, and *experience* how beautiful and functional luxury appliances can be.

You are Invited!

Clarke invites you to one of their exciting appliance showrooms...**call for your appointment today!**

Hopkinton, MA 800-842-5275
South Norwalk, CT 866-838-9385

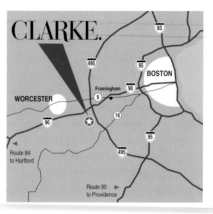

Hopkinton

Exit 21B off Route 495, just south of the Mass Pike (Route 90). At the first light, take a left onto South Street.

South Norwalk

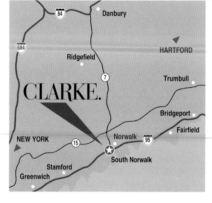

From the north:
I-95 south to exit 15... Maritime Center lane. Left onto West Avenue. Travel five lights and bear left at pharmacy onto North Main Street. Proceed under railroad bridge (becomes South Main). Clarke is on your left (about two blocks).

From the south: I-95 north to exit 14. Turn right at top of ramp Bear left at the first light and then straight through second light. Just past Klaff's, take a right onto South Main Street. Clarke is on your left (about two blocks).

CLARKE.

New England's Premier Luxury Kitchen Resource

63 South Street • Hopkinton, MA 01748
508-435-6226 • 800-842-5275 • FAX 508-435-6860

64 South Main Street • South Norwalk, CT 06854
203-838-9385 • 866-838-9385 • FAX 203-838-9451

www.clarkecorp.com

First one to boil water wins . . .

. . . we put the heat where it belongs!

The
Definitive Source
For
Home Appliances

Authorized Sales - Service - Delivery & Installation for all Major Appliances

PLANET T.V.
& APPLIANCES

900 High Ridge Rd | Stamford, CT 06905
(203) 968-1515 | www.planettv.com

A staff of friendly and knowledgeable appliance experts
providing answers and solutions - one customer at a time.

If cooking is your passion, welcome to the honeymoon suite.

Viking products are marketed under the *Ultraline®* brand name in Canada.

Celebrate your love of food in a Viking kitchen. The superior performance of the world's only complete professional-type kitchen stokes gourmet flames to divine new heights. With all the available sizes, colors, and fuel options, you'll find the perfect match for your kitchen. But you should probably let the delivery guys carry it over the threshold.

VIKING

Only the best at:

Albano Appliance & Service, LLC

Family owned and operated for 3 generations

Coffee for the true connoisseur

The Miele Built-in Coffee System brings that perfect cup of coffee, espresso, cappuccino or latte right into your kitchen.

Miele
anything else is a compromise

from the kitchens of
the world's greatest chefs

DIVA DE PROVENCE

PASCO, FRANCE

www.divadeprovence.com

33 Westchester Ave.   914-764-4051
Pound Ridge, NY   (Mon- Sat 9am-5pm)

~ Since 1952 ~

Things that matter SM

Thermad

◮HADCO

Things that matter SM

877.887.6157
www.hadco.net

Call for a dealer near you.

So much to do…so little time. And family time is precious. We know that at the end of the day, you'd rather be helping with homework than saddled with housework. That's why every product we offer is designed to get the job done better…and faster. Take Thermador's CM oven, combining convection, microwave and radiant heat to reduce cooking time by 50%. Now you have twice as much time for the things that matter.

Smart products are things that matter…bringing to life the things that matter to you.

GAGGENAU

Things that matter [SM]

In this kitchen, everything is made to order...

With a Gaggenau kitchen, you can start from scratch and cook up the kitchen of your dreams. Take one Gaggenau cooktop, add a barbecue grill, and combine with an electric deep fryer. Mix in one built-in steamer, and you've whipped up a masterpiece!

Create your own recipe for a totally personalized kitchen with Gaggenau and you'll know it will always be well done.

Smart products are things that matter... bringing to life the things that matter to you.

⬛HADCO

877.887.6157
www.hadco.net

Call for a dealer near you.

French Country Cooks!

Anybody – well
almost anybody –
can learn how to
cook the French way.
It is very basic, and for
seemingly centuries, very good.
It's all about the ingredients, the care and
concern of the cook, and the satisfaction from the plate.
These new Provencale Kitchen cabinets and fixtures from
France are just as delicious and mouth watering as your favorite recipes.
Made of solid French oak throughout with a hand painted finish. Let French
Country Living's designers put a French accent on your upcoming kitchen
plans. This is a kitchen that makes opening a bottle of wine feel like a trip to
Provence.

French Country Living

The soul of Provence in the heart of Greenwich

Complete Interior Design Services by Jani Caroli & Associates

34 East Putnam Avenue   **Greenwich, CT 06830**
Tel: 203.869.9559   **Fax: 203.869.9790**

Photo courtesy of **Drexel S. Frye Inc.**
Photo by **Olson Photographic**

CUSTOM WOODWORKING, METALWORKING, HARDWARE & GLASS

331
Paying Attention to the Details

338
Custom Millwork

347
Custom Cabinets

354
Stairways

360
Hardware

362
Windows & Doors

367
Custom Metalwork

371
Garage Doors

New England St

The region's indu

CUSTOM WOODWORKING,
METALWORKING,
HARDWARE & GLASS

"Stairways of distinction fo

From breathtaking, grand stairways,
New England Stair Company has been t
Combing old world craftsmanshi
innovative design, we produce stairways

800-8

ir Company, Inc.

y leader since 1975

more than twenty-six years"

...designs, of simple elegance,
...eader for over a quarter century.
...tate of the art technology, and
...nsurpassed quality and timeless beauty.

-6620

New England Stair Company, Inc

The region's industry leader since 1975

P.O. Box 763
1 White Street Extension
Shelton, CT 06484

800-822-6620 (outside local area)
203-924-0606
203-924-0165 (fax)

sales@newenglandstair.com

Paying Attention to the Details

W hat is it that makes a home truly original? Interior architectural elements handcrafted by the finest artisans contribute greatly to the uniqueness of a custom home.

Techniques with wood, metal, and glass have evolved over millennia. These ancient crafts are now ready to enhance your home. Cabinetry, moldings, ceiling medallions, chair rails, staircases, mirrors and mantels tell your story and reflect your unique tastes. Doors, windows and hardware should function in accord with the way you live, whether you want bay windows with storage drawers below, double French doors that open up the space between rooms, or hardware that simply reflects your style.

Photo courtesy of **Mark P. Finlay Architects**
Photo by **Nancy Hill**

PRICING A POWER LIBRARY

- A 15 ft. x 16 ft. library, fully paneled in cherry, mahogany or oak, some cabinets, with moldings, desk with hidden computer, coffered ceilings: $20,000 to $30,000.
- In a 16 ft. x 24 ft. two-story study, less paneling and more cabinetry of cherry, mahogany or oak, heavy with moldings, and radius work, desk with more pull out and hidden compartments for fax machine, small copier, bar with leaded glass cabinet fronts and a marble top, built-in humidor, and heavily coffered ceilings with multiple steps: $40,000.

HOW TO RECOGNIZE CUSTOM CABINET QUALITY

1. Proper sanding which results in a smooth, beautiful finish.
2. Superior detail work, adding unexpected elegance.
3. Classic application of design features and architectural details.
4. Beautiful, functional hardware selections.
5. High-quality hinges and drawer glides.
6. Superior overall functionality.

Nowhere is the commitment to elegant living through quality materials more apparent than in the selection of cabinets and millwork. Representing a significant percentage of the overall cost of a new or renovated home, sophisticated homeowners use this opportunity to declare their dedication to top quality.

Architectural millwork, made to order according to a set of architectural drawings, is becoming an increasingly popular luxury upgrade. Such detailing creates a richly nostalgic atmosphere that reminds homeowners of the comfort and security of a grandparents' home or the elegance of a club they've been in.

Elegant libraries, dens or sitting rooms dressed with fashionable raised panel cabinetry and special moldings are often included in the plans for new homes and remodeling projects. As a homeowner considering how and where to install millwork, ask yourself questions like these:

- How is the room used? Will a study be used for work or for solitude? Entertaining or a second office? Will it have to function as both a working office and an elegant room?

- How are the cabinets and shelves used? Books, collectibles, audio-video equipment, computer, fax or copy machines?

- What look do you want? You may want to consider "dressing" your rooms in different woods. You may like the rich look and feel of cherry paneling in your library, mahogany in the foyer, oak in a guest room and plaster in a dining room.

- Will the interior millwork choices work with the exterior architecture? A colonial home reminiscent of Mount Vernon should be filled with authentic details, like "dog-ear" corners, that create classic luxury. Using millwork inside a modern home can add interest and warmth to one or many rooms.

TAKE TIME TO MAKE A STATEMENT

Handcrafted high quality woodwork cannot be rushed. Millwork specialists encourage clients to contact them as early as possible with a clear idea of what kind of architectural statement they wish to make. The earlier you plan these details, the more options you'll have. Wainscoting with raised panels has to be coordinated with electrical outlets, window and door openings; beamed ceilings with light fixtures, and crown moldings with heating vents.

Hold a preliminary meeting before construction begins while it's early enough to incorporate innovative or special requirements into your plans. The more time you can devote to design (two to three weeks is recommended), the better your result will be. You're creating a custom millwork package that's never been designed for anyone before. Investments made on the front end are the most valuable. Ask about design fees, timelines and costs per revision. Keep your builder up to date on all of your millwork plans.

Drawings can be as detailed as you require. If you want to see the intricacies of a radius molding before you contract for it, let the millwork specialist know your requirements. Ask to see wood samples, with and without stain or paint.

Try to visit installed projects to get a firsthand feel for the quality of a specialist's work and to develop clearer ideas for your own home.

Changes made after an order is placed are costly. Therefore, if you're unsure, don't make a commitment. Add accessory moldings and other details as you see the project taking shape.

Expect a heavily laden room to take at least five to eight weeks to be delivered, about the time from the hanging of drywall to the installation of flooring. Installation takes one to three weeks, depending on the size and scope of the project.

THE SIGNATURE STATEMENT OF CUSTOM CABINETRY

Handcrafted custom cabinets are a recognizable standard of excellence which lend refinement and beauty to a home. Built in a kitchen, library, bathroom, or closet, or as a freestanding entertainment system or armoire, custom cabinets are a sophisticated signature statement.

DESIGNING HANDSOME CABINETRY

Cabinetry is a major element in your dream home, so let your imagination soar. Collect pictures of cabinets, noting the particular features you like. Cabinet makers appreciate visual examples because it's easier to interpret your desires from pictures than from words. Pictures crystallize your desires.

When you first meet with a cabinet maker, take your blueprints, and if possible, your builder, architect or designer. Be prepared to answer questions like:

• What is the exterior style of your home and do you want to continue that style inside?

• How will you the use the cabinets? Cutlery trays, pullout bins? Shelves for books, CDs, computer software, collections?

• What styles and embellishments do you like? Shaker, Prairie, Country English, Contemporary?

WHY YOU WANT A PROFESSIONAL DESIGNER

• They rely on experience to deliver you a custom product. Computer tools are great, but nothing replaces the experienced eye.
• They have established relationships with other trades, and can get top-quality glass fronts for your cabinets, or granite for a bar top.
• Their design ability can save you significant dollars in installation.
• They know how to listen to their clients and help them get the results they dream of.

PRICING OF CUSTOM KITCHEN CABINETS

• Deluxe Kitchen - Face frame-style cabinets of oak, maple or pine, with raised panel doors; crown molding on upper cabinetry, decorative hardware, wood nosing (cap) around counter tops: $10,000 - $20,000
• Upgrade to - Shaker inset-style cabinets in cherry-wood, painted finish: $20,000 additional.

Fancy moldings, wainscoting, inlaid banding? Use your Idea Notebook to communicate your preferences.

• Do you prefer particular woods? Cherry, oak, sycamore, or the more exotic ebony, Bubinga or Swiss pearwood? (Species must be selected on the basis of the finish you want.)

• Will cabinetry be visible from other rooms in the house? Must it match previously installed or selected flooring or countertops? (Take samples.)

MANAGING THE LENGTHY PROCESS OF A CUSTOM CABINET PROJECT

With plenty of unhurried time, you can be more creative, while allowing the woodworkers the time they need to deliver a top quality product. Take your blueprints to a cabinet maker early. Although installation occurs in the latter part of the construction, measuring usually takes place very early on.

If your project is carefully thought out, you won't be as likely to change your mind, but a contingency budget of 10 to 15 percent for changes (like adding radiuses or a lacquered finish) is recommended.

Custom cabinets for a whole house, (kitchen, butler's pantry, library, master bath, and three to four additional baths) may take 10 to 15 weeks, depending on the details involved (heavy carving adds significant time). Cabinets for a kitchen remodeling may take two months.

EXCEPTIONAL STAIRCASES

Take full advantage of the opportunity to upgrade your new or remodeled home with a spectacular staircase by contacting the stairmakers early in the design phase. Their familiarity with products, standards and building codes will be invaluable to you and your architect, contractor or interior designer.

Visit a stair showroom or workroom on your own or with your architect, interior designer or builder during the architectural drawing phase of your project. Discuss how you can achieve what you want at a cost-conscious price. Choosing a standard size radius of 24 inches, in place of a custom 25 ½ inch radius, for example, will help control costs.

Although your imagination may know no bounds in designing a staircase, hard and fast local building codes may keep your feet on the ground. Codes are not static, and stairmakers constantly update their files on local restrictions regarding details like the rise and run of a stair, and the size and height of rails.

USING PLASTER DETAILING

Plaster architectural detailing and trim add a distinctive look to any home. Most often used in out-of-the-way places, like in ceiling medallions or crown moldings, the high relief detailing is especially impressive.

PRICES OF CUSTOM STAIRS

Stairs can cost anywhere from $200 to $95,000, depending on size, materials and the complexity of design:
• Red Oak spiral staircase, up-graded railing: $10,000
• Red Oak circle stairs, standard railings on both sides and around upstairs landing: $13,000
• Six flights of Red Oak circle stairs stacked one atop the next, with landings at the top of each stair: $95,000
• Walnut or mahogany adds 50 percent to the overall cost.

THE STAIR-BUILDING PROCESS

The design of your stairs should be settled in the rough framing phase of the overall building project. If you work within this time frame, the stairs will be ready for installation after the drywall is hung and primer has been applied to the walls in the stair area.

Stairs can be built out of many woods. The most popular choice is red oak, but cherry, maple, walnut and mahogany are also used. If metal railings are preferred, you'll need to contact a specialist.

A top quality stair builder will design your stairs to your specifications. Consider the views you want of the house while on the stairs, and what kind of front entrance presentation you prefer. You may want to see the stairs from a particular room. An expert also can make suggestions regarding comfort and safety, and what styles will enhance the overall architecture.

Plans that are drawn on a computer can be changed with relative ease and can be printed at full size. This is very helpful to homeowners who want to see exactly what the stairs will look like in their home. The full-size plans can be taken to the job site and tacked to the floor to be experienced firsthand.

LOOKING AT THE BEAUTY OF CUSTOM GLASS AND MIRROR

A room can be transformed through the use of custom decorative glass and mirrors. Artists design intricately patterned, delicately painted glass to add light and architectural interest in all kinds of room dividers and partitions. Glass artistry can be based on any design, playing on the texture of carpet, the pattern of the brick, or repeating a fabric design. A glass block wall or floor panel can add the touch of distinction that sets a home above the others. Stained glass, usually associated with beautiful classic styling, can be designed in any style – from contemporary to art deco to traditional.

Top specialists, like those presented in the following pages, take great care in designing and delivering unique, top quality products. They work with top quality fabricated products, with the highest quality of beveling and edge work.

THE ARTISTIC PROCESS

Glass specialists will visit your home or building site to make recommendations and estimate costs and delivery time. Study their samples and if they have a showroom, go take a look. Perhaps you could visit an installed project. Seeing the possibilities can stimulate your imagination and open your eyes to new ideas in ways pictures simply cannot.

DOOR #1, #2, OR #3?

- Door #1 - Six panel oak door with sidelights of leaded glass: $1,700 - $2,000
- Door #2 - Six panel oak door with lead and beveled glass: $3,000
- Door #3 - Oversized, all matched oak, with custom designed leaded glass and brass, sidelights, elliptical top over door: $15,000
- Allow $500 to $1,500 for door-knobs, hinges and other hardware.

LUXURY GLASS & MIRROR

- **Mirrored Exercise Room:** Floor to ceiling, wall to wall mirrors, on two or three walls. Allow at least a month, from initial measuring, to squaring off and balancing walls, to installation. Price for polished mirror starts around $9 per square foot. Cutouts for vent outlets cost extra.
- **Custom Shower Doors:** Frameless, bent or curved shower doors are popular luxury upgrades. Made of clear or sandblasted heavy glass - 1/2 in. to 3/8 in. thick. $2,000 and up.
- **Stained Glass Room Divider:** Contemporary, clear on clear design, with a hint of color. Approximately 4 ft. x 6 ft., inset into a wall. $4,500.
- **Glass Dining Table:** Custom designed with bevel edge, 48 in. x 96 in. with two glass bases. $1,200.

Allow a month to make a decision and four weeks for custom mirror work delivery, and ten to 14 weeks for decorated glass.

In order to have the glass or mirror ready for installation before the carpet is laid, decisions must be made during the framing or rough construction phase in a new home or remodeling job. Mirrored walls are installed as painting is being completed, so touch-ups can be done while painters are still on site.

Expect to pay a 50 percent deposit on any order after seeing a series of renderings and approving a final choice. Delivery generally is included in the price.

THE BEAUTY AND CHARM OF CUSTOM WINDOWS AND DOORS

Just as we're naturally drawn to establish eye contact with each other, our attention is naturally drawn to the "eyes" of a home, the windows, skylights and glass doors.

These very important structural features, when expertly planned and designed, add personality and distinction to your interior while complementing the exterior architectural style of your home.

After lumber, windows are the most expensive part of a home. Take the time to investigate the various features and qualities of windows, skylights and glass doors. Visit a specialty store offering top of the line products and service and take advantage of their awareness of current products as well as their accumulated knowledge.

Visit a showroom with your designer, builder or architect. Because of the rapidly changing requirements of local building codes, it's difficult for them to keep current on what can be installed in your municipality. In addition, the dizzying pace of energy efficiency improvements over the past five years can easily outrun the knowledge of everyone but the window specialist. Interior designers can help you understand proper placement and scale in relation to furnishings and room use.

As you define your needs ask questions about alternatives or options, such as energy efficiency, ease of maintenance, appropriate styles to suit the exterior architecture, and interior.

Top quality windows offer high-energy efficiency, the best woodwork and hardware, and comprehensive service and guarantees (which should not be prorated). Good service agreements cover everything, including the locks.

Every home of distinction deserves an entry that exudes a warm welcome and a strong sense of homecoming. When we think of "coming home," we envision an entry door first, the strong, welcoming look of it, a first impression of the home behind it. To get the best quality door, contact a door or millwork specialist with a reputation for delivering top quality products. They can educate you on functionality, and wood and size choices and availability, as well as appropriate style. Doors are also made of steel or fiberglass, but wood offers the most flexibility for custom design.

Since doors are a permanent part of your architecture, carefully shop for the design that best reflects the special character of your home. Allow two to three weeks for delivery of a simple door and eight to 12 weeks if you're choosing a fancy front door. Doors are installed during the same phase as windows, before insulation and drywall.

DESIGN FLAIR HINGES ON FANTASTIC HARDWARE

Door and cabinet hardware, towel bars and accessories add style and substance to interiors. Little things truly do make the difference – by paying attention to the selection of top quality hardware in long-lasting, great-looking finishes, you help define your signature style and commitment to quality in a custom home. There are hundreds of possibilities, so when you visit a specialty showroom, ask the sales staff for their guidance. They can direct you towards the products that will complement your established design style and help you stay within the limits of your budget. When a rim lock for the front door can easily cost $500, and knobs can be $10 each, the advice of a knowledgeable expert is priceless.

Most products are readily available in a short time frame, with the exception of door and cabinetry hardware. Allow eight weeks for your door hardware, and three to four weeks for cabinetry selections. Since accessory hardware is usually in stock, changing cabinet knobs, hooks and towel bars is a quick and fun way to get a new look.

If you're looking to add a creative touch, blacksmithing as decorative art has come to the fore as a way for homeowners to express their personal style. Whether reproductions of period pieces or a new, original design, ornamental iron combines strong, functional purpose with graceful art. ■

THREE TIPS FOR DOOR HARDWARE

1. Use three hinges to a door - it keeps the door straight.
2. Match all hardware - hinges, knobs, handles, all in the same finish. Use levers or knobs - don't mix.
3. Use a finish that will last.

Custom Millwork

ALL STAR WOODWORKING...**(914) 769-9161**
401 Claremont Avenue, Thornwood   Fax: (914) 747-4038
See Ad on Page: 342
Principal/Owner: Les Vissers
e-mail: allstar@bestweb.net
Additional Information: Build and install fine interior woodwork, including kitchens, libraries, vanities since 1978.

BLOOM DESIGN LLC ....**(203) 773-9992**
315 Peck Street, New Haven   Fax: (203) 773-9785
See Ad on Page: 341
Principal/Owner: Paul Bloom
Website: bloom-design.net e-mail: office@bloom-design.net
Additional Information: Custom furniture and interiors that balance art and function. Unexpected junctures in wood, stone and glass. Design or design/build – exactly what you want.

CRANE WOODWORKING, INC....**(203) 852-9229**
15 Rockland Road, South Norwalk   Fax: (203) 853-4799
See Ad on Page: 340
Principal/Owner: Doug Crane
Website: cranewoodworking.com e-mail: craneww.snet.net
Additional Information: High-end architectural millwork and custom cabinetry.

DESCOM WOODWORKING COMPANY ....**(914) 941-5383**
100 Spring Street, Ossining   Fax: (914) 941-1729
See Ad on Page: 344, 345
Principal/Owner: Chris Marconi
e-mail: chrismarconi@earthlink.net
Additional Information: For over 40 years Descom Woodworking Company has been creating beautiful custom cabinetry and architectural elements for the discriminating homeowner..

DREXEL S. FRYE, INC. ....**(860) 663-3202**
14 Route 80, Killingworth   Fax: (203) 483-4161
See Ad on Page: 350,351
Principal/Owner: Eric M. Rose
e-mail: dfrye@drexelsfrye.com
Additional Information: The finest cabinetry and millwork for the finest architects.

FAIRFIELD COUNTY MILLWORK...**(203) 367-9755**
955 Connecticut Avenue, Bridgeport   Fax: (203) 367-9385
See Ad on Page: 346
Principal/Owner: John Ianiri
Website: www.fcmillwork.com e-mail: fcm1@optonline.net
Additional Information: High-end custom millwork and cabinetry manufacturers.

K.L.R. WOODWORKING...**(203) 854-5190**
97 Richards Avenue, Norwalk   Fax: (203) 854-5190
See Ad on Page: 339
Principal/Owner: Khris Rozwadowski

338

K.L.R. Woodworking

■   ■   ■   ■   ■

Specializing in Architectural Trim

15 Rockland Road

BLOOM DESIGN LLC
FURNITURE + INTERIORS

Photo by: Rick Scanlan

FURNITURE YOU IMAGINE BUT CANNOT FIND.
EXACTLY WHAT YOU WANT.

315 PECK STREET   NEW HAVEN   CT   06513
203.773.9992 T   203.773.9785 F   OFFICE@BLOOM-DESIGN.NET

ALL STAR
WOODWORKING

THORNWOOD
ARCHITECTURAL MILLWORK

Fine Woodworking Since 1978

Member **AWI**

401 CLAREMONT AVE   THORNWOOD, NY 10594
TEL: 914-769-9161   FAX: 914-747-4038

Bayberry

WOODWORKING

Specialists in the installation of fine architectural trim and cabinetry, our attention to detail has made Bayberry Woodworking a top choice among contractors, leading architects, and discerning homeowners since 1989. Each and every member of the Bayberry crew is a master craftsman – we think you'll find our workmanship *unparalleled*.

...because it's in the

Details

Contact: Andrew Gallen

203.938.2684

Fax: 203.938.0677

Redding, Connecticut

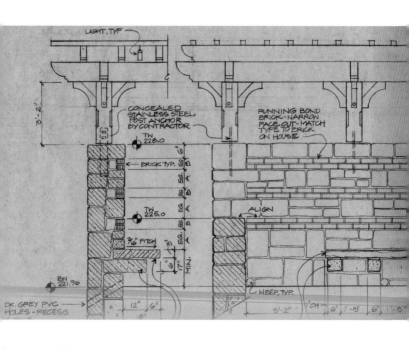

LIGHT, TYP

CONCEALED
STAINLESS STEEL
POST ANCHOR
BY CONTRACTOR

RUNNING BOND
BRICK - NARROW
FACE OUT - MATCH
TYPE TO BRICK
ON HOUSE

TW 228.0

BRICK TYP.

TW 225.0

3/16" PITCH

ALIGN

BW 221.90

WEEP, TYP.

DK. GREY PVC
HOLES - RECESS

12"   6"

3'-2"   1'-0"   6"   1'-9"   6"   1'-9"

MIN.

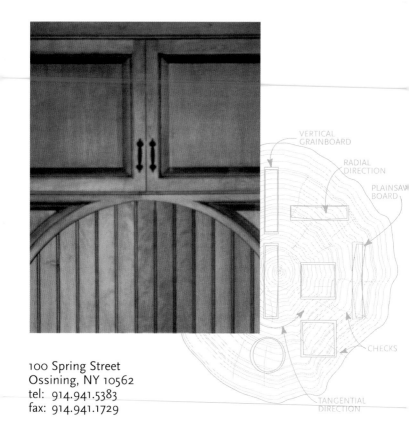

VERTICAL
GRAINBOARD

RADIAL
DIRECTION

PLAINSAW
BOARD

CHECKS

TANGENTIAL
DIRECTION

100 Spring Street
Ossining, NY 10562
tel: 914.941.5383
fax: 914.941.1729

DESCON WOODWORKING COMPANY
Craftsmanship from another era.

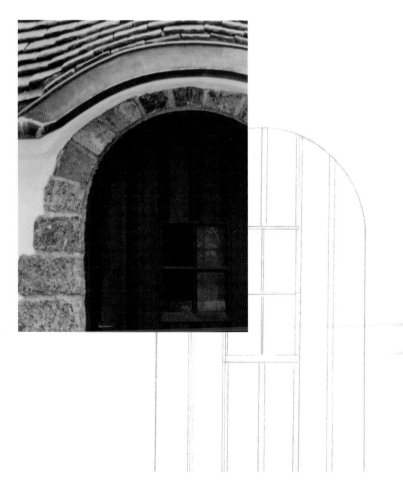

Fairfield County Millwork

Fine Cabinetry and Architectural Millwork

Est.1983

Member
Architectural
Woodwork
Institute

955 Connecticut Ave. Suite 4109 • Bridgeport, CT 06607
tel.203.367.9755 • fax 203.367.9385
Visit our website at www.fcmillwork.com
Email us at fcml@optonline.net

Custom
Cabinets

DREXEL S. FRYE, INC. ....**(860) 663-3202**
14 Route 80, Killingworth   Fax: (203) 483-4161
See Ad on Page: 350, 351
Principal/Owner: Eric M. Rose
e-mail: dfrye@drexelsfrye.com
Additional Information: The finest cabinetry and millwork for the finest architects.

MASTERWORKS CABINETRY, INC. ....**(203) 791-2034**
17 Diamond Avenue, Bethel   Fax: (203) 791-2473
See Ad on Page: 348, 349
Principal/Owner: Raymond P. Menard, President
Website: www.masterworkscabinetry.com

ROOMS OF ENGLAND ....**(203) 226-7550**
1027 Post Road East, Westport   Fax: (203) 226-6848
See Ad on Page: 290, 291
Principal/Owner: Matt Cowan

TOP DRAWER CUSTOM CABINETRY CORP. ....**(914) 632-4222**
11 Lincoln Avenue, New Rochelle   Fax: (914) 637-0843
See Ad on Page: 312
Principal/Owner: Jerry Tomic

WESTCHESTER DESIGN CENTER/EMPIRE KITCHENS ....**(914) 242-9011**
193 Main Street, Mt. Kisco   Fax: (914) 242-4603
See Ad on Page: 310, 311, 352, 353
Principal/Owner: John Mansor

347

MASTERWORKS CABINETRY, INC

CUSTOM WOODWORKING DESIGN & DETAILS

17 Diamond Avenue • Bethel, Connecticut • 06801
Phone: (203) 791-2034 • Fax: (203) 791-2473

www.masterworkscabinetry.com

We are professional designers
who engineer and build the
products we provide.

Serving allied professionals and
private clients, throughout
New England, since 1984.

Raymond P. Menard, President

Elaine C. Murdoch, CKD
Certified Kitchen Designer

Uncompromised Quality - Uncommon Servic

Photography by Maggie Cole

DREXEL S. FRYE, INC.

ARCHITECTURAL WOODWORKING

Modern

Classical

DREXEL S. FRYE, INC.
ARCHITECTURAL WOODWORKING

Antique

**From Modern to Artistic,
Your architect's ideas are our reality.**

Custom Cabinets • Architectural Woodwork

14 Route 80 • Killingworth, CT 06419
tel 860.663.3202 • fax 203.483.4161

EMPIRE KITCHENS at

The Westchester Design Center

193 Main Street • Mount Kisco, New York 10549
Telephone (914) 242-9011 • Fax (914) 242-4603

QUALITY
CUSTOM CABINETRY
INC.

EMPIRE OF GREENWICH
Fine Cabinets and Cabinetry, Inc.
95 Putnam Avenue, Putnam, CT 06830
Telephone (203) 863-9690

Stairways

NEW ENGLAND STAIR COMPANY, INC. ....**(800) 822-6620**
P.O. Box 763, 1 White Street , Shelton   Fax: (203) 924-0165
See Ad on Page: 331-333, 355-359
<u>Principal/Owner</u>: William Silvia
<u>Website</u>: newenglandstaircompany.com <u>e-mail</u>: info@newenglandstair.com
<u>Additional Information</u>: Manufacturers of custom stairways and balustrades of distinction. The region's industry leader since 1975.

New England Stair Company, Inc
The region's industry leader since 1975

Our Windsor Estate™ model gives this grand foyer a classic, stately look

The timeless Nantucket™ Lighthouse Newel is a warm welcome beacon to any foyer

Design innovation and attention to detail

This stairway features Lexington™
box newels, one of many popular
choices from our extensive
box newel collection

New England Stair Company, Inc

The region's industry leader since 1975

P.O. Box 763
1 White Street Extension
Shelton, CT 06484

800-822-6620 (outside local area)
203-924-0606
203-924-0165 (fax)

sales@newenglandstair.com

Hardware

INTERSTATE LUMBER/LAKELAND LUMBER ....**(203) 531-8050**
184 South Water Street, Greenwich   Fax: (203) 531-1373
See Ad on Page: 361, 363
<u>Principal/Owner</u>: Sheldon Kahan
<u>Website</u>: interstatelumber.com <u>e-mail</u>: sksieber@lakelandlumber.com
<u>Additional Information</u>: Providing quality building products for over 80 years.

MARVIN
Windows and Doors

Made for you.™

Windows and doors made for the way you look at the world.

Visit the experts at the Interstate Design Center and experience the quality of Marvin.

Interstate Design Center
A division of

INTERSTATE IL LAKELAND • LUMBER est. 1922

239 Mill Street • Greenwich
203.531.8820

Windows &
Doors

AMERICAN FRAMELESS ....**(203) 227-1785**
42 Riverside Avenue, Westport   Fax: (203) 226-7976
See Ad on Page: 364, 365
Principal/Owner: Dennis Grimaldi

INTERSTATE LUMBER/LAKELAND LUMBER ....**(203) 531-8050**
184 South Water Street, Greenwich   Fax: (203) 531-1373
See Ad on Page: 361, 363
Principal/Owner: Sheldon Kahan
Website: interstatelumber.com e-mail: sksieber@lakelandlumber.com
Additional Information: Providing quality building products for over 80 years.

LAKELAND LUMBER ....**(203) 531-8080**
184 South Water Street, Greenwich   Fax: (203) 531-1373
See Ad on Page: 361, 363
Principal/Owner: Archie Leonardis
Website: interstatelumber.com e-mail: sksieber@lakelandlumber.com

RINGS END LUMBER ....**(203) 656-7515**
181 West Avenue, Darien   Fax: (203) 656-7586
See Ad on Page: 366
Principal/Owner: Craig Sinclair

$\mathscr{S}$ECURITY
for exceptional homes

Nothing compares to the timeless elegance of crafted brass. Baldwin estates locking products combine the lustrous beauty of brass with meticulously designed and solidly crafted locking systems that assure ultimate security for exceptional homes.

- Mortise locks, knobs and levers.

- Solid, forged brass construction.

- Industry's broadest selection of styles and finishes.

BALDWIN®

GREENWICH, CT   STAMFORD, CT   BETHEL, CT

LAKELAND • LUMBER   est. 1922

SHRUB OAK, NY   CROTON FALLS, NY

203-531-8050 / 914-939-2500

Providing Quality Service & Building Products For Over 80 Years

I'm proud to say that throughout our 45 years, The Westport Glass Company has treated our client's homes and offices as if they were our own ... with personalized attention to the design, manufacturing and fabrication requirements ... with courteous, neat and on-time installations ... backed by our warranty and on-going maintenance support.

We look forward to making your ideas in glass a delightful reality.

Dennis Grimaldi
President

Log onto our
Ideas In Glass Website
AMERICANFRAMELESS.COM

42 RIVERSIDE AVENUE
WESTPORT, CT 06880

800 • 606 •1776

Our Semi-Frameless & Framed Enclosure Systems for sliding and pull type doors are an economical yet beautiful form of bath & shower enclosures. And these systems are available in a variety of glass and hardware finish options.

American Frameless
Shower Door
A WESTPORT GLASS COMPANY

• *residential* • *architectural*

Crystal Clear Elegance

in Bath & Shower Enclosures

Our Frameless Enclosure Systems feature the simple elegance of free floating structural glass doors ... hung without conventional hardware and rail devices. The result is a sleek, minimalist, custom fit to almost any enclosure dimension ... thereby accentuating the classic lines and clarity of the glass.

We also offer scratch & stain resistant Teflon-Coated Diamond Fusion™ glass.

Think
of the possibilities.

...for your
home

Whether you're about to embark upon build
ing a new home or remodeling or renovating an
existing one, windows and doors will be an integra
part of your plans. But where do you begin? W
hope with Ring's End and Marvin Windows and
Doors. With Marvin's 11,000 standard sized win
dows and doors, and an unlimited number of cus
tom sizes, we'll make sure that you get the right windows and doors with jus
the right features and options for your home and living style.

Here are just a few of the services Ring's End can provide

Factory Trained & Certified Marvin Windows and Doors Coordinator
Computer Aided Design • Blueprint Take-Offs
In Field Service • Contractor Referrals • Free Quotations • Free Deliver

"Your Marvin Signature Dealer"

DARIEN	**BETHEL**	**LEWISBORO**	**NEW MILFORD**	**NIANTIC**
181 West Ave.	9 Taylor Ave.	Rt. 123, Vista NY	140 Danbury Rd.	28 Hope Stree
(203) 655-2525	(203) 797-1212	(914) 533-2517	(860) 355-5566	(860) 739-54

Lumber • Hardware • Building Materials • Kitchens • Millwork • Moulding • Fencing • Pai

Custom
Metalwork

ARTISTIC IRON WORKS, LLC..**(203) 838-9200**
11 Reynolds Street, Norwalk   Fax: (203) 852-9002
See Ad on Page: 370
<u>Principal/Owner</u>: Renata Jankowksa Singh
<u>Additional Information</u>: Specializing in custom wrought iron railings, estate gates, fences, and decorative architectural blacksmithing of all kinds.

CREATIVE METAL FAB, LLC ....**(203) 323-4090**
293 Selleck Street, Stamford   Fax: (203) 323-4412
See Ad on Page: 368, 369
<u>Principal/Owner</u>: John Pampea

CREATIVE METAL FAB, LLC

293 Selleck St. Stamford, CT 06902
Tel. 203 323-4090   Fax 203 323-4412

CMF is the premier custom architectural metals shop servicing NYC, Fairfield and Westchester counties. The design professionals choice for fabrication, design and installation of a wide array of projects. Visit our website! See our capabilities.

 www.cmfmetals.com

ARTISTIC IRON WORKS, LLC

Distinctive design, quality craftsmanship and exceptional customer service. We will implement your concept into a beautiful work of art. Specializing in custom wrought iron railings, estate gates, fences,decorative, architectural and artistic blacksmithing of all kinds.

11 Reynolds Street
Norwalk, CT 06855
Phone (203) 838-9200
Fax (203) 852-9002
www.artisticironwork.com

Garage
Doors

ED'S GARAGE DOORS ....**(203) 847-1284**
9 Cross Street, Norwalk   Fax: (203) 855-8259
See Ad on Page: 373
Principal/Owner: Richard A. Cunningham
Website: www.edsgaragedoors.com   e-mail: edsgaragedoors@aol.com
Additional Information: Fairfield County's premium supplier of high-end quality garage doors since 1972.

DANBURY
Overhead Door
Family Owned and Operated

Olson Photography

26 Federal Road
Danbury, CT 06810

203.744.3001

fax 203.792.1765
jeanne@ohddct.com

Model 511
Honduras
Mahogany

Model E308A
Western Red
Cedar

Model EX08S
Western Red
Cedar

The Perfect Enhancement to the Extraordinary Home

Discover one of Fairfield County's premium suppliers of quality doors and electric
door operators. Featuring a full line of wood doors, carriage style doors and matching
entry doors. We can offer the perfect complement to any architectural design and
lifestyle - from traditional manor homes to sophisticated contemporaries.

GARAGE DOORS, LTD.

9 Cross Street, Norwalk, CT 06851
Phone: 203-847-1284 Fax: 203-855-8259
Website: www.Edsgaragedoors.com

Lift-Master
The Professional Line

Sales * Installation * Service * Since 1972
(203) 847-1284

Location,
Location,
Location!

What better LOCATION for your advertisement than the CONNECTICUT/WESTCHESTER COUNTY HOME BOOK!

Just as our readers realize how important location is when choosing a home, we realize that it's just as important to you when allocating your advertising dollars. That's why we have successfully positioned the CONNECTICUT/WESTCHESTER COUNTY HOME BOOK to reach the high-end consumers you want as clients.

Call 203-323-7400 to find out about our unique marketing programs and advertising opportunities.

Published by
The Ashley Group
1234 Summer St., Stamford, CT, 06905
203-323-7400 fax 203-326-5177
E-mail: ashleybooksales@ReedBusiness.com

FLOORING

& COUNTERTOPS

375
Surfacing in Style

382
Carpeting & Area Rugs

386
Marble, Tile & Granite

390
Flooring

*Come in and view our enormous
selection of antique, semi-antique
and contemporary rugs, needlepoints,
broadlooms, wilton and custom rugs.*

Open To The Trade

A. T. PROUDIAN INC
Fine Carpets and Their Care   Established 1923

120 East Putnam Avenue
Greenwich, CT 06830
203-622-1200

736 Main Street
New Rochelle, NY 10801
914-632-4848

DORELLO

CARPETS & AREA RUGS

DORELLOCARPETS.COM

594 MAIN AVENUE NORWALK, CT 06851
(203) 847-0335 • FAX: (203) 750-0267

Your Full Line   *Karastan*®   Rug & Broadloom Dealer

Surfacing in Style

The feel of a home is indelibly tied to the materials that make up its surfaces, and its floors and countertops are two of the most conspicuous. Ceramic tile, red oak, and marble floors, for example, each evoke vastly different responses. Depending on your goals, you can choose materials that make you feel casual and relaxed, cozy and warm, or powerful and prestigious.

As the world becomes smaller due to the ease of global travel, exotic woods, stone and tile are increasingly available. And manmade countertop materials come in an increasing array of colors and styles.

The suppliers and artisans featured in the following pages can offer you a whole new world waiting just below (or on top of) the surface.

Photo courtesy of **Zoltan European Floors Inc.**

DISTINGUISHED FLOOR COVERINGS...
CARPETS & RUGS

From a room-sized French Aubusson rug to a dense wool carpet with inset borders, "soft" floor treatments are used in area homes to make a signature statement, or blend quietly into the background to let other art and furnishings grab the attention.

Selecting carpeting and rugs requires research, a dedicated search, and the guidance of a well-established design plan. Because the floor covers the width and depth of any room, it's very important that your choices are made in concert with other design decisions — from furniture to art, from window treatments to lighting.

Your interior designer or a representative at any of the fine retail stores featured in the following pages is qualified to educate you as you make your selections.

Rug and carpet dealers who cater to a clientele that demands a high level of personal service (from advice to installation and maintenance) and top quality products, are themselves dedicated to only the best in terms of service and selection. Their accumulated knowledge will be a most important benefit as you select the right carpet for your home.

THE WORLD AT YOUR FEET

Today's profusion of various fibers, colors, patterns, textures, and weights make carpet selection exciting and challenging. Your search won't be overwhelming if you realize the requirements of your own home and work within those boundaries.

Begin where the carpet will eventually end up – that is, in your home. Consider how a carpet will function by answering questions like these:

• What is the traffic pattern? High traffic areas, like stairs and halls, require a stain resistant dense or low level loop carpet for top durability in a color or pattern that won't show wear. Your choices for a bedroom, where traffic is minimal, will include lighter colors in deeper plush or velvets.

• How will it fit with existing or developing decors? Do you need a neutral for an unobtrusive background, or an eye-catching tone-on-tone texture that's a work of art in itself?

• Will it flow nicely into adjoining rooms? Carpet or other flooring treatments in the surrounding rooms need to be considered.

• What needs, other than decorative, must the carpet fill? Do you need to keep a room warm, muffle sound, protect a natural wood floor?

ORIENTAL RUGS

The decision to invest in an Oriental rug should be made carefully. Buying a rug purely for its decorative beauty and buying for investment purposes require two different approaches. If you're buying for aesthetics, put beauty first and condition second. Certain colors and patterns are more significant than others; a reputable dealer can guide you. Check for quality by looking at these features:
• Regularity of knotting.
• Color clarity.
• Rug lies evenly on the floor.
• Back is free of damage or repair marks.

BEYOND TRADITIONAL

Solid surfacing is now being used to make custom faucets, decorative wall tiles, and lots of other creative touches for the home. Their rich colors (including granite), famed durability and versatility are perfect for bringing ideas to life. Check with your countertop supplier for information and ideas.

• How is the room used? Do teenagers and toddlers carry snacks into the family room? Is a finished basement used for ping-pong as well as a home office?

THE ARTISTRY OF RUGS

N othing compares to the artful elegance of a carefully selected area rug placed on a hard surface. Through pattern, design, texture and color, rug designers create a work of art that is truly enduring. If you have hardwood, marble or natural stone floors, an area rug will only enhance their natural beauty. From Chinese silk, to colorful Pakistanis, to rare Caucasian antiques, the possibilities are as varied as the world is wide.

If you're creating a new interior, it's best to start with rug selection. First, it's harder to find the "right" rug than it is to find the "right" fabric or paint: there are simply fewer fine rugs than there are fabrics, patterns or colors. However, don't make a final commitment on a rug until you know it will work with the overall design. Second, rugs usually outlive other furnishings. Homeowners like to hang on to their rugs when they move, and keep them as family heirlooms.

In recent years, many rug clients have been enjoying a bounty of beautiful, well-made rugs from every major rug-producing country in the world. As competition for the global market intensifies, rugs of exceptionally high caliber are more readily available. Getting qualified advice is more important than ever.

Fine rug dealers, like those showcased in the following pages, have knowledgeable staff members who are dedicated to educating their clientele and helping them find a rug they'll love. Through careful consideration of your tastes, and the requirements of your home, these professionals will virtually walk you through the process. They'll encourage you to take your time, and to judge each rug on its own merits. They'll insist on you taking rugs home so that you can experience them in your own light (and may also provide delivery). And their companies will offer cleaning and repair service, which may well be important to you some day.

WARMING UP TO HARDWOOD

A hardwood floor is part of the dream for many custom homeowners searching for a warm, welcoming environment. Highly polished planks or fine parquet, the beauty of wood has always been a definitive part of luxurious homes and as the design "warming trend" continues, a wood floor figures prominently in achieving this feeling.

FOR SUCCESSFUL CARPET SHOPPING

1. Take along blueprints (or accurate measurements), fabric swatches, paint chips & photos.
2. Focus on installed, not retail price.
3. Take samples home to experience it in the light of the room.
4. Be aware of delivery times; most carpet is available within weeks; special orders or custom designs take much longer.
5. Shop together. It saves time in the decision-making process.

With new product options that make maintenance even easier, wood floors continue to add value and distinction in upscale homes throughout the area and the suburbs. Plank, parquet, and strip wood come in a wide variety of materials, and scores of styles and tones. Consider what effect you're trying to achieve.

Plank wood complements a traditional interior, while parquet wood flooring offers a highly stylized look. Designs stenciled directly on to floorboards create an original Arts and Crafts feel.

Brazilian cherry wood and tumbled travertine quarried from Italy are simply more accessible today, and the door is open to previously obscure materials such as Australian jarrah eucalyptus or American antique red heart cypress (also known as tidewater or bald cypress).

VINYL AND LAMINATES

Vinyl or laminated floor coverings are no longer considered candidates for immediate rehab. As a matter of fact, they're among the most updated looks in flooring. Stylish laminates are made to convincingly simulate wood, ceramic tile and other natural flooring products, and are excellent choices for heavy traffic areas. They come in hundreds of colors and patterns, and offer great compatibility with countertop materials.

THE RENAISSANCE OF CERAMIC TILE

Ceramic tile has literally come out of the back rooms and into the spotlight with its color, beauty and unique stylistic potential. As sophisticated shoppers gain a better understanding of the nature and possibilities of tile, its use has increased dramatically. Homeowners who want added quality and value in their homes are searching out hand painted glazed tiles for the risers of a staircase, quirky rectangular tiles to frame a powder room mirror, and ceramic tiles that look exactly like stone for their sun porch or kitchen. From traditional to modern, imported to domestic, ceramic tile offers a world of possibilities.

It is the perfect solution for homeowners who want floor, walls, countertops or backsplashes made of top quality, durable and attractive materials. A glazed clay natural product, ceramic tile is flexible, easy to care for, and allows for a variety of design ideas. It is easily cleaned with water and doesn't require waxing or polishing. And, like other natural flooring and counter products, ceramic tile adds visible value to a luxury home.

BUDGETING FOR WOOD FLOOR

• 2 1/4" strip oak - $10/sq. ft. Wider plank or parquet, glued & nailed - $15/sq. ft. Fancy parquet, hand-finished plank or French patterns (Versailles, Brittany) - $30/sq. ft. and up.
• Estimates include finishing and installation; not sub-floor trim.

378

THE NUMBER ONE WAY TO DECIDE ON A RUG

Do you like the rug enough to decorate around it? There's your answer.

SELECTING CERAMIC TILE

Not all tile works in all situations, so it's imperative that you get good advice and counsel when selecting ceramic tile for your home. Ceramic tile is wear-rated, and this standardized system will steer you in the right direction. Patronize specialists who can provide creative, quality-driven advice. Visit showrooms to get an idea of the many colors, shapes and sizes available for use on floors, walls and counters. You'll be in for a very pleasant surprise.

If you're building or remodeling, your builder, architect, and/or interior designer can help you in your search and suggest creative ways to enliven your interior schemes. Individual hand-painted tiles can be interspersed in a solid color backsplash to add interest and individuality. Tiles can be included in a glass block partition, on a wallpapered wall, or in harmony with an area rug.

Grout, which can be difficult to keep clean, is now being addressed as a potential design element. By using a colored grout, the grout lines become a contrast design element – or can be colored to match the tile itself.

THE SOPHISTICATED LOOK OF NATURAL STONE

For a luxurious look that radiates strength and character, the world of natural stone offers dazzling possibilities. As custom buyers look for that "special something" to add to the beauty and value of their homes, they turn to the growing natural stone marketplace. A whole world of possibilities is now open to involved homeowners who contact the master craftsmen and suppliers who dedicate their careers to excellence in stone design, installation and refurbishing.

Marble and granite, which have always been options for homeowners, are more popular than ever. With luxurious texture and color, marble is often the choice to add dramatic beauty to a grand entryway or a master bath upgrade. Granite continues to grow in popularity especially in luxury kitchens – there is no better material for countertops. It's also popular for a section of countertop dedicated to rolling pastry or dough. Rustic, weathered and unpolished, or highly polished and brilliant, granite brings elegance and rich visual texture that adds easily recognizable value to a home. Beyond marble and granite, the better suppliers of stone products also can introduce homeowners to slates, soapstone, limestone, English Kirkstone, sandstone, and travertine, which can be finished in a variety of individual ways.

DON'T GET COLD FEET

Stone and tile floors are known for their chilly feel. Electrical products are available now to help warm the surfaces of natural products. Installed in the adhesive layer under the flooring, these warming units are available at the better suppliers and showrooms.

379

CERAMIC TILE AS STONE

With textured surfaces and color variations, ceramic tile can look strikingly like stone. You can get the tone on tone veining of marble, or the look of split stone, in assorted shapes, sizes and color.

BREAKING IN STONE PRODUCTS IN THE HOME

Like Mother Nature herself, natural stone is both rugged and vulnerable. Each stone requires specific care and maintenance, and homeowners often experience a period of adjustment as they become accustomed to the requirements of caring for their floors or countertops.

Ask an expert about the different requirements and characteristics. Soapstone, for example, is a beautiful, soft stone with an antique patina many people love. Accumulated stains and scratches just add to the look. Granite, on the other hand, will not stain.

A professional can educate you about the specific characteristics of each stone product so you make an informed decision on what products will best serve the lifestyle of your family.

CHOOSING STONE – A UNIQUE EXPERIENCE

Once a decision to use a natural stone is made, begin your search right away. By allowing plenty of time to discover the full realm of choices, you'll be able to choose a stone and finish that brings luster and value to your home, without the pressure of a deadline. If you order imported stone, it can take months for delivery. Be prepared to visit your supplier's warehouse to inspect the stone that will be used in your home. Natural stone varies – piece to piece, box to box – a slab can vary in color from one end to the other. If you understand this degree of unpredictable irregularity is unavoidable, it will help you approach the selection in a realistic way.

STRONG AND ELEGANT COUNTERTOPS

The quest for quality and style does not stop until the countertops are selected. Today's countertop marketplace is brimming with man-made products that add high style without sacrificing strength and resiliency.

As the functions of kitchens become broader, the demand for aesthetics continues to increase dramatically. For lasting beauty with incredible design sensibilities, manmade solid surfaces are a very popular choice. The overwhelming number of possibilities and combinations in selecting countertops makes it vital to work with specialists who are quality-oriented. Countertops represent a significant investment in a custom home, and quality, performance and style must be the primary considerations in any decision. Established professionals, like those introduced in your Home Book, have a reputation for expert installation and service of the top quality products that define luxury.

PRICING FOR NATURAL STONE

As with all flooring and countertop materials, get an installed, not a retail quote. Installation can drive the cost up significantly. Preparing a realistic quote may take days of research, due to the tremendous variety of factors that can influence price. As a general guideline, the installed starting price per square foot:

- Granite: $30
- Tumbled marble, limestone, slate: $20
- Engineered stone/quartzite: $25
- Antique stone, with intricate installation: $75
- Granite slab countertop: $70

SOLID SURFACING SHOWS UP ON TILES

Durable, non-porous solid surface materials are now being used to make decorative wall tiles. Check with your countertop supplier for information and ideas.

MAKE COUNTERTOP CHOICES EARLY

Since decisions on cabinetry are often made far in advance, it's best to make a countertop choice concurrently.

Expect to spend at least two weeks visiting showrooms and acquainting yourself with design and materials. Take along paint chips, samples of cabinet and flooring materials, and any pictures of the look you're trying to achieve. Expect a solid surface custom counter order to take at least five weeks to arrive.

AN ARRAY OF COUNTERTOP CHOICES

You'll face a field of hundreds of colors and textures of solid surfacing, laminates, ceramic tile, natural stone, wood and stainless or enameled steel. Poured concrete counters also are finding their way into luxury kitchens in the area.

Laminate or color-through laminate offer hundreds of colors, patterns and textures, many of which convincingly mimic the look of solid surfacing or granite. Enjoying growing popularity in countertop application, are the natural stones, those staggeringly gorgeous slabs of granite, marble or slate, which offer the timeless look of quality and luxury. Naturally quarried stone is extremely durable and brings a dramatic beauty and texture to the kitchen or bath. For endless color and pattern possibilities, ceramic tile is a highly durable option. Manmade resin-based solid surfacing materials offer many of the same benefits as stone. These surfaces are fabricated for durability and beauty, and new choices offer a visual depth that is astounding to the eye. It can be bent, carved, or sculpted. Elaborate edges can be cut into a solid surface counter and sections can be carved out to accommodate other surface materials, such as stainless steel or marble. Best known for superior durability, solid surfaces stand up to scratches, heat and water.

FINDING THE BEST SOURCE FOR MATERIALS

If you're building or remodeling your home, your designer, builder or architect will help you develop some ideas and find a supplier for the material you choose. Reputable suppliers, like those featured in the Home Book, are experienced in selecting the best products and providing expert installation. Go visit a showroom or office – their knowledge will be invaluable to you. The intricacies and idiosyncrasies of natural products, and the sheer volume of possibilities in fabricated surfaces, can be confounding on your own. ∎

BE CREATIVE!

Mix and match counter top materials for optimum functionality and up-to-date style. Install a butcher block for chopping vegetables and slicing breads, a slab of marble for rolling pastry and bakery dough, granite on an island for overall elegance, and solid surfaces for beauty and durability around the sinks and cooktop areas.

381

MAKE IT CONCRETE

This material is a versatile and indestructible choice, available in a variety of colors and textures. Sealed concrete can be made with creative borders, scored, sandblasted or stained. A strong, natural material, it can be made to look like other materials and natural stone.

Carpet
& Rugs

A.T. PROUDIAN INC....**(203) 622-1200**
120 E. Putnam Avenue, Greenwich   Fax: (203) 622-1713
See Ad on Page: 375, 376
Principal/Owner: Armen Proudian

CCA CARPET CO-OP OF AMERICA ....**(800) 466-6984**
4301 Earth City Expressway, Earth City, MO   Fax: (314) 291-7970
See Ad on Page: 383
Principal/Owner: Shari Carder
e-mail: scarder@swholesale.com

CLASSIC CARPET & RUG ....**(203) 359-3622**
83 Harvard Avenue, Stamford   Fax: (203) 445-0598
See Ad on Page: 384
Principal/Owner: Jack Breiner

DORELLO CARPETS & AREA RUGS ....**(203) 847-0335**
594 Main Street, Norwalk   Fax: (203) 750-0267
See Ad on Page: 377
Principal/Owner: James & Andrew Vecchiariello
Website: www.dorellocarpets.com

HOUSE OF TIBET RUGS INC. ....**(203) 341-0705**
9 Post Road West, Westport   Fax: (203) 341-8724
See Ad on Page: 385
Principal/Owner: Nima Lama
Website: www.houseoftibetrugs.com   e-mail: Houseoftibet@yahoo.com
Additional Information: Hand-crafted Tibetan traditional rugs from master weavers. Pure 100% Tibetan sheep wool, directly imported from our own carpet factory in Nepal. We specialize in custom orders in any dimension.

PROSOURCE WHOLESALE FLOOR COVERING ....**(800) 466-6984**
4301 Earth City Expressway, Earth City   Fax: (314) 291-7970
See Ad on Page: 383
Principal/Owner: Shari Carder
e-mail: scarder@swholesale.com

Designer flooring served up beautifully.

Low Wholesale Prices – All Name Brands

ProSource is a complete floorcovering resource designed to meet the unique needs of the trade professional. From the most elegant to the economical, we've gathered the world's largest selection of name brand flooring products from around the globe into one convenient Showroom that Members can use as their own. Carpet, vinyl, ceramic tile, wood, laminates and more—all at the lowest wholesale prices available in the market.

Membership is limited to the flooring trade professional. If you are not a member of the trade, have your professional call ProSource for you today.

Check out these Showrooms in the greater Connecticut area:

CLASSIC
CARPET & RUG

HOUSE OF TIBET RUGS, Inc.
TIBETAN RUGS

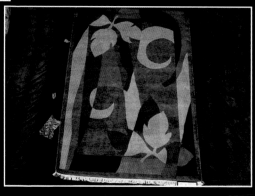

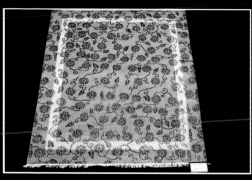

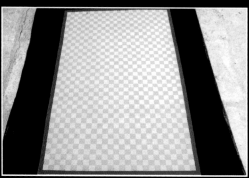

and Crafted Tibetan Traditional Rugs From Master Weavers

Pure Tibetan 100% sheep wool, directly imported from our own carpet factory in Nepal. We specialize in custom orders in any shape and size. We also make wool/silk combination carpets

House of Tibet Rugs, Inc
9 Post Rd. West
Westport, CT 06880
Tel: 203.341.0705
Fax: 203.341.8724

Our main shownroom
457 Mass Avenue,
Arlington, MA-02474
Tel: 781-641-3060
Fax; 781-641-3959

Marble, Tile & **Granite**

NEW CANAAN MARBLE & TILE...**(203) 966-7339**
3 Morse Court, New Canaan   Fax: (203) 966-1346
See Ad on Page: 388, 389
<u>Principal/Owner</u>: Kevin Pezeshkian

PARAMOUNT STONE CO ....**(203) 353-9119**
338 Courtland Avenue, Bridgeport   Fax: (203) 353-9094
See Ad on Page: 387
<u>Principal/Owner</u>: Steve Riviere
<u>Website</u>: ParamountStone.com   <u>e-mail</u>: info@ParamountStone.com
<u>Additional Information</u>: Importer, distributor and fabricator of all natural stone products.

ZOLTAN EUROPEAN FLOORS, INC. ....**(203) 790-4926**
87 Mill Plain Road, Danbury   Fax: (203) 790-8854
See Ad on Page: 392, 393
<u>Website</u>: www.zoltanfloors.com   <u>e-mail</u>: zoltan@zoltanfloors.com
<u>Additional Information</u>: The one-stop shop for designers, builders and homeowners.
Home Furnishing & Decorating

PARAMOUNT STONE INC.

338 Courtland Avenue, Stamford, CT 06906
203 353 9119 • 203 353 9094(Fax)
email: Info@Paramountstone.com

QUALITY

SERVICE

COMMITMENT

Photography by: Olson Photographic, LLC

Building Your Tomorrow One Stone At A Time.

NEW CANAAN MARBLE & TILE

A Showroom Specializing in the Sale, Fabrication, and Installation of Fine Ceramic Tiles and Natural Stones

3 Morse Court   *Phone (203) 966-7339*
New Canaan, CT 06840   *FAX (203) 966-1346*

Flooring

A.T. PROUDIAN INC...**(203) 622-1200**
120 E. Putnum Avenue, Greenwich   Fax: (203) 622-1713
See Ad on Page: 375, 376
<u>Principal/Owner</u>: Armen Proudian

PHOENIX HARDWOOD FLOORING ....**(203) 845-8094**
1 Muller Avenue, Norwalk   Fax: (203) 845-8099
See Ad on Page: 391
<u>Principal/Owner</u>: Jeffrey Samoncik
<u>Website</u>: phoenixfloors.com
<u>Additional Information</u>: A full service wood flooring company serving all of New England and
New York.

PIANETA LEGNO FLOORS USA INC. ....**(212) 755-1414**
1100 Second Avenue, New York   Fax: (212) 755-0112
See Ad on Page: 394
<u>Principal/Owner</u>: S. Kutun

ZOLTAN EUROPEAN FLOORS ....**(203) 790-4926**
87 Mill Plain Road, Danbury   Fax: (203) 790-8854
See Ad on Page: 392, 393
<u>Principal/Owner</u>: Zoltan Vincze
<u>Website</u>: www.zoltanfloors.com <u>e-mail</u>: zoltan@zoltanfloors.com
<u>Additional Information</u>: The one-stop shop for designers, builders and homeowners.

1 Muller Avenue, Norwalk, CT 06851

(203) 845-8094

301 Soundview Road, Guilford, CT 06437

(203)453-5708

HARDWOOD FLOORING AND TILE SHOWR
87 Mill Plain Road • Danbury, CT 06811
Showroom open 7 days a week.
Phone: 203 790 4926 • Fax: 203 790 8854

Engineered, pre-finished hardwood floors

"New focal point of your home"

Pianeta Legno Floors now offers the world's finest engineered and pre-finished hardwood flooring for those seeking warmth of real wood and stability of engineered structure.

Engineered to last Italian made exotic wood collection of Pianeta Legno, has the thickest top layer of the industry and with its built in sub floor, it can be used on radiant heated floors. Pre finished with 8 coats of UV cured polyurethane, Pianeta Legno Floors will hold up to years to come with an elegant touch of select wood collection of Italian taste.

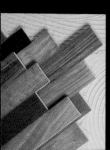

PIANETA LEGNO

The Ashley Group Luxury Home Resource Collection

The **Ashley Group (www.theashleygroup.com)** is pleased to offer as your final destination when searching for home improvement and luxury resources the following **Home Books** in your local market. Available now: *Chicago, Washington D.C., South Florida, Los Angeles, Dallas/Fort Worth, Detroit, Colorado, New York, Atlanta, Arizona, Philadelphia, San Diego, North Carolina, Boston, Houston* and *Las Vegas.* These comprehensive, hands-on guides to building, remodeling, decorating, furnishing, and landscaping a luxury home, are required reading for the serious and selective homeowner. With over 500 full-color, beautiful pages, the **Home Book** series in each market covers all aspects of the building and remodeling process, including listings of hundreds of local industry professionals, accompanied by informative and valuable editorial discussing the most recent trends.

Order your copies today and make your dream come true!

THE ASHLEY GROUP LUXURY HOME RESOURCE COLLECTION

Yes! Please send me the following Home Books! At $39.95 for each, plus $4.00 Shipping & Handling and Tax per book.

	# of Copies		# of Copies
☐ Dallas/Fort Worth Home Book *Premier Ed.*	_____	☐ Detroit Home Book *Premier Ed.*	_____
☐ New York Home Book *Premier Ed.*	_____	☐ Colorado Home Book *Premier Ed.*	_____
☐ Chicago Home Book *6th Ed.*	_____	☐ Los Angeles Home Book *2nd Ed.*	_____
☐ Washington DC Home Book *2nd Ed.*	_____	☐ South Florida Home Book *2nd Ed.*	_____
☐ North Carolina Home Book *Premier Ed.*	_____	☐ Las Vegas Home Book *Premier Ed.*	_____
☐ San Diego Home Book *Premier Ed.*	_____	☐ Philadelphia Home Book *Premier Ed.*	_____
☐ Arizona Home Book *Premier Ed.*	_____	☐ Atlanta Home Book *Premier Ed.*	_____
☐ Boston Home Book *Premier Ed.*	_____	☐ Houston Home Book *Premier Ed.*	_____

I ordered (# Of Books) _____ X $43.95 = $ _____   Total amount enclosed: $ _____

Please charge my: _____ Visa _____ Mastercard _____ American Express

Credit Card #: _____   Exp. Date: _____

Name: _____ Phone: _____

Signature: _____

Address: _____ Email: _____

City: _____ State: _____ Zip Code: _____

Send order to: Attn: Book Sales—Marketing, The Ashley Group—Reed, 2000 Clearwater Drive, Oak Brook, Illinois 60523
Or Call Toll Free at: 1-888-458-1750 • Or E-mail ashleybooksales@ReedBusiness.com • Visit us on-line at www.theashleygroup.com

All orders must be accompanied by check, money order or credit card # for full amount.

Finally...
Connecticut/
Westchester County's Own
Home & Design
Sourcebook

The ***Connecticut/Westchester County Home Book*** is your final destination when searching for home remodeling, building and decorating resources. This comprehensive, hands-on sourcebook to building, remodeling, decorating, furnishing and landscaping a luxury home is required reading for the serious and discriminating homeowner. With more than 500 full-color, beautiful pages, the ***Connecticut/Westchester County Home Book*** is the most complete and well-organized reference to the home industry. This hardcover volume covers all aspects of the process, includes listings of hundreds of industry professionals, and is accompanied by informative and valuable editorial discussing the most recent trends. Ordering your copy of the ***Connecticut/Westchester County Home Book*** now can ensure that you have the blueprints to your dream home, in your hand, today.

O R D E R   F O R M

THE CONNECTICUT/WESTCHESTER COUNTY HOMEBOOK

☐ YES, please send me ____ copies of the CONNECTICUT/WESTCHESTER COUNTY HOME BOOK at $39.95 per book, plus $4 Shipping & Handling per book.

Total amount enclosed: $_____ Please charge my: ☐ VISA ☐ MasterCard ☐ American Express

Card # _____ Exp. Date _____

Signature _____

Name _____ Phone (___) _____

Address _____ E-mail _____

City _____ State _____ Zip Code _____

Send order to   Attn: Marketing Department—The Ashley Group, 2000 Clearwater Drive, Oak Brook, Illinois 60523
Or Call Toll Free: 888-458-1750 Fax: 630-288-7949 E-mail ashleybooksales@ReedBusiness.com
All orders must be accompanied by check, money order or credit card # for full amount.

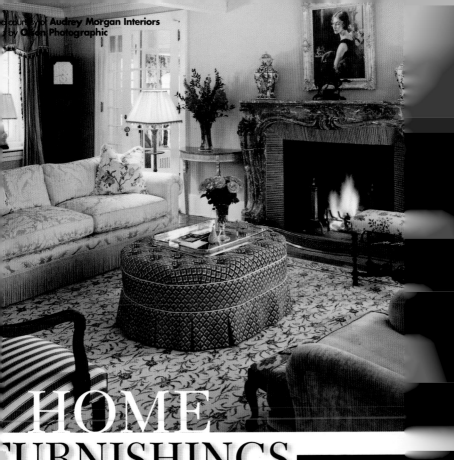

courtesy of Audrey Morgan Interiors
by Olson Photographic

HOME
FURNISHINGS
&
DECORATING

397
**The Finishing
Pieces**

404
Home Furnishings

411
**Home Office, Closet
& Garage**

417
**Arcitectural
Elements**

419
**Specialty Wall
Finishes**

424
**New in the
Showroom**

426
**Window Coverings
& Upholstery**

431
Home Gyms

433
Billiards

436
Lighting

438
Fireplaces

FROM TRADITIO

THE PLACE TO

FURNITURE f

Jesign center

FAX (203) 299-1703   WWW.CONNECTICUTDESIGNCENTER.COM

CONTEMPORARY...

OR HOME FASHION

TERIOR DESIGN

connecticut design center

TRADITIONAL   CONTEMPORARY

FURNITURE   INTERIOR
                                               DESIGN

666 WEST AVENUE • NORWALK, CT 06850
(203) 299-1700 • WWW.CONNECTICUTDESIGNCENTER.COM • FAX (203) 299-1703

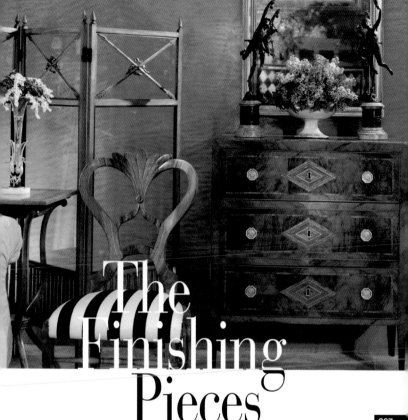

The Finishing Pieces

Home furnishings are the frosting on the cake that is your dream home. While your home's location, construction and architecture may be exactly as you have wished, they provide but the stage for your homelife. It is the objects that fill your home, from the furniture to window treatments to lighting, that truly express your personal style and the way you want to live.

Today's homeowners, whether they're in their first or final home, have the elevated taste that comes from exposure to good design. Choice is abundant in the home furnishing industry; one item is more amazingly gorgeous than the next, and anything you can imagine can be yours. This freedom can be overwhelming, even intimidating, if you don't keep a sharp focus.

By visiting the finest stores, specialty shops, and artisans, like those presented in the following pages, you can begin to refine your options and choose the items which best suit your home, tastes and lifestyle. Knowledgeable professionals will be available to guide you. Enjoy.

Photo courtesy of **Christianson Lee Studios Inc.**

TAKE TIME TO CHOOSE FURNITURE

You'll be living with your choices for many years to come, so take your time. Try to define why you like what you like. Look through shelter magazines, visit decorator homes and furniture showrooms. When you see a piece or arrangement you like, try to analyze what you like about it. Is it the color, the style of the piece, the texture of the fabric? Recognizing common elements you are drawn to will help you hone and refine your personal style.

As you start out, be sure to ruthlessly assess your current interior. Clear out pieces that need to be replaced or no longer work with your lifestyle, even if you have no clear idea of what you'll be replacing them with. Sometimes empty space makes visualizing something new much easier.

When furnishing a new room, consider creating a focus by concentrating on an architectural element or selecting one important piece, like a Chinese Chippendale-style daybed or an original Arts & Crafts spindle table. Or, make your focus a special piece you already own.

To make the most of your time when visiting showrooms, take along your blueprint or a detailed drawing with measurements, door and window placements, and special architectural features. If your spouse or anyone else will be involved in the final decision, try to shop together to eliminate return trips. The majority of stores can deliver most furniture within eight weeks, but special custom pieces may take up to 16 weeks.

Be open-minded and accept direction. Rely on your interior designer or a qualified store designer to help direct your search and keep you within the scale of your floor plan. Salespeople at top stores can help you find exactly what you're seeking, and, if you ask them, guide you away from inappropriate decisions toward more suitable alternatives. Their firsthand knowledge of pricing, products and features is invaluable when it comes to finding the best quality for your money.

As you seek these tangible expressions of your personal style, keep these thoughts in mind:

• What are your priorities? Develop a list of "must have," "want to have," and "dreaming about."

• What major pieces will be with you for a long time? Allow a lion's share of your budget for these.

• What colors or styles are already established through the flooring, walls, windows, or cabinetry? Keep swatches with you, if possible.

• Does the piece reflect your tastes? Don't be influenced too strongly by what looks great in a showroom or designer house.

FOCUS

Is there an architectural focus point in the room, a fireplace, a skylight or brilliant picture window? If not, consider creating focus with a significant piece of furniture, possibly custom designed, like an elaborate entertainment center in the family room or an elegant headboard in the master bedroom.

ACHIEVING A BALANCE

For a calming, soothing home, consider designing your rooms around the ancient Chinese study of Feng Shui. Not a religion, the science of Feng Shui is used to organize furnishings and decorative accessories in a natural way to balance the energy of the home and create a harmonious environment. Indoor water features, strategic placement of mirrors and open vessels, along with careful consideration of the arrangement of furniture in each room are all part of designing a Feng Shui environment.

• Does the piece fit the overall decorating scheme? Although the days of strict adherence to one style per room are over, it's still necessary to use coordinated styles.

• Is the piece comfortable? Before you buy, sit on the chair, recline on the sofa, pull a chair up to the table.

• Can you get the furnishings through the doorway, up the elevator, or down the stairs?

• Will a piece work for your family's lifestyle? Choose upholstery fabrics, colors and fixtures that will enhance, not hinder, your everyday life.

DESIGNED FOR YOU

The ultimate in expression of personal style, a piece of custom designed furniture is akin to functional art for your home. A custom furniture designer can create virtually any piece you need to fill a special space in your home and satisfy your desire for owning a unique, one-of-a-kind.

Some of the most talented, best known designers working in this area today are listed in the following pages of the Home Book. You can contact them directly, or through your interior designer. At an initial meeting you'll see examples of the designer's work and answer questions like:

• What kind of piece do you want? Freestanding entertainment system, dining table, armoire?

• What functions must it serve? It is a piece of art, but the furniture still must function in ways that make it practical and usable. Explain your needs clearly.

• Do you have favorite woods, materials or colors? As with ordering custom woodwork, the possibilities are almost unlimited. Different woods can be painted or finished differently for all kinds of looks. It's best to have some ideas in mind.

• Are you open to new ideas and approaches? If you'd like the designer to suggest new ways of reaching your goal, let him or her know.

Seek out a furniture designer whose portfolio excites you, who you can communicate with, and who you trust to deliver your project in a top quality, professional manner. Ask for a couple of design options for your piece. Make sure you and the designer are in agreement regarding finishes, materials, stain or paint samples you want to see, and a completion date. Most charge a 50 percent deposit at the beginning with the balance due upon completion. If you decide not to go ahead with construction of a piece, expect to be billed a designer's fee. A commissioned piece of furniture

FROM THE FLOOR UP

Your carpets, rugs or flooring set the stage for your design. Whether a simple backdrop or the starring role, it's important to determine which part you want your floor treatments to take at the outset of your decorating project.

'FAUX' FINISH TROMPE L'OEIL?

Any painting technique replicating another look is called a 'faux' (false) finish. There are many methods to achieve wonderful individual effects. Trompe l'oeil (fool the eye) is a mural painting that creates illusion through perspective. A wall becomes an arched entry to a garden.

WHAT'S YOUR STYLE?

Consider these characteristics of different styles: **Formal**-Dark, polished woods; smooth, tightly woven fabrics; symmetrically placed furnishings. **Casual**-Lighter woods; textured, loosely woven fabrics, asymmetric placement. **Contemporary-Artistic**, sculptural furnishings with smooth, clean lines; bold splashes of color and carefully placed artwork. **French Country**-Aged, carved wood furnishings; textiles feature earth-tones mixed with intense colors; accessorized with wrought iron, pottery and baskets. **Rustic**-Sturdy, extremely textural furnishings of polished logs, softened with cushions and pillows in colorful fabrics. **Shabby Chic**-White furniture and accents, slipcovers, overstuffed upholstery and "old" looking accessories. **Tuscan**-Sturdy heavily distressed wood furnishings with terra cotta tile, stone or marble accents; bright fabrics; washed or faux-finished painted surfaces.

requires a reasonable amount of time to get from start to finish. If you want an entertainment system for Super Bowl Sunday, make your final design decisions when you take down the Halloween decorations. Keep in mind that the process cannot be rushed.

ILLUMINATING IDEAS

Lighting can be the focal point of a room, or it can be so subtle that it's almost invisible. The trick is knowing what you want to accomplish. Indeed, when we remember a place as cozy and elegant, or cold and uncomfortable, we're feeling the emotional power of illumination.

The industry is filled with options and combinations, from fixtures and bulbs to dimmers and integrated systems. Top lighting retailers in the area employ in-house design consultants to guide you, or you can employ a residential lighting designer.

To deliver a superior lighting scheme, a designer must know:

• What are your needs? Lighting falls into three categories – general, task, and atmospheric. A study/work area, a cozy nook or a kitchen each require different lighting.

• What feeling are you trying to create?

• What "givens" are you working with? Where are your windows or skylights? The use of artificial, indoor light depends to a great degree on the natural light coming in.

• What materials are on the floor and what colors are on the walls and ceiling? This affects how well your lighting will reflect, or "bounce."

• Where is your furniture placed, and how big are individual pieces? This is especially important when you're choosing a dining room chandelier.

• If you're replacing lighting, why are you replacing it? Know the wattage, for instance, if a current light source is no longer bright enough.

• Are there energy/environmental concerns? Lighting consumes 12 to 15 percent of the electricity used in the home. An expert can develop a plan that maximizes energy efficiency.

WINDOW DRESSING

The well-appointed room includes window treatments in keeping with the style of the home and furnishings. Yet it's also important to consider how your window treatments will need to function in your setting. Will they be required to control light, or provide privacy as well? Some windows in your home may need just a top treatment as a finishing touch, while a soaring window wall might require sun-blocking draperies or blinds to minimize heat build-up or ultraviolet damage.

How window treatments will be installed is another design question to consider–inside or outside the window frame, from the top of the window to the sill or from ceiling to floor? Take these points into consideration when designing your window treatments:

• How much privacy do you require? If you love the look of light and airy sheers, remember they become transparent at night and you may need blinds or shades as well.

• Is light control necessary? This is usually a must for bedroom window treatments, as well as for windows with southern or western exposures

• Do you want to take advantage of a beautiful view of the landscape or hide an unsightly view of the building next door?

• Are there any structural elements such as built-in cabinets, outlets or vents near the window to consider?

• Are your windows a focal point of the room or the background that puts the finishing touch on your room design?

• What role will the choice of fabric play? The fabric can unify the whole, standout as the focus, or add another note to the rhythm of the room.

PAINTING OUTSIDE THE FRAMES

Through their travels, reading and exposure to art and design, sophisticated homeowners are aware of the beauty that can be added to their homes with specialty decorative painting. They see perfect canvases for unique works of art in walls, furniture and fabrics. The demand for beautiful art applied directly to walls, stairs or furniture has created a renaissance in decorative painting. Faux finishes, trompe l'oeil and murals have joined the traditional finishes of paint, wallpaper and stain for consideration in outstanding residential interiors.

Specialty painters can help you fine-tune your idea, or develop a concept from scratch. At your initial meeting, discuss your ideas, whether they're crystal clear or barely there. Don't be apprehensive if you don't have a clear idea. Artists are by profession visually creative, and by asking questions and sharing ideas, you can develop a concept together.

Ask to see samples of his or her other work, and if possible, visit homes or buildings where the work has been done. Ask for, and call, references. Find out

CUSTOM DESIGNING A CHERRY WOOD TABLE

What might it actually cost to have a custom designed piece of furniture made for you?
Here is a general estimate of the costs involved in the custom design and construction of a 48 in. x 96 in. dining room table.
• Trees harvested (felled) ($30/hr x 2 hours):
    $60
• Trees sawn and dried:
    $175
• Design (included in the project cost)
• Labor cost (fine sanding, construction, varnishing):
    $5,000
• Special materials (included in cost)

    Total:
    $5,235

401

RECLAIMING CHARACTER

Magnificently unique custom-designed furnishings can be made of wood reclaimed from building renovations or demolitions. Another option is to use new wood, hand-distressed to lend it the character of an older piece.

THE PRICE OF GETTING ORGANIZED

• An 8 ft. closet, round steel chrome plated rods, double and single hang, with a five-drawer unit: $800 to $1,000
• His-and-Hers walk-in closet, full length and double hang rods, two five-drawer units, foldable storage space, mirrored back wall, shoe rack: $1,000 to $4,000
• Conversion of a full-size bedroom into closet area with islands, custom designed cabinets with full extension drawers and decorative hardware, mirrors, jewelry drawers, and many other luxury appointments: $15,000
• Customized desk area, with file drawers, computer stand and slide shelves for printer, keyboard and mouse pad, high pressure surface on melamine with shelves above desk: $3,000
• Average garage remodel, with open and closed storage, sports racks for bikes and fishing poles, a small workbench, and a 4 ft. x 8 ft. pegboard, installed horizontally: $2,500

if the work was completed on time and on budget. Based on your initial conversations, a painter can give you a rough estimate based on the size of the room and the finish you've discussed. You can expect the artist to get back to you with sample drawings, showing color and technique, usually within a week.

Surface preparation, such as stripping and patching, is not usually done by the specialty painter. Ask for recommendations of professionals to do this work if you don't have a painter you already use.

THE GREAT OUTDOORS

As homeowners strive to expand comfortable living space into their yards, top quality outdoor furniture manufacturers respond with new and innovative styles. Before you shop for outdoor furniture, think about:

• What look do you like? The intricate patterns of wrought iron? The smooth and timeless beauty of silvery teak wood? The sleek design of sturdy aluminum?

• What pieces do you need? Furnishing larger decks and terraces requires careful planning.

• Will you store the furniture in the winter or will it stay outdoors under cover?

• Can you see the furniture from inside the house? Make sure the outdoor furnishings won't distract from the established inside or outside design.

TICKLING THE IVORIES

A new or professionally reconditioned piano makes an excellent contribution to the elegance and lifestyle of a growing number of area homes. Pianos add a dimension of personality that no ordinary piece of furniture can match. They are recognized for their beauty, visually and acoustically.

First time piano buyers may be astonished at the range of choices they have and the variables that will influence their eventual decision. Go to the showrooms that carry the best brand name pianos. Not only will you be offered superior quality instruments, but you'll also get the benefit of the sales staff's professional knowledge and experience. Questions that you need to answer will include:

• Who are the primary players of the instrument?

• What level of players are they (serious, beginners)?

• Who are their teachers?

• What is the size of the room the piano will be

laced in?

What are your preferences in wood color or leg hape?

Are you interested in software packages that convert our instrument into a player piano?

Pianos represent a significant financial investment, one that will not depreciate, and may actually appreciate over time. If a new piano is out of your financial ange, ask about the store's selection of reconditioned nstruments that they've acquired through trades. he best stores recondition these pieces to a uniformly high standard of excellence and are good options for ou to consider. These stores also hold occasional romotions, when special pricing will be in effect or a period of time.

THE HOME OFFICE COMES INTO ITS OWN

The home office has become a "must have" room for many homeowners. More businesses re being operated from home, and increasing numbers of companies are allowing, even encouraging, elecommuting. Spreading out on the dining room able or kitchen table is no longer an efficient option.

Because the home office often requires specific viring and lighting, be sure your architect, designer and builder are involved in the planning process. If you're simply outfitting an existing room to be your home office, designers on staff at fine furniture stores can guide you. However, it's still most practical o get some architectural input for optimum comfort and functionality of the space.

While some aspects of home furnishings may be easy to overlook, such as storage and lighting, you should give great attention to all of them. The construction of your dream home will give you a place to live, but the way it is furnished will let you ive in the style you want. ■

PROJECT FILE

A project file with carpet, fabric, wallpaper and paint samples, floor plans, a tape measure, a calendar, and a phone list of everyone working on your project can really enhance your decorating experience. With your file in hand, decisions can be made on the spot without having to check if the piece matches or fits into your overall plan.

403

Home
Furnishings

ASIAN COLLECTIBLES ....**(203) 637-7866**
123 Mason Street, Greenwich   Fax: (203) 637-7646
See Ad on Page: 405
<u>Principal/Owner</u>: Renata Horstmann De Pepe

BLOOM DESIGN LLC ....**(203) 773-9992**
315 Peck Street, New Haven   Fax: (203) 773-9785
See Ad on Page: 341
<u>Principal/Owner</u>: Paul Bloom
<u>Website</u>: bloom-design.net   <u>e-mail</u>: office@bloom-design.net
<u>Additional Information</u>: Custom furniture and interiors that balance art and function. Unexpected junctures in wood, stone and glass. Design or design/build – exactly what you want.

CLASSIC SOFA...**(212) 620-0485**
5 West 22nd Street, New York
See Ad on Page: 409
<u>Principal/Owner</u>: Jeff Stone

CONNECTICUT DESIGN CENTER ....**(203) 299-1700**
666 West Avenue, Norwalk   Fax: (203) 299-1703
See Ad on Page: 397-399
<u>Principal/Owner</u>: Martin L. Abbatiello
<u>Website</u>: www.connecticutdesigncenter.com   <u>e-mail</u>: ctdesign@att.net
<u>Additional Information</u>: Why travel to New York City? The Connecticut Design Center, with a myriad of elegant and cutting edge furniture, designer fabrics, custom window treatments, floor coverings, lighting and unique accessories is a stone's throw away. Styles from traditional to contemporary, together with our talented staff designers, will make your decorating wishes become reality.

FRENCH COUNTRY LIVING ....**(203) 869-9559**
34 East Putnam Avenue, Greenwich   Fax: (203) 869-9790
See Ad on Page: 406, 407

GO TO YOUR ROOM ....**(203) 532-9701**
21 Mill Street, Byram   Fax: (203) 532-1943
See Ad on Page: 410
<u>Principal/Owner</u>: Fernando Martinez
<u>e-mail</u>: go2uroombehappy@compuserve.com
<u>Additional Information</u>: All furniture designed, built and painted by Fernando Martinez.

HOUSE OF FINS...**(203) 661-8131**
99 Bruce Park Avenue, Greenwich
See Ad on Page: 408
<u>Principal/Owner</u>: Robert Bray
<u>Additional Information</u>: House of Fins specializes in the design, installation, stocking and maintenance of custom aquatic environments.

Asian Collectibles & Design
RENATA HORSTMANN DE PEPE, LTD

123 MASON STREET *greenwich* CONNECTICUT 06830

203 983 6360 *fax* 203 983 6361 renatap@acninc.net

Finally...
Connecticut/
Westchester County's Own
Home & Design
Sourcebook

The **Connecticut/Westchester County Home Book** is your final destination when searching for home remodeling, building and decorating resources. This comprehensive, hands-on sourcebook to building, remodeling, decorating, furnishing, and landscaping a luxury home is required reading for the serious and discriminating homeowner. With more than 500 full-color, beautiful pages, the **Connecticut/Westchester County Home Book** is the most complete and well-organized reference to the home industry. This hardcover volume covers all aspects of the process, includes listings of hundreds of industry professionals, and is accompanied by informative and valuable editorial discussing the most recent trends. Ordering your copy of the **Connecticut/Westchester County Home Book** now can ensure that you have the blueprints to your dream home, in your hand, today.

Order your copy now!

Published by
The Ashley Group
1234 Summer St., Stamford, CT 06905
203-323-7400 fax 203-326-5177
E-mail: ashleybooksales@ReedBusiness.com

French Country
Is Always In.

In the South of France, in the magic that is Provence, you'll find what they call French Country Living. Luxuriate in fabulous interiors furnished in Cherry, Walnut, and Chestnut woods. Blush under beautifully patina-ed light fixtures of iron and copper. Warm to mustard, lavender, and poppy accents that color this rustic yet elegant decor. Discover room after room, filled with French country antiques and French reproductions. But don't wait for your next trip to France to delight in this visual *tour de force*, you'll find all this and more at French Country Living in Greenwich at 34 East Putnam Avenue.

French Country Living

The soul of Provence in the heart of Greenwich

Complete Interior Design Services by Jani Caroli & Associates

34 East Putnam Avenue   Greenwich, CT 06830
Tel: 203.869.9559   Fax: 203.869.9790

*Providing custom residential and commercial aquariums for
distinctive homes and offices for over twenty five years*

HOUSE OF FINS

GREENWICH CT

Tel: (203) 661-8131   www.houseoffins.com   Fax: (203) 661-1864

SHIP SOURCE

CUSTOM
CRAFTED
2 WEEK
DELIVERY

JUST IN TIME
STYLE

EW YORK CITY
VEST 22ND STREET
W YORK, NY 10010
IONE (212) 620-0485

REENWICH, CT
EAST PUTNAM AVENUE
REENWICH, CT 06830
IONE (203) 863-0005

DGEWOOD, NJ
EAST RIDGEWOOD AVENUE
DGEWOOD, NJ 07450
IONE (201) 447-5800

ANHASSET, LI
00 NORTHERN BOULEVARD
ANHASSET, NY 11030
IONE (516) 365-4441

w.classicsofa.com

CLASSIC SOFA®

Go To Your Room

Fine hand-crafted furniture & accessories
for children and some grownups, too!

234 Mill Street • Byram, Connecticut
(Exit 2 off I-95-In town of Greenwich)
(203) 532-9701

Home Office, Closet
& Garage Systems

CALIFORNIA CLOSETS ....**(914) 592-1001**
5 Skyline Drive, Hawthorne Fax: (914) 592-4554
See Ad on Page: 412,413
<u>Principal/Owner</u>: Robert J. Westenberg
<u>Website</u>: www.calclosets.com
<u>Additional Information</u>: California Closets will reorganize your clothes closet, set up an entertainment center or home office, or put your kitchen pantry to better use - wherever you've got clutter. Our designers are dedicated to helping you simplify your life and will walk you through the entire process of creating an organized system.

CLASSY CLOSETS..**(800) 772-8089**
22 Shelter Rock Ln, Danbury Fax: (203) 778-6441
See Ad on Page: 414
<u>Principal/Owner</u>: Pete Krajcsik / Guy Verfaillie
<u>Website</u>: windquestco.com <u>e-mail</u>: classyclosets@aol.com
<u>Additional Information</u>: Specializing in custom storage systems for closets, pantries, and home office. Systems come in a variety of colors and finishes to satisfy any need or budget.

CLOSET FACTORY ....**(203) 854-9767**
2291 Fairfield Avenue, Bridgeport Fax: (203) 854-9740
See Ad on Page: 415
<u>Principal/Owner</u>: Elizabeth May
<u>Website</u>: www.closetfactory.com
<u>Additional Information</u>: #1 rated closet company specializing in expert design consultation, manufacturing and installation of any organizational furniture for the home or business.

GARAGE TEK ....**(800) 427-3545**
22 Shelter Rock Lane, Danbury Fax: (203) 778-6441
See Ad on Page: 416
<u>Principal/Owner</u>: Peter Krajcsik
<u>Website</u>: www.garagetek.com <u>e-mail</u>: garagetek200@aol.com
<u>Additional Information</u>: A flexible system of patented wall panels that work in conjunction with racks, shelves, cabinets, bins and books to organize your garage.

411

©2001 California Closet Company, Inc. All rights reserved. All franchises independently owned and operated.

life, stuff, storage – The Walk-In. The Home Office.

The home is the heart of life. An ever changing story of ourselves, our family, our friends. A welcome retreat where we protect, nurture and sustain all that is needed and loved.

Let California Closets share 25 years experience with you to create the finest custom storage solutions for all the areas of your home. Live the way you dream. Call today for a complimentary consultation in your home.

800.339.2567 • www.calclosets.com

WESTCHESTER
5 SKYLINE DRIVE
HAWTHORNE
914.592.1001

ROCKLAND, ORANGE
845.368.1575

MANHATTAN
1625 YORK AVENUE
(Between 85 & 86 St.)
212.517.7877

DUTCHESS
845.454.5647

CALIFORNIA CLOSETS®

Classy Closets

22 Shelter Rock Lane
Danbury, CT 06810
Phone: (203) 743-2800
Fax: (203) 778-6441

© 2002, The Closet Factory. All rights reserved.

IF ONLY YOUR LIFE
WERE THIS ORGANIZED.

At Closet Factory, we create custom storage solutions that fit your home exactly.
Our Designers are masters at making closets, entertainment centers, offices and
garages efficient and easy to manage. With that out of the way, you'll have more
time for carpools and grocery shopping. Lucky you.

203.854.9767   888.793.7576   closet*factory*

Call for a free design consultation

www.closetfactory.com

With renovations on the rest of the house getting more expensive, more homeowners are taking a new look at their garage. GarageTek's patented wall panel is completely moisture repellent and weather resistant, signifying that it will never rot, peel, warp, splinter, expand or contract. This revolutionary system transforms unfinished garage space into an attractive versatile, organized area. In addition to being a smart-looking product it is easy to clean and stronger then drywall. The GarageTek system is a fully integrated unit that offers a means of furnishing extra work, storage and living space to the home.

22 Shelter Rock Lane
Danbury, CT 06810
Toll Free 800.472.3545
www.garagetek.com

Architectural
Elements

COLONIAL COLLECTIONS OF NEW ENGLAND, INC. ....**(203) 254-4495**
1476 Post Road, Fairfield   Fax: (203) 254-4496
See Ad on Page: 418
Principal/Owner: Len & Renee D'Andrea
Website: www.colonialcollection.com
Additional Information: The store for your "finishing touches". Colonial Collections specializes in
decorative accessories such as upscale address markers, mailboxesand post systems, hand-
crafted weathervanes and cupolas, as well as handcrafted copper & brass lighting fixtures.
Although many of our products fit well with a colonial design home, we have designs for most
homes.

FISHE BROS., MERCHANTS OF INTEREST ....**(203) 840-1345**
625 Main Avenue, Route 7, Norwalk   Fax: (203) 849-8775
See Ad on Page: 269
Principal/Owner: Peggy Ann White
Website: Sculpturedgardens.com e-mail: Fishebro@optonline.com
Additional Information: Fishe Bros. offers Fairfield County's most unique selection of garden
ornaments from across the states and Europe, including Vicenza, limestone, cast iron, granite
and fine estate statuary.

417

Colonial Collections
of New England, Inc.

The store for your "Finishes Touches". Colonial Collections specializes in decorative accessories such as upscale Address Markers, Mailboxes and Post Systems, Handcrafted Copper Weathervanes and Cupolas, as well as Handcrafted Copper & Brass Lighting Fixtures. Although many of our products fit well with a colonial design home, we have designs for most homes.

1476 POST ROAD, FAIRFIELD, CT 06430
PH 203.254.4495   FAX 203.254.4496
w w w . c o l o n i a l c o l l e c t i o n s . c o m

Specialty
Wall Finishes

BURDO PAINTING COMPANY, LLC ....**(203) 972-2755**
226 Algonquin Trail, Trumbull   Fax: (203) 268-3217
See Ad on Page: 420
<u>Principal/Owner</u>: Pat Burdo
<u>e-mail</u>: pburdo2704@aol.com
<u>Additional Information</u>: High-end residential general painting company. Family owned since 1977. Very detail oriented. Neatness and cleanliness, an absolute must.

CHRISTIANSON LEE STUDIOS, INC. ....**(203) 798-0098**
44 Old Mill Road, Ridgefield   Fax: (203) 798-0098
See Ad on Page: 421
<u>Principal/Owner</u>: J. Nels Christianson / Eva Lee
<u>Website</u>: www.christiansonlee.com <u>e-mail</u>: eva@christiansonlee.com
<u>Additional Information</u>: Fine decorative painting and finishes. Our services include murals, woodgraining, marbling, glazing, encaustic, stencillling, painted furniture, gilding, carved glass, reverse painting on glass, antiqued mirror, and verre eglomise. We will complete your project with creativity, attention to detail, courtesy, and promptness.

COULEUR PROVENCE ....**(203) 655-9775**
863 Boston Post Road, Darien   Fax: (203) 655-9775
See Ad on Page: 422
<u>Principal/Owner</u>: Michelle, Pierre Gagnon
<u>Additional Information</u>: Provencal home decoration with Trompe L'oeil and faux finishes. Artist on the premises. Fabrics and potteries from the South of France. Artist works with his own colors.

GIORGIO'S UPHOLSTERY INTERIOR DECORATING INC.........................**(203) 762-2150**
363 Main Avenue, Norwalk
See Ad on Page: 427
<u>Principal/Owner</u>: Giorgio & Despina Taiyanides
<u>Additional Information</u>: We provide custom made furniture, re-upholstery and custom window treatments. We carry a full line of designer fabrics and offer interior design services.

HOME WORKS...**(914) 934-0907**
509 North Main Street, Port Chester
See Ad on Page: 430
<u>Principal/Owner</u>: Adam Gibbs

J.S.J. WINDOW TREATMENTS..**(203) 661-5123**
3 Strickland Road, Cos Cob   Fax: (203) 661-6096
See Ad on Page: 428,429

JERRY LIOTTA DECORATIVE ARTIST ....**(203) 226-5560**
65 Kings Highway North, Westport
See Ad on Page: 423
<u>Principal/Owner</u>: Jerry Liotta

PIERRE GAGNON INTERIORS ....**(203) 655-9775**
863 Boston Post Road, Darien
See Ad on Page: 422
<u>Principal/Owner</u>: Pierre Gagnon
<u>Additional Information</u>: Provencal home decoration with Trompe L'oeil and faux finishes. Artist on the premises. Fabrics and potteries from the South of France. Artist works with his own colors.

419

Burdo Painting Co.

Fine Residential Painting

Our Services

Interior:

General Painting Services

Wallcovering of any description

Plaster Repair

Faux Finish

Minor Carpentry

Exterior:

General Painting Services

Power Sanding

Reglaze Windows

Oil Wood Roofs

Minor Carpentry

Burdo Painting Co.

New Canaan (203) 972-2755   Fax (203) 268-3217

CHRISTIANSON LEE STUDIOS

Fine Decorative Painting & Finishes

murals
woodgraining
marbling
glazing
encaustic
stencilling

carved glass
reverse painting
antiqued mirror
verre églomisé
gilding
painted furniture

44 OLD MILL ROAD, RIDGEFIELD, CT 06877
TEL/FAX: (203)798-0098
WWW.CHRISTIANSONLEE.COM

Pierre Gagnon Interiors

863 Boston Post Road • Darien, CT 06820
Tel: 203.655.9775

Hand Painted Surface Art

A world of possibilities

A recreation of an Etruscan mural (approx. 6x8 feet)

Two of the many surface techniques and finishes professionally executed, which include furniture, interior and exterior surfaces.

JERRY LIOTTA

65 Kings Hwy.
Westport CT 06880

telephone or fax
203-226-5560

A wall of trompe l'oeil shutters

WILTON LAMP
LIGHT & SHADE

Hot Air Balloon Chandelier:
This piece is called the hot air balloon ballroom chandelier. It is made in a variety of colors and bead combinations. Since every homeowner has different needs, offsite consultation is available. Often it takes a great deal of communication between designer and homeowner to determine what style best suits their needs.

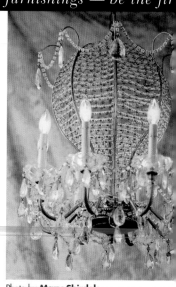

Photo by **Mary Shirdek**

WALPOLE WOODWORKING

Chippendale Entrance Gates:
Recently, there has been an upswing in the demand for entrance gates that provide home security as well as charm. We now offer a variety of styles that feature steel frames and pillars that have tough steel cores and are ready for automatic door openers. Driveway and entrance security gates in contemporary and classic styles are available. This Chippendale entrance gate is a custom wooden gate made from mahogany, and it features a fine lattice panel at the bottom and a Chippendale-style design at the top. Security codes and an intercom system can be installed, and the gate can be remotely controlled from several hundred yards away.

ASIAN COLLECTIBLES

Antique Candlesticks:
This pair of rare brass and cloisonnee candlesticks dates from the Chien Lung dynasty, 1736-1796. The beautiful antiques measure 19 in. tall, with a 5½ in. base.

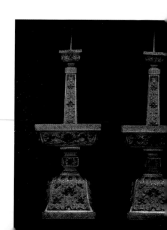

CONNECTICUT DESIGN CENTER
Bar/TV Cabinet:
From the Georgian Collection by Wesley Bober, the Kenwood is a fine reproduction of English-style furniture. This piece is crafted by hand for the discerning home-owner who wants that special bar or TV unit that will be the pinnacle of their room. The bar includes a 20-piece set of Swarovski crystal. A humidore may be ordered. The TV features a built-in cable connection.

425

CHRISTIANSON LEE STUDIOS, INC.
Gilded Hands: These gilded hands will brighten any décor with their elegance and originality. They are perfect for the discerning and bold home decorator. Whether used as tiebacks or towel rings, accessorizing with these hands in any room will recall the visionary filmmaker Jean Cocteau's use of gilded hands as sconces in his imaginative version of "Beauty and the Beast." Each life-sized hand is cast in resin and leafed in 22k gold, then burnished, and antiqued to a fine finish. They are also offered in other finishes.

CLASSY CLOSETS
Custom Closet/Storage Organizational Systems:
This custom closet/storage organizing system utilizes the Easy Track system. Each closet is designed around homeowner needs and preferences. The custom design will keep everything well-organized and within easy reach.

GARAGE TEK
Garage Organizational System:
This new system transforms garages into an attractive, versatile, organized area. The system is a fully integrated unit that offers not only functionality, but also a cost-effective means of furnishing extra work, storage and living space to the home.

Window Coverings,
Fabrics,
& Wall Coverings

GIORGIO'S UPHOLSTERY INTERIOR DECORATING INC............................**(203) 762-2150**
363 Main Avenue, Norwalk
See Ad on Page: 427
Principal/Owner: Giorgio & Despina Taiyanides
Additional Information: We provide custom made furniture, re-upholstery and custom window treatments. We carry a full line of designer fabrics and offer interior design services.

HOME WORKS...**(914) 934-0907**
509 North Main Street, Port Chester
See Ad on Page: 430
Principal/Owner: Adam Gibbs

J.S.J. WINDOW TREATMENTS...**(203) 661-5123**
3 Strickland Road, Cos Cob   Fax: (203) 661-6096
See Ad on Page: 428,429

GIORGIO'S UPHOLSTERY INTERIOR DECORATING, Inc.

363 Main Ave. (route 7) Norwalk, Ct 06851
203.762.2150

For over 50 years, Hunter Douglas has been the worldwide leader in window coverings - continually introducing exciting concepts that anticipate the needs of the marketplace and provide superior solutions. Whatever your design or budgetary considerations, Hunter Douglas has the optimal answer - window fashions that are the last word in aesthetics and performance. They also offer coverings for all types of custom designed and specialty-shaped windows.

HunterDouglas
window fashions

J S J WINDOW TREATMENTS, INC.
Showroom: 3 Strickland Rd., Cos Cob, CT 06807
Phone: (203) 661-5123 Fax: (203) 661-6096

couture

custom
window treatments

&

upholstery

Design Services Available

SONO
81 Washington Street
So. Norwalk, CT 06854
203. 838. 4663

MT. KISCO
510 Lexington Avenue
Mt. Kisco, NY 10549
914. 242. 9300

PORT CHESTER
509 N. Main Street
Port Chester, NY 10573
914. 934. 0907

SOHO
529 Broome Street
New York, NY 10013
212. 343. 9900

HOME
WORKS

Home
Gyms

HOME GYM DESIGN, INC. ....**(914) 997-6313**
Fax: (914) 949-2018

See Ad on Page: 432
<u>Principal/Owner</u>: Ruth Tara
<u>Website</u>: www.HomeGymDesign.Net <u>e-mail</u>: HomeGymDesign@aol.com
<u>Additional Information</u>: Specializing in designing and equipping custom residential fitness centers, Home Gym Design, Inc. will create a workout room as beautiful and functional as all the other rooms in your home. Our experts coordinate with you, your architect and contractor to design the layout and choose exercise equipment that fits your individual needs, space and budget. From personalized equipment selection to lighting, climate controls, entertainment and wall/floor coverings, workouts in YOUR HOME GYM will be enjoyable and effective!

Home Gym Design, Inc.

Creators of Custom Home Gyms

Your **Home...**

Your **Gym...**
Our **Design.**

NY-CT-NJ

914.997.6313

www.HomeGymDesign.net

Billiards

DESIGNS BY KAYE ....**(203) 254-1013**
1385 Post Road East, Westport
See Ad on Page: 434, 435
<u>Principal/Owner</u>: Arnold Kaye
<u>Additional Information</u>: Handcrafted unique billiard and game tables.

"Executive"

"Greenwich"

"Westport"

"Reflections"

Southport II

"Rainbow"

*F*or over forty years Arnold Kaye, designer and
CEO of Designs by Kaye, has created and
handcrafted some of the finest and unique
billiard tables on the market. He has worked with
customers and/or their designers to create
a one-of-a-kind table to coordinate with their
decor. Many of his designs have been copied, but
the quality has never been duplicated. Others
have not been able to reproduce the expert
workmanship and singular attention to
detail which is the benchmark of
Designs by Kaye.

DESIGNS BY
KAYE 1385 POST ROAD, EAST WESTPORT, CT 06880
PH. 203.254.1013 FX. 203.259.6901 DESIGNSBYKAYE.COM

Lighting

WILTON LAMP LIGHT & SHADE ....**(203) 762-3004**
35 Danbury Road, Wilton, CT   Fax: (203) 762-7132
See Ad on Page: 437
Principal/Owner: Sandra L. Zemola
Website: www.smartpages.com/ctwiltonlamplight
Additional Information: After 29 years of experience this lighting showroom is a lighting boutique specializing in the unusual, still offering all major lighting and lamp lines. Our staff takes time to know you with on or off site consultation. This personalized service helps create a decorative llighting scheme especially for you. Other services include sales of shades, shade recovery, lamp repair and home furnishings.

Wilton Lamps Light & Shade

WHEN THE ORDINARY IS UNACCEPTABLE

Featuring

Major Lighting Manufactures • Designer Lamps
Antique & Unique Chandeliers• Shades & Shade Recovery
Decorative Mirrors • Expert Lamp Repair & on Premises

Your Local Lighting Source

5 Danbury Road, Wilton, CT • (203) 762-3004

Just north of TJ Max. Look for our Green Awning.
Mon.-Fri. 10-5:30; Sat. 10-5

Fireplaces

HOMEFIRES ....**(704) 376-9747**
307 L West Tremont Ave., Charlotte, NC   Fax: (704) 376-0268
See Ad on Page: 439
Principal/Owner: Chad Smith
Website: www.homefiresusa.com e-mail: homefires@mindspring.com
Additional Information: U.S. importer of English gas-fueled firebaskets; grates are hand-made from solid brass, cast iron and polished steel; available with company's own gas coils and gas 1 yr.

© Leslie Wright Dow

The Number One Choice of Number Ten Downing.

A complete selection of London's finest gas-fueled firebaskets. Handmade of solid brass, cast iron or polished steel. Available with gas coals or gas logs. Designed to be the most realistic in the world—from the U.S.A.'s exclusive distributor of Real Flame® products. Call 1-800-749-4049 for information or your free catalog.

HOMEFIRES

P.O. Box 11313 • Charlotte, NC 28220 • 704-376-9747 • Fax: 704-376-0268
www.homefiresusa.com

Location,
Location,
Location!

What better LOCATION for your advertisement than the CONNECTICUT/WESTCHESTER COUNTY HOME BOOK!

Just as our readers realize how important location is when choosing a home, we realize that it's just as important to you when allocating your advertising dollars.
That's why we have successfully positioned the CONNECTICUT/WESTCHESTER COUNTY HOME BOOK to reach the high-end consumers you want as clients.

Call 203-323-7400 to find out about our unique marketing programs and advertising opportunities.

Published by
The Ashley Group
1234 Summer St., Stamford, CT, 06905
203-323-7400 fax 203-326-5177
E-mail: ashleybooksales@ReedBusiness.com

oto courtesy of **Benchmark Builders**

ART&
ANTIQUES

441
The Beauty of Rarity

451
Antiques

446
Art Galleries

448
Framing

ART & ANTIQUES

Distinctive 17th, 18th and 19th Century Engl

G. SERGEA

G. Sergeant Antiques invites yc
visit our converted barn/gallery
historic Woodbury Connecticut.
where you will find the finest in
English, Continental and Amer
furniture. Our inventory dates f
the late 17th century through th
mid-19th century and hails from
the great periods of original desi
and construction.

88 North Main Street
203-266-

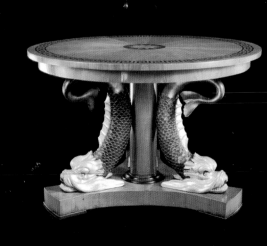

ntinental and American Furniture from Fine Estates.

ANTIQUES

Museums, designers, collectors
d private individuals have come to
ly on Gary Sergeant's thirty years
xperience and discriminating eye
hen looking for distinctive period
eces. Each item has its own unique
d classic form which will add style
d value to any collection.

terior Decorating Services Available

6 • Woodbury, CT 06798
w.gsergeant.com

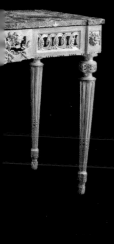

An important 18th century American architectural breakfront in painted and parcel gilt surface with glazed upper doors, a very rare raised paneled interior, fluted and carved relief frieze having bellflower garlands and an oval neoclassic medallion. The lower closed cabinet sections are adorned with rosette and fluted bordered doors and a square plinth platform. Made in the Mid-Atlantic region, probably Philadelphia. A wonderful piece of English inspired, Adam period, architectural design. Microanalysis conclusively indicates that this piece is made of American white pine.
Height: 107″ Width: 101″ Depth: 17″

G. SERGEANT
ANTIQUES

Distinctive 17th, 18th and 19th century
English, Continental and American
furniture from fine estates.

88 North Main Street • Route 6
Woodbury, CT 06798 • 203-266-4177
www.gsergeant.com
Interior decorating services available

441

The Beauty of Rarity

Art and antiques can connect with us in a way that no other objects in our homes can. A favorite piece of art can transport us to another place, set a mood for a room, give visitors a glimpse of our personalities, and provide us with a canvas for the way we feel. Fine art speaks to the soul of the owner. An antique can bring part of the past into our homes, and can bring us thoughts of other times, other places and the people who lived in them. They tell their stories through the generations.

Art and antiques, unlike so many other pieces purchased for the home, have the potential to become a family's heirlooms. Even an inexpensive "find" may someday become a most treasured item because of the warm memories it calls to mind. Truly, these choices are best made with the care and guidance of an experienced professional who understands the significance of these items in your home.

Photo courtesy of **Handwright Gallery & Framing**

A PIECE OF THE PAST

442

Part of the pleasure of collecting art or antiques is learning about them. Many homeowners buy a particular painting or sculpture they love, and find that following the art form or the artists becomes a lifetime passion.

The best place to start to familiarize yourself with art is at one of the many wonderful museums in your area. Wander through historic homes in the different historic neighborhoods of the city and get an idea of what the art feels like in a home environment. Go to auctions. Buy the catalog and attend the viewing. At the sale, you'll begin to get an idea of the values of different types of items. Finally, get to know a dealer. Most are pleased to help you learn and want to see more people develop a lifetime love affair with art, similar to their own. If a dealer seems too busy or isn't genuinely interested in helping you, then go to another dealer.

Haunt the local bookstores and newsstands. There are many publications dedicated to these fields.

Homeowners find their way to a love of antiques by many different paths. Some are adding to an inherited collection that connects them with past generations of family or with the location of their birth. Some are passionate about pottery or porcelain, clocks or dolls, and want to expand their knowledge while building a lifetime collection.

Antique furniture, artwork and collectibles also can be used to make a singular statement in an interior. Through a 19th Century English chest, an American Arts & Crafts table, or a beloved collection of Tiffany glass vases, homeowners put a personal signature on their interior design.

Making the right selection is as much a matter of knowledge and experience as it is taste and personal aesthetic. As top quality antique paintings, photographs and other desirable items become more difficult to find, getting expert guidance in identifying good and worthwhile investments is crucial. An interior designer or the knowledgeable professionals at the top galleries in the area can help you determine the value of pieces you are considering by assessing these four characteristics:

• Rarity-In general, the more difficult it is to find similar pieces, the greater the value. Try to determine how many comparable pieces exist. However, it is possible to be too rare. If there are too few similar pieces in circulation, there may be limited demand.

• Quality-The quality of the original materials and workmanship affects the value significantly.

• Provenance-The history of a piece, how many owners it has had, is its provenance. A piece with only a few owners has a better provenance.

• Condition-The more that remains of the original finish, the more valuable the piece. However, in some cases, small imperfections can help to establish authenticity.

When you visit an antique store or gallery, be prepared to seriously consider what type of investment you wish to make and how it will work in a given interior.

If you are pursuing pieces to add to an existing collection, do your research to determine which dealers and galleries in the area cater to your interests. Or, check with a favorite gallery for information. Be open to ideas and suggestions, especially when you're just beginning a collection, or a search for a special antique. There is so much to know about so many different objects, time periods, and design, that it truly does take a lifetime to develop an expertise.

VISITING ART GALLERIES

More than anything else, choosing to make beautiful, distinctive art objects a part of your home brings the joy of living with beautiful things into the daily life of yourself, your family and your guests.

The most important rule to know as your begin or continue to add art to your home is that there truly are no "rights or wrongs." Find what reaches you on an emotional level, and then begin to learn about it.

Use your eyes and react with your heart. Look at art magazines and books. Visit the museums in town, and those in other cities as you travel. Go to the galleries. Visit many of them for the widest exposure to different possibilities. Use the Internet to visit gallery and museum sites from all over the world. Let only your sense of beauty and aesthetics guide you at this point. Consider other constraints after you've identified the objects of your desire.

EXPERT ADVICE

The most reputable art gallery owners and dealers have earned their reputation by establishing an expertise in their field, and serving their clients well.

Buying from these established, respected professionals offers many benefits. Their considerable knowledge of and exposure to art translates into opinions that mean a great deal. You can trust the advice and education they offer you. They've done considerable research and evaluation before any item gets placed in their gallery, and determined that it's a good quality item, both in terms of artistic merit and market value. You can also rest assured that they will stand behind the authenticity of what they present in their galleries. Most offer free consultations, trade-back arrangements, and installation, and will help you with selling your art at some point in the future as your collection grows, you change residences, or your tastes change.

VALUE JUDGMENTS

Buy for love, not money. This is the advice we heard time and again from the best art galleries. Not all art appreciates financially – often it fluctuates over the years according to the artist's career, consumer tastes, and the state of the overall economy. If you love what you own and have been advised well by a knowledgeable professional, you'll be happiest with your investment.

TARNISH OR PATINA?

If your collection includes decorative metal objects like an engraved silver platter or brass handles on an antique chest, tarnish may become an issue. In some cases, the tarnish, caused by oxidation, can add subtle shadings and a beautiful patina to the piece. Before you polish, decide if the piece is more authentic with the tarnish. If so, relax and enjoy.

443

MAKE AN APPOINTMENT

When you have identified a gallery or dealer you admire, call for an appointment to discuss your needs. Most professionals appreciate knowing you will be visiting at a specific time so they can have additional help on hand to attend to other customers.

THE FINESSE OF FINE ART

You know what you like, but how much might it actually cost to fill your home with art? Following is one example, for the analysis, research and procurement of six art pieces.

Before the project begins, a budget is established based on the type of art desired (sculpture, drawings, paintings, tapestry), the quality of the art, scale, and provenance.

The art:
A print for the hallway;
a 4-ft. tall classical bronze sculpture;
a still-life painting;
two tapestries;
a Dufy painting;
Total: $55,000

Additional expenses:
Appraisal services;
framing;
insurance;
consultation fees;
security;
Total; $19,750

Grand Total: $74,750

Note: a project such as this one usually lasts 12 to 18 months.

444

Set a working budget (possibly a per-piece budget) and let the gallery know at the outset what the guidelines are. This saves both you and the gallery time and energy. You'll be able to focus on items that are comfortably within the range of your budget. Buy the best quality possible in whatever category you like. You will appreciate the quality for years. Don't hesitate to do some comparison shopping. Although each art object is unique in itself, you may find another piece in the same style that you enjoy equally as well.

The best dealers understand budgets, and respect your desire to get good quality at a fair price. They are happy to work with enthusiastic clients who want to incorporate beautiful art into their lives.

Only deal with dealers who are helpful and present their art fairly. If you feel intimidated in a gallery, or feel the dealer isn't giving you the time and information you deserve to make intelligent choices, visit another gallery. Never buy art under pressure from a dealer, or to meet a deadline imposed by your interior design timetable.

GO TO AN AUCTION HOUSE

Attending an auction is an excellent way to learn about decorative arts, develop and add to a collection, and simply have a good time. Whether you attend as a buyer, seller, or observer, an auction is an experience that will enrich your understanding and enjoyment of the art and antiques world.

If you're a novice, it's important to choose a well-established auction house with a reputation for reliability. Try to be a patient observer and learn about the process as well as the value of items you may be interested in later on.

Buy a copy of the catalog and attend the viewing prior to the beginning of the auction itself. Each item, or "lot," that will be available for sale at the auction will be listed, and a professional estimate of selling price will be included. Professionals will be available during the viewing to answer questions and help you become familiar with the art objects as well as the process.

CHOOSING AN AUCTION

Find out about interesting auctions from the proprietors of galleries you like, or ask to be added to the mailing list of a reputable auction house. With these sources of information, you'll be informed of events that will feature quality items of interest to you. The established auction houses that have earned a reputation for reliability and expertise generally have a single location where they hold their auctions. Sometimes an auction will be held at an estate site, or a seller's location.

Before attending the auction, spend some time researching the art or antique you're interested in bidding on, so you'll be informed about its value and can make an informed decision. Talk to people at the galleries. Visit Internet sites to research your interests, or for information on upcoming auctions and recent auction prices. There also are books available that publish recent auction sales to help you get an idea of price and availability. Check your library or bookseller for publications like Gordon's Price Annual.

There seems to be an air of mystery and sophistication that surrounds auctions, but don't let that discourage you from discovering the auction experience. They are enjoyable and educational for anyone who is interested in obtaining or learning about art and antiques.

BE REALISTIC

For many of us, an auction might seem an opportunity to pick up an item at a bargain price. Realize that there may be bargains to be found, but in general, auctioned items are sold for a fair price. There may be a "reserve price," which is a private agreement between the seller and the auctioneer on the amount of a minimum bid.

If you educate yourself about the category you're interested in, you'll be at an advantage at an auction. It's equally important to research the market value of any lot you may be considering. Remember that there is an auctioneer's commission of 10 to 15 percent of the hammer price, to be paid in addition to the purchase price, as well as applicable sales taxes.

While you won't end up making the top bid simply by tugging your ear, it's important to pay attention when you're bidding. Be aware of the way the auctioneer communicates with the bidders and always listen for the auctioneer's "fair warning" announcement just before the gavel falls. ■

THE FALL SEASON

Fall signals the beginning of the art season. Galleries will open exhibits and the excitement is contagious. Ask to get on gallery mailing lists to stay informed of fall openings.

VISIT OUR MUSEUMS

As you develop your passion for art and items of antiquity, take advantage of the collections and public education opportunities at some of Connecticut's distinguished art museums, like:

445

Bruce Museum of Arts and Science One Museum Dr. Greenwich, CT 06830 816.561.4000 www.brucemuseum.org

Bush Holley Historic Site 39 Strickland Rd. Cos Cob, CT 06807 203.869.6899 www.hstg.org

Art
Galleries

ACCENT PICTURE FRAMING ....(203) 655-6633
576 Boston Post Road, Darien   Fax: (203) 655-4670
See Ad on Page: 450
<u>Principal/Owner</u>: Tom & Ann Geary
<u>Website</u>: gearygallery.com   <u>e-mail</u>: tom@gearygallery.com
<u>Additional Information</u>: We offer expert workmanship, reasonable prices, full restoration services and the widest selection of custom and finished frames in FairfieldCounty. We work closely with each customer to make the most of each piece - from treasured heirloom to inexpensive "finds".

BARNEY'S PLACE ....(203) 661-7369
107 Greenwich Avenue, Greenwich   Fax: (203) 661-6946
See Ad on Page: 447
<u>e-mail</u>: BarneyArt@aol.com
<u>Additional Information</u>: Under a new energetic leadership, Barney's Place, a 27-year old feature on Greenwich Avenue, provides its unparalleled expertise in on site framing to many satisfied Greenwich customers. After many successful shows exhibiting artists from all around the world, the art gallery is now a "must stop" for every distinguished art lover and artists alike.

GEARY GALLERY ....(203) 655-6633
576 Post Rd., Darien   Fax: (203) 655-4670
See Ad on Page: 450
<u>Principal/Owner</u>: Tom Geary
<u>Website</u>: gearygallery.com   <u>e-mail</u>: tom@gearygallery.com

HANDWRIGHT GALLERY & FRAMING L.L.C. ....(203) 966-7660
93 Main Street, New Canaan   Fax: (203) 966-7663
See Ad on Page: 449
<u>Principal/Owner</u>: Betsy Jesup
<u>Website</u>: handwrightgallery.com   <u>e-mail</u>: bjesup@aol.com
<u>Additional Information</u>: Experienced framers that offer a large selection of American and European frames. After 28 years in framing enjoys an excellent reputation among artists, decorators, and long time customers for expert design, fine art framing, and knowledgeable restoration services.

446

Barney's Place, a 27 year old feature on Greenwich Avenue is much more than an Art Gallery. We provide in house custom framing, ranging from period framing to the finest finished corner frames made. We also supply serious artists as well as students with the most recognizable brands of art supplies available.

Where Moulding Becomes Art!

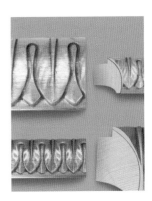

Barney's Place
and Art Gallery

107 Greenwich Ave.
Greenwich, Connecticut 06830
(203) 661-7369 • Fax (203) 661-6946

WINSOR & NEWTON

Framing

ACCENT PICTURE FRAMING..**(800) 452-0718**
576 Boston Post Road, Arts & Antiques   Fax: (203) 655-4670
See Ad on Page: 450
Principal/Owner: Tom & Anne Geary
Website: gearygallery.com e-mail: tom@gearygallery.com
Additional Information: We offer expert workmanship, reasonable prices, full restoration services and the widest selection of custom and finished frames in Fairfield County. We work closely with each customer to make the most of each piece - from treasure to heirloom to inexpensive "finds".

BARNEY'S PLACE..**(203) 661-7369**
107 Greenwich Avenue, Greenwich   Fax: (203) 661-6946
See Ad on Page: 447
e-mail: BarneyArt@aol.com
Additional Information: Under a new energetic leadership, Barney's Place, a 27-year old feature on Greenwich Avenue, provides its unparalleled expertise in on site framing to many satisfied Greenwich customers. After many successful shows exhibiting artists from all around the world, the art gallery is now a "must stop" for every distinguished art lover and artists alike.

GEARY GALLERY..**(203) 655-6633**
576 Post Rd., Darien   Fax: (203) 655-4670
See Ad on Page: 450
Principal/Owner: Tom Geary
Website: gearygallery.com e-mail: tom@gearygallery.com

HANDWRIGHT GALLERY & FRAMING L.L.C. ....**(203) 966-7660**
93 Main Street, New Canaan   Fax: (203) 966-7663
See Ad on Page: 449
Principal/Owner: Betsy Jesup
Website: handwrightgallery.com e-mail: bjesup@aol.com
Additional Information: Experienced framers that offer a large selection of American and European frames. After 28 years in framing enjoys an excellent reputation among artists, decorators, and long time customers for expert design, fine art framing, and knowledgeable restoration services.

448

Handwright Gallery & Framing

Fine Art, Sculpture & Antique Prints
Conservation Framing
Restoration Art Services
Certified Picture Framer
28 Years Experience
Member P.P.F.A.

Tuesday-Saturday: 10-5:30

93 Main Street,
New Canaan, CT
Phone: 203-966-7660
Fax: 203-966-7663   www.handwrightgallery.com

Sculpture by Christopher Smith

Private Parking in Rear

GEARY GALLERY

One of the leading galleries of fine artwork, Accent Picture Framing/Geary Gallery can handle all your needs for quality art. For over eighteen years Accent Picture Framing and Restoration has enjoyed developing multi-leveled relationships with artists of varied mediums. Our reputation for quality custom framing has attracted accomplished artists who are now part of our Gallery family. We offer one of the largest selections of frame mouldings; mat board and glass types to create the perfect final touch for your piece of art. Custom designing for every decor has made this firm respected and well known. Your picture framing is done in a collaborative artistic effort assuring your satisfaction.

The Geary Gallery is becoming known as a pre-eminent Fairfield County showcase for representational art. We maintain an ambitious exhibition schedule, changing shows approximately every three months. We feature Connecticut-based artists with national reputations and well-known artists from the eastern seaboard. We specialize in originals, lithographs, prints and limited editions. We also concentrate on fine oil painting restoration with free in-house consultations. Services offered are custom framing, art appraisals, oil painting restoration and cleaning and frame restoration.

Accent Picture Framing
Geary Gallery
Accent Restoration

576 Boston Post Road, Darien, CT • (203) 655-663

Antiques

B & D JOHNSON ANTIQUES, LLC ....**(203) 618-0009**
122 East Putnam Avenue, Greenwich   Fax: (203) 618-0009
See Ad on Page: 458
Principal/Owner: Brent & Derek Johnson
e-mail: bdjant@prodigy.net
Additional Information: The area's best source for period antiques and fine art.

BRIGGS HOUSE ANTIQUES ....**(914) 381-0650**
566 East Boston Post Road, Mamaroneck   Fax: (914) 381-7649
See Ad on Page: 463
Principal/Owner: Lorraine Bauchmann

ELEISH VAN BREEMS ANTIQUES ....**(203) 263-7030**
487 Main Street South, Woodbury   Fax: (203) 263-7032
See Ad on Page: 454
Principal/Owner: Rhonda Eleish & Edith Van Breems
Website: www.evbantiques.com e-mail: evba@evbaantiques.com

G. SERGEANT ANTIQUES ....**(203) 266-4177**
88 Main Street North, Woodbury   Fax: (203) 266-4179
See Ad on Page: 441-443
Principal/Owner: Andrew Rowan
Website: www.gsergeant.com e-mail: gary@sergeant.com
Additional Information: Distinctive 17th, 18th & 19th C. English, Continental and American furnishings from fine estates. Interior decorating services available.

HARBOR VIEW CENTER FOR ANTIQUES ....**(203) 325-8070**
101 Jefferson Street, Stamford   Fax: (203) 325-4704
See Ad on Page: 455
Principal/Owner: Gary Rubinstein/ Michael Ortenau
Website: www.harborviewantiques.com e-mail: sales@harborviewantiques.com
Additional Information: Antique center featuring 70 international dealers specializing in fine 18th and 19th century antiques.

continued on page **456**

Quai Volta
Gree

Guy F. FLichy
378 Greenwich Avenue
Greenwich, CT 06830

e Antiques
n, CT

Tel. 203.618.9777
Fax. 203.618.9191
gfflichy@qvantiques.com

ELEISH & VAN BREEMS ANTIQUES

...alizing in 18th and 19th Century Scandina... Northern European antiques, garden eleme... ...orative accessories and reproduction furnitu...

www.evbantiques.com

487 Main Street South
Woodbury, CT 06798
Tel. 203.263.7030   Fax 203.263.7032
evba@evbantiques.com

HARBOR VIEW CENTER
OVER 70 INTERNATIONAL DEALERS
IN FINE ANTIQUES

FINE 18TH & 19TH CENTURY ANTIQUES
HARBOR VIEW CENTER FOR ANTIQUES
101 JEFFERSON STREET   STAMFORD, CT   06902
203.325.8070   WWW.HARBORVIEWANTIQUES.COM

Antiques

LE BARN ....**(203) 253-7286**
457 Webbs Hill Road, Stamford   Fax: (203) 322-0948
See Ad on Page: 459
<u>Principal/Owner</u>: Kathy Sachs
<u>e-mail</u>: Afromum@aol.com
<u>Additional Information</u>: Unique building displaying small settings of antiques, art work, and home accessories to finish your rooms. Personal guidance and sense of interior design offered.

QUAI VOLTAIRE ANTIQUES ....**(203) 618-9777**
378 Greenwich Avenue, Greenwich   Fax: (203) 618-9191
See Ad on Page: 452,453
<u>Principal/Owner</u>: Guy Flichy

VALLIN GALLERIES LLC...**(203) 762-7441**
516 Danbury Road, Wilton   Fax: (203) 761-9469
See Ad on Page: 462
<u>Principal/Owner</u>: Peter L. Rosenberg
<u>Website</u>: vallingalleries.com <u>e-mail</u>: peter@vallingalleries.com
<u>Additional Information</u>: Chinese and Asian art and antiques. Established 1940.

WAYNE PRATT INTERIORS ....**(203) 263-5676**
346 Main Street South, Woodbury   Fax: (203) 266-4766
See Ad on Page: 460,461
<u>Principal/Owner</u>: Corey Boure

WOODBURY ANTIQUES DEALERS ASSOCIATION ....**(203) 266-4177**
88 Main Street North, Woodbury   Fax: (203) 266-4179
See Ad on Page: 457
<u>Principal/Owner</u>: Andrew Rowan

WOODBURY
ANTIQUES CAPITAL
OF CONNECTICUT™

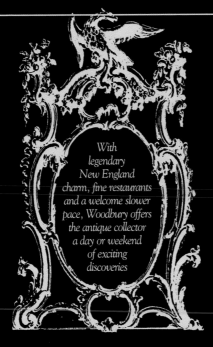

With legendary New England charm, fine restaurants and a welcome slower pace, Woodbury offers the antique collector a day or weekend of exciting discoveries

www.antiqueswoodbury.com

Monique Shay Antiques

Country Loft Antiques

La Belle France Antiques L.L.C.

Eleish -Van Breems Antiques

Authantiques

Joel Einhorn Antiques

The Elemental Garden

Tucker Frey Antiques

Norma Chick / Autumn Pond

East Meets West

Wayne Pratt Antiques

High Ridge Antiques

Martell & Suffin Antiques

Jennings and Rohn Antiques

B. Bourgeois Antiques

Hitchcock House Antiques

David A. Schorsch Antiques

Antiques on Main

Art Pappas Antiques

Main Street Antiques Center

Lisa Demuro Antiques

Woodbury Guild

Robert S. Walin - American Antiques

Grass Roots Antiques & Reruns

Thomas Schwenke Antiques

Antique Talk

G. Sergeant Antiques

Hamrah's Oriental Rug Co.

Eagle Antiques

Fayence Antique

Galpin Brook Antiques & Rugs

Mill House Antiques

Charles & Rebekah Clark

David Dunton

The Liebson's

West Country Antiques

WOODBURY ANTIQUES
DEALERS ASSOCIATION

B & D JOHNSON ANTIQUES, L.L.C.

A RARE PAIR...

FINE AND RARE:
18thc. English Mahogany Window Bench
Serpentine Shaped Seat

One of a Pair, in the Chinese Taste, Circa 1760
Height 25"   Length 55"   Depth 20"
GREENWICH PROVENANCE

*From our Extensive
Collection of Fine
Antiques.*

Brent C. Johnson
Derek A. Johnson

122 East Putnam Ave.
Greenwich, CT 06830

Telephone: 203.618.0009

LE BARN

Mirror • French Country Antiques • Garden Pot

Print • Painted Furniture • Pottery • Lamps • Paintings

Chairs • Lamps • Pottery • Wicker • Accessories • Trunks

Copper Cauldron • Ceramics • Desk • Armoires

Unique estate hosts a renovated barn showing
personally collected French country armoires, farm
tables, rush-seated chairs, and mirrors. Painted
furniture, baskets, copper pots, garden accessories
and hard-to-find small objects will make your room
a home. Call for a visit.

457 Webb Hill Road
Stamford, CT 06903
(203) 253-7286
Fax (203) 322-0948
Open daily Thursday through Saturday 10-4

Wayne Pratt, Inc.

AMERICAN ANTIQUES

Celebrating Thirty-Three Years of Experience

346 Main Street South, Woodbury, CT 06798
(203) 263-5676 • Fax (203) 266-4766

28 Main Street Nantucket, Massachusetts 02554
(508) 228-8788 • Fax (508) 228-8137
www.prattantiques.com

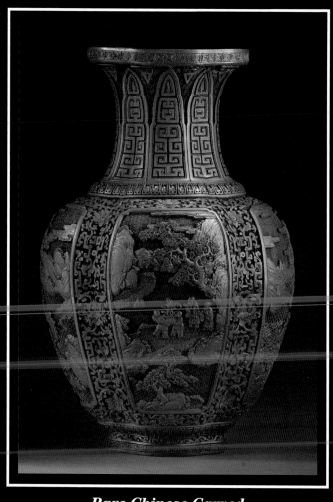

***Rare Chinese Carved
Red and Ochre Lacquer Vase***
Qianlong Reign, 1736-96, 17 h.

Vallin Galleries

*516 Danbury Road (Route7)
Wilton, Connecticut 06897
203 762-7441 Fax 203 761-9469
www.vallingalleries.com
e-mail: peter@vallingalleries.com*

Briggs House Antiques

A comprehensive collection
of imported furniture and
decorative accessories.
Housed in 8,000 square feet
of showrooms.

566 East Boston Post Road
Mamaroneck, New York
T 914.381.0650   F 914.381.7649

Finally...
Connecticut/
Westchester County's Own
Home & Design
Sourcebook

The ***Connecticut/Westchester County Home Book*** is your final de.
tination when searching for home remodeling, building and decoratir
resources. This comprehensive, hands-on sourcebook to building,
remodeling, decorating, furnishing and landscaping a luxury home is
required reading for the serious and discriminating homeowner. With
more than 500 full-color, beautiful pages, the
Connecticut/Westchester County Home Book is the most complet
and well-organized reference to the home industry. This hardcover vc
ume covers all aspects of the process, includes listings of hundreds o
industry professionals, and is accompanied by informative and valuab
editorial discussing the most recent trends. Ordering your copy of the
Connecticut/Westchester County Home Book now can ensure tha
you have the blueprints to your dream home, in your hand, today.

O R D E R   F O R M

THE CONNECTICUT/WESTCHESTER COUNTY HOMEBOOK

☐ YES, please send me _____ copies of the CONNECTICUT/WESTCHESTER COUNTY HOME BOOK at $39.95 per book, plus $4 Shipping & Handling per book.

Total amount enclosed: $_____   Please charge my: ☐ VISA   ☐ MasterCard   ☐ American Express

Card # _____   Exp. Date _____

Signature _____

Name _____   Phone (_____) _____

Address _____   E-mail _____

City _____   State _____   Zip Code _____

Send order to   Attn: Marketing Department—The Ashley Group, 2000 Clearwater Drive, Oak Brook, Illinois 60523
Or Call Toll Free: 888-458-1750 Fax: 630-288-7949 E-mail ashleybooksales@ReedBusiness.com

All orders must be accompanied by check, money order or credit card # for full amount.

Photo courtesy of **Audio Excellence**

HOME
THEATER

&

TECHNOLOGY

465
**High Tech
Comes Home**

468
**Home Theater
Design**

473
**Integrated Home
Systems**

PERFORMANCE IMAGING
System Integrators

115 East Putnam Avenue
Greenwich, CT 06830
(203) 862-9600

sales@pi-ma
www.performanceimagin

@CRESTRON   ⚡LUTRON.   TANDBERG

PERFORMANCE **IMAGING**
SYSTEMS INTEGRATOR

115 East Putnam Avenue   Greenwich, CT 06830   (203) 862-960
sales@pi-mail.net   www.performanceimaging.ne

Theaters ➘ System Integration ➘ Multimedia/Video Conferencing Rooms ➘ L
Multi-Room A/V ➘ Private Theaters ➘ System Integration ➘ Multimedia/Vide
ation ➘ Multimedia/Video Conferencing Rooms ➘ Lighting & Window Automa
Theaters ➘ System Integration ➘ Multimedia/Video Conferencing Rooms ➘ L
Multi-Room A/V ➘ Private Theaters ➘ System Integration ➘ Multimedia/Vide
ation ➘ Multimedia/Video Conferencing Rooms ➘ Lighting & Window Automa
Theaters ➘ System Integration ➘ Multimedia/Video Conferencing Rooms ➘ L
Multi-Room A/V ➘ Private Theaters ➘ System Integration ➘ Multim
ation ➘ Multimedia/Video Conferencing Rooms ➘ Lighti
Theaters ➘ System Integration ➘ Multimedia
Multi-Room A/V ➘ Private Thea
ation ➘ Multimedia/Vid
Theaters ➘ System Inte
Multi-Room A/V ➘ Priv
ation ➘ Multimedia/Vic
Theaters ➘ System In
Multi-Room A/V ➘ Pri
ation ➘ Multimedia/V
Theaters ➘ System !
Multi-Room A/V ➘ F
ation ➘ Multimedia/
Theaters ➘ System
Multi-Room A/V ➘
ation ➘ Multimedia
eaters ➘ System
ulti-Room A/V ➘
ion ➘ Multimedia/
eaters ➘ System
ulti-Room A/V ➘
ion ➘ Multimedia
eaters ➘ System
lti-Room A/V ➘ Privat
on ➘ Multimedia/Video Confere
eaters ➘ System Integratic
lti-Room A/V ➘ Private
on ➘ Multimedia/Video Con
eaters ➘ System Integration ➘ Multimedia/Video Conferencing Rooms ➘ Lig
lti-Room A/V ➘ Private Theaters ➘ System Integration ➘ Multimedia/Video
on ➘ Multimedia/Video Conferencing Rooms ➘ Lighting & Window Automati
eaters ➘ System Integration ➘ Multimedia/Video Conferencing Rooms ➘ Lig
lti-Room A/V ➘ Private Theaters ➘ System Integration ➘ Multimedia/Video
on ➘ Multimedia/Video Conferencing Rooms ➘ Lighting & Window Automati

Performance Imaging LLC (PI) is the premier specialist in audio
and video design, installation, and integration in the tri-state area.
What sets Performance Imaging apart from its competitors is its
innovation, attention to detail, product knowledge, and superior
customer service.

Theaters ➘ System Integration ➘ Multimedia/Video Conferencing Rooms ➘ L
ulti-Room A/V ➘ Private Theaters ➘ System Integration ➘ Multimedia/Vide
tion ➘ Multimedia/Video Conferencing Rooms ➘ Lighting & Window Automa

High Tech Comes Home

465

The modern home is a hub of technology. Tech wizards continue to deliver better and more powerful products that are less obtrusive and more affordable than ever. From lighting and security systems that can be operated from half-way around the globe to home theaters that rival the quality of commercial movie houses, these once rare luxury items have become priorities for homeowners.

Sophisticated homeowners have had their level of appreciation for quality in sight and sound elevated through the years of experience in concert halls, movie theaters and sports arenas. As they gravitate toward making the home the focus of their lifestyle, and strive to incorporate that high level of performance into their leisure time at home, new technological advances become a more desirable and practical investment.

Photo courtesy of **The Electronics Connection**

THE IMPORTANCE OF A HOME THEATER DESIGN SPECIALIST

Home theater is widely specified as a custom home feature today. The sophisticated homeowner with a well-developed eye (and ear) for quality demands the latest technology in a home entertainment system that will provide pleasure for many years. Because of the fluid marketplace, the vast possibilities of the future, and the complexity of the products, it's crucial to employ an established professional to design and install your home theater.

The experts presented on the following pages can advise you on the best system for your home. They can find an appropriate entertainment center, masterly install your system, and teach you to use it. Their expertise will make the difference.

THE HOME THEATER DESIGN PROCESS

Tell your builder or remodeling specialist early on if you want a home theater, especially if built-in speakers or a ceiling-mounted video projection unit are part of the plan.

Inform the interior designer so proper design elements can be incorporated. Window treatments to block out light and help boost sound quality, furnishings or fabrics to hide or drape speakers, and comfortable seating to enhance the media experience should be considered. If you plan to control the window treatments by remote control, these decisions will have to be coordinated.

When visiting showrooms, be ready to answer these questions:

• What is your budget? There is no upper limit.

• Do you want a High Definition Television (HDTV) or projection video system? A DVD player? Built-in or free-standing speakers?

• Do you want Internet access for your television?

• What style of cabinetry and lighting do you want? Do you want specialized lighting? A built-in bar? How much storage is needed?

• What are the seating requirements? Seating should be at least seven feet from the screen.

• Do you want whole-house control capability so you can distribute and control the system from different rooms of the house?

• How will you incorporate the system with the rest of the room? Must the room meet other needs?

• Do you want extra luxuries, like multiple screens, or a remote control system that allows you to dim the lights and close the draperies?

PLAN AHEAD

Even if you aren't installing a home theater system right away, have a room designed to serve that purpose later. Get the wiring done and build the room an appropriate shape and size. Get the right antenna. Ask for double drywall for noise control.

SAVE AN AISLE SEAT

For the best seat in the house, your home theater will need the following:
A large screen television and/or projection video system (from 32-inch direct view up to 200-inches, depending on the size of the room). New, compact products are available now.
A surround-sound receiver to direct sound to the appropriate speaker with proper channel separation.
A surround-sound speaker system, with front, rear, and center channel speakers and a sub-woofer for powerful bass response.
A comfortable environment, ideally a rectangular room with extra drywall to block out distractions.

466

Will this room function in the future? As technology continues to change our lifestyle, plan for this room to grow and change as well. Ask your salesperson for advice.

Home theaters are installed at the same time as security and phone systems, before insulation and drywall. In new construction or remodeling, start making decisions at least two months before the drywall is hung. Allow four weeks for delivery and installation.

AUTOMATED HOME MANAGEMENT

It's like clockwork: Your alarm clock wakes you, and while you are rubbing the sleep from your eyes, a path from your bed to the master bath to the kitchen is lit for you. The stone floor of your bath has warmed and the climates of the rooms you'll be walking through this morning are all in sync. Once your eyes have opened, you walk to the kitchen, where a hot, fresh, pot of coffee is waiting for you and the television is already tuned to your favorite morning news program. Once you've left home, there's no need to worry about whether you've locked all of the doors or have turned the lights off, because those things are also handled automatically. But just in case, for your own peace of mind, you can check on the status of your home's locks, lights and windows from a remote computer or even a cell phone, and lock, close or turn off whatever you may have forgotten about.

Such are the advantages of automated home management. Home automation brings an added, virtually impenetrable layer of ease and security to the home. Energy can be saved by keeping the heat or air-conditioning at a low level while you're out of the house, then as you're on the way home from the office or your daily errands, you can bring the home climate back to your comfort level. Criminals can be thwarted by lighting that not only automatically switches on at night, but comes on at random times, in random rooms, to make it look as if your home is "lived in" when you're away.

You don't have to be a computer wizard to operate these automated home systems. Voice recognition software allows you to simply say, "Turn lights on at 7 p.m. for four hours," and it's done. Systems have become smarter: while a direct line to the police department can be activated by an object coming into contact with a door or window at 3 a.m., the homeowner, while at the office or the golf course, can be alerted first when something is detected at 3 p.m. A quick check on any computer, which will give him or her a view from the home's security cameras, can let the homeowner know that the afternoon incident was caused by children who have been told not to play soccer so close to the house.

While it all may have seemed unbelievably futuristic not long ago, modern home technology is making homeowner's lives easier, more peaceful and much more enjoyable. ∎

YOUR PERSONAL SCREENING ROOM

Here's an example of the costs involved with outfitting a room in the mid- to high-scale price range for a home theater
Labor (at $55/hour): $3,500
50-inch television: $4,000
DVD player: $900
Amplifier with surround-sound decoder: $10,000
Six speakers with subwoofer: $10,000
Satellite dish (high definition): $1,000
Delivery/installation: $2,500
Seating: Eight leather module seats, $15,000
Infrared sensors to control lighting, motorized drapes, security system: $10,000

Total: $57,000

BEST TIP:

Have phone lines, DSL or cable modems connected to every TV outlet in the house for Internet access and satellite reception.

Home Theater
Design

A-ARCH, INC. ....**(845) 279-8884**
16 Mt. Ebo Rd. South, Suite # 5, Brewster   Fax: (845) 279-8587
See Ad on Page: 478, 479
Principal/Owner: Glenn Gentilin
Website: acousticarchitecture.com
Additional Information: Design & installation of background stereo music systems, multi-zone keypad systems, surround sound and dedicated home theaters.

AUDIO VIDEO EXCELLENCE, LLC ....**(914) 747-1411**
343 Manville Road, Pleasantville   Fax: (914) 773-7054
See Ad on Page: 477
Principal/Owner: Michael Esposito
Website: www.audiovideoex.com

AUDIODESIGN, INC...**(203) 336-4401**
1955 Black Rock Turnpike, Fairfield   Fax: (203) 335-7026
See Ad on Page: 472
Principal/Owner: Ira Fagan
Website: www.audiodesign.com e-mail: ira@audiodesign.com
Additional Information: Audiodesign sells, designs and services all home electronic systems, specializing in home theater, multi-room audio/video systems and home automation.

COUNTY TV & APPLIANCE ....**(203) 968-1515**
900 High Ridge Road, Stamford   Fax: (203) 968-8640
See Ad on Page: 324
Principal/Owner: Steven Prisco

OPUS AUDIO/VIDEO/CONTROL INC. ....**(203) 498-0407**
85 Willow Street, New Haven   Fax: (203) 498-2938
See Ad on Page: 470,471
Website: www.opusavc.com e-mail: info@opusavc.com

PERFORMANCE IMAGING ....**(203) 862-9600**
115 East Putnam Avenue, Greenwich   Fax: (203) 862-9079
See Ad on Page: 465-467
Principal/Owner: Mark Risi

WESTFAIR TV...**(203) 255-1671**
1961 Post Road, Fairfield   Fax: (203) 255-0364
See Ad on Page: 469
Principal/Owner: Glenn Levinson

we Install the System . . .

AUTHORIZED BRANDS
Sony
Sony ES
Sony CiS
Klipsch
Definition Technology
Sonance
Lexicon
Elan
Creston

ON-SITE REPAIR SHOP

SMART HOME DESIGN
&
INSTALL

**Celebrating
Our 40th
Year**

. . . then You take Control

WESTFAIR TV
Custom Audio-Visual Systems
1961 Post Road, Fairfield, CT · (203) 255-1671

A PASSION FOR PERFECTION

OPUS AUDIO|VIDEO|CONTROL INC

multi-room audio, video and data
integrated control systems and
home theater since 1990

O P U S
AUDIO|VIDEO|CONTROL

85 WILLOW STREET NEW HAVEN, CT 06511 (203) 498-0407 WWW.OPUSAVC.COM

ILLUMINATED
IN EVERY DETAIL

OPUS LIGHTING LLC

lighting control systems
that enhance your home's aesthetics,
convenience and security

85 WILLOW STREET NEW HAVEN, CT 06511 (203) 453-5211 WWW.OPUSLIGHTING.COM

World class home theater
design and installation

- Home Theater Portfolio
- Multi-Room Audio/Video
- Custom Design & Installation
- Dedicated Media Rooms
- Home Automation
- Retail Showroom

view our portfolio and more online at...

www.audiodesign.net

audiodesign

1955 black rock turnpike fairfield ct 06432   203 336 440

Integrated
Home Systems

DESIGN INSTALLATIONS ....**(203) 847-2777**
4 New Canaan Avenue, Norwalk   Fax: (203) 849-7700
See Ad on Page: 474
Principal/Owner: Dean A. Smith
e-mail: dean@designinstallations.com
Additional Information: Designing and installling high-end home theatres, multi-room audio systems and lighting control by Lutron since 1984.

ELECTRONICS CONNECTION, THE ....**(914) 273-0099**
517 Main Street, Armonk   Fax: (914) 273-2946
See Ad on Page: 475
Principal/Owner: Gregg A. Bilotta

473

continued on page **481**

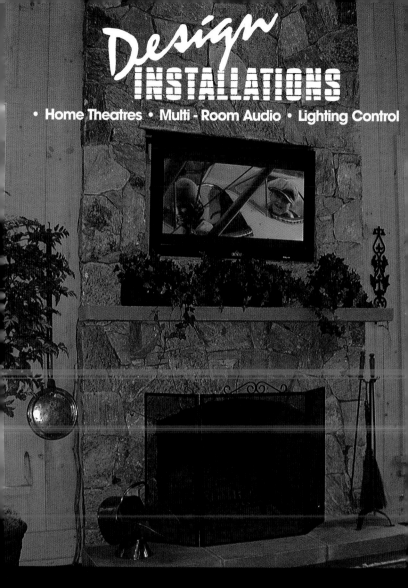

Design Installations...

a name aptly derived from what we do best...design and installation. More specifically: the custom creation of audio/video interiors that are aesthetically pleasing, intuitive to operate and a joy to experience. Multi-room audio systems from casual to sublime, home theatres of intimate atmosphere to those of truly cinematic proportions and lighting control systems from basic to all encompassing ....we'll help make being at home your most favorite place to be.

4 New Canaan Avenue
Norwalk, Connecticut 06851
P 203.847.2777   F 203.849.7700
www.designinstallations.com

- **Home Theaters • Multi-Room Audio • HDTV**
- **Telephone Systems • Home Automation**

517 Main Street, Armonk, NY 10504
(914) 273-0099
www.hometheatres.tv

ALL THE

comforts

OF *home*

HOME TECHNOLOGY DESIGN & INSTALLATION · MEDIA ROOMS
WHOLE HOUSE AUDIO · MULTI-ZONE, MULTI-SOURCE SYSTEMS
HOME THEATER · LIGHTING CONTROL · SECURITY SYSTEMS
PHONE SYSTEMS · RESIDENTIAL CABLING

HOMETRONICS *Lifestyles*

800.468.9418 · www.hometronicslifestyles.com

Home Automation

Custom Home Theaters

Multi Room Audio Video

Lighting Controls

Structured Wiring

Security

Audio Video Excellence, LLC
Designing Home Automation Since 1986

(914) 747-1411
www.audiovideoex.com

Acoustic Architecture best describes the work performed by A-Arch, Inc. We combine form and function by incorporating custom Audio Video systems into our client's lifestyles. We work closely with the homeowners to determine their needs and design the appropriate systems. These can run from basic stereo music systems to multi-source keypad systems to smart-home whole house control systems, and from simple surround sound to dedicated home theaters. For design and installation with attention to detail, call us today.

- High-Definition TV
- Touch-Screen Controls
- Home Theater Specialists

A-Arch, Inc.
Custom Audio Video
Design & Installation

Brewster, NY   Phone: 845-279-8584

www.acousticarchitecture.com

CEDIA

CUSTOM
ELECTRONIC
DESIGN &
INSTALLATION
ASSOCIATION

For Ultimate Home Theater...

...We're Your Ticket to the Best Seat in the House.

SONY	HDTV PLASMA & LCD	**MITSUBISHI**
⋀ Atlantic Technology.	PROJECTION & REAR SCREEN HDTV	**ONKYO**
harman/kardon	THX CERTIFIED AUDIO COMPONENTS	**ENERGY**
⊓⊓⊓	TOUCH SCREEN CONTROL SYSTEMS	*Pioneer*
DENON	LIGHTING & SOUND CONTROLS	*Definitive Technology*
Panasonic	SMART HOME AUTOMATION SYSTEMS	**DOLBY** DIGITAL
HUGHES	VIDEOCONFERENCING SUITES	**HITACHI**

Authorized Sales - Service - Installation for Residential and Commercial.

900 High Ridge Rd - Stamford, CT 06905
(203) 968-1515 - www.planttv.com - sprisco@planettv.com

Engineering ▪ Design ▪ Build ▪ Equip ▪ Install
Visit our showroom for an informative demonstration.

Integrated
Home Systems

HOMETRONICS LIFESTYLES ....**(800) 468-9418**
6 Way Road, Middlefield   Fax: (860) 349-7087
See Ad on Page: 476
Principal/Owner: Jim Sweeney
e-mail: jim@ss-hometech.com

OPUS LIGHTING LLC ....**(203) 453-5211**
458 Three Mile Course, Guilford   Fax: (203) 453-1631
See Ad on Page: 470, 471
Website: www.opuslighting.com e-mail: info@opuslighting.com

PLANET TV & APPLIANCE ....**(203) 968-1515**
900 High Ridge Road, Stamford   Fax: (203) 321-8640
See Ad on Page: 325, 480
Principal/Owner: Steven Prisco

The Ashley Group Luxury Home Resource Collection

The **Ashley Group (www.theashleygroup.com)** is pleased to offer as your final destination when searching for home improvement and luxury resources the following **Home Books** in your local market. Available now: *Chicago, Washington D.C., South Florida, Los Angeles, Dallas/Fort Worth, Detroit, Colorado, New York, Atlanta, Arizona, Philadelphia, San Diego, North Carolina, Boston, Houston* and *Las Vegas.* These comprehensive, hands-on guides to building, remodeling, decorating, furnishing, and landscaping a luxury home, are required reading for the serious and selective homeowner. With over 500 full-color, beautiful pages, the **Home Book** series in each market covers all aspects of the building and remodeling process, including listings of hundreds of local industry professionals, accompanied by informative and valuable editorial discussing the most recent trends.

Order your copies today and make your dream come true!

THE ASHLEY GROUP LUXURY HOME RESOURCE COLLECTION

Yes! Please send me the following Home Books! At $39.95 for each, plus $4.00 Shipping & Handling and Tax per book.

- ☐ Dallas/Fort Worth Home Book *Premier Ed.* ___ # of Copies
- ☐ New York Home Book *Premier Ed.* ___ # of Copies
- ☐ Chicago Home Book *6th Ed.* ___ # of Copies
- ☐ Washington DC Home Book *2nd Ed.* ___ # of Copies
- ☐ North Carolina Home Book *Premier Ed.* ___ # of Copies
- ☐ San Diego Home Book *Premier Ed.* ___ # of Copies
- ☐ Arizona Home Book *Premier Ed.* ___ # of Copies
- ☐ Boston Home Book *Premier Ed.* ___ # of Copies

- ☐ Detroit Home Book *Premier Ed.* ___ # of Copies
- ☐ Colorado Home Book *Premier Ed.* ___ # of Copies
- ☐ Los Angeles Home Book *2nd Ed.* ___ # of Copies
- ☐ South Florida Home Book *2nd Ed.* ___ # of Copies
- ☐ Las Vegas Home Book *Premier Ed.* ___ # of Copies
- ☐ Philadelphia Home Book *Premier Ed.* ___ # of Copies
- ☐ Atlanta Home Book *Premier Ed.* ___ # of Copies
- ☐ Houston Home Book *Premier Ed.* ___ # of Copies

I ordered (# Of Books) _____ X $43.95 = $ _____ Total amount enclosed: $ _____

Please charge my: _____ Visa _____ Mastercard _____ American Express

Credit Card #: _____ Exp. Date: _____

Name: _____ Phone: _____

Signature: _____

Address: _____ Email: _____

City: _____ State: _____ Zip Code: _____

Send order to: Attn: Book Sales–Marketing, The Ashley Group–Reed, 2000 Clearwater Drive, Oak Brook, Illinois 60523
Or Call Toll Free at: 1-888-458-1750 • Or E-mail ashleybooksales@ReedBusiness.com • Visit us on-line at www.theashleygroup.com

All orders must be accompanied by check, money order or credit card # for full amount.

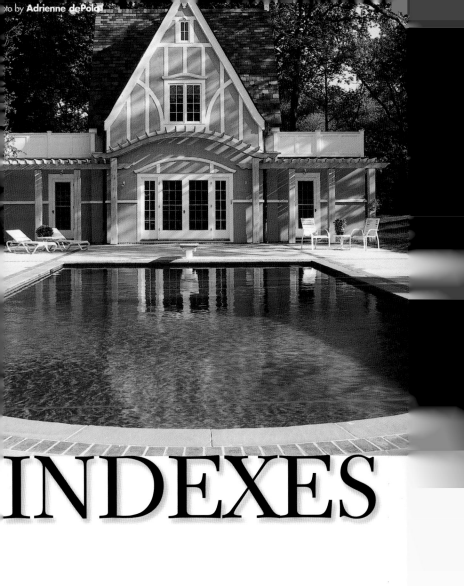

to by **Adrienne dePoto**

INDEXES

483
Alphabetical Index

486
Professional

Woodsmith Building Corp
Ph: 914•723•5033 Fax: 914•723•1322

Gary Neil Saritzky Architect
Ph: 914•723•3316 Fax: 914•723•5914

P.O. Box 566
Scarsdale, NY 10583

AUSTIN
PATTERSON
DISSTON

ARCHITECTS

376 Pequot Avenue, Southport, CT 06490 • (203) 255-4031
4 Midland Street, Quogue, NY 11959 • (631) 653-1481
www.apdarchitects.com

Alphabetical Index

A

A & G Contracting Inc. 174
A Matter of Style .309
A.P. Savino LLC 133
A.T. Proudian In. 375,376
A-Arh, In. 478,479
Aent Picture Framing 450
ACI General Contracting, In. 128,129
Advanced Roofing In. 179
Albano Aliane & Servie, LLC 326,327
Albis Turlington Architects, LLC 71
Alexa Wheeler Interiors 195
Alfredo LDC .235-237
All American Custom
        Pool & Spas, Inc 266,267
All Star Woodworking 342
American Development Cororation 166,167
American Frameless 364,365
Anthony & Sylvan Pools 264
Anthony Totilo, Architect 90
Architects' Guild 94
Architreasures Interiors 200
Artisans, In. 114, 115
Artistic Iron Works, LLC 370
Asian Collectibles 405
Audio Video Exellence, LLC 477
Audiodesign, In. .472
Audrey Morgan Interiors 181-183
Austin Patterson Disston 89

B

B & D Johnson Antiques, LLC 458
B. Hirsch Landworks, LLC 249,257
Bamman Building 171
Banks Design Associates, Ltd 57
Barchella
        Contracting Company, Inc. 250,251
Barney's Place 447
Barrington Building Company, LLC 143
Bayberry Woodworking, LLC 343
Beautiful Home .191
Bedford Stone & Masonry 252-259
Benchmark Builders, LLC 173
Bilotta Home Center 301
Blansfield Builders, Inc. 116, 117
Bloom Design LLC 341
Bourke & Mathews 157
Brenner Builders 138,139
Briggs House Antiques 463
Brindisi & Yaroscak LLC 141
Budd & Allardyce Interiors LLC 188,189
Building Designs, LLC 98,99
Burdo Painting Company, LLC 420

C

California Closets 412,413
Cannondale Building & Design 111
Cardillo Pools & Spas LLC 265
CCA Carpet Co-Op of America 383
Champa Interiors 201
Chary & Sigüenza Architects, LLP 95
Chris Carlo Electrical Contractors, Inc. 177
Christianson Lee Studios, Inc. 421
Christman Stuart Interiors 205
Clarke 324-331

Clarke Builders Inc. 140
Classic Carpet & Rug 384
Classic Sofa 409
Classy Closets 414
Closet Factory 415
Cole Harris CH2K
        Architecture Interiors 64,65
Colonial Collections
        of New England, Inc. 418
Connecticut Bomanite Systems, Inc. 261
Connecticut Design Center 397-399
Connecticut Fencemen, Inc, The 272
Connecticut Kitchen & Bath 312-319
Construction Concepts Corp. 135,199,289
Contadino Architects, AIA 86
Coppola & Sons Construction Co. Inc. 258
Cornerstone Building, LLC 126,127
Couleur Provence 422
Country Club Homes, Inc. 152,153
Country Design, Inc. 207
Country Kitchens, LLC 313
County TV & Appliance 324
Crane Woodworking, Inc. 340
Creative Bath At
        Danbury Plumbing Supply 317
Creative Metal Fab, LLC 368,369
Custom Kitchens & Baths 304
Custom Landscape & Lighting, LLC . . .274,275

D

D.L.T.C., Inc. 246
Dacor 322,323
Danbury Overhead Door 372
Daniel L. Colbert, Architect 91
Davenport & Co. 192, 193
Davenport Contracting, Inc. 158
De Motte Architects, PC 67
Décor of Greenwich 190
Descom Woodworking Company 344,345
Design Installations 474
Design Lighting By Marks 276,277
Designs By Kaye 434,435
Diana Sawicki Interior Design, Inc. 194
Dorello Carpets & Area Rugs 377
Drexel S. Frye, Inc. 350,351
Drexel S. Frye, Inc. 350,351
Dujardin Design Associates 204

E

E.M. Rose Builders, Inc. 105
Edelmann Kitchen,
        Bath & Interior Design 209,297
Ed's Garage Doors 373
Electronics Connection, The 475
Eleish Van Breems Antiques 454
Empire Kitchens 310,311,352,353
Eric Michaels Architects, LLC 55,56,88

F

Fairfield County Millwork 346
Femia Landscaping, Inc. 253
Fenimore Plumbing Supply 318
Fishe Bros., Merchants of Interest 269
French Country Living 406,407

483

Alphabetical Index

G

G. Sergeant Antiques 441-443
Gallery of Kitchens 290,291
Garage Tek 416
Garon Fence Company Inc. 279
Gary Neil Savitzy/
    Woodsmith Building 483,484
Geary Gallery 450
Geitz Design Associates 93
Giorgio's Upholstery
    Interior Decorating 427
Girouard Associates, Inc. 103,104,168
Go To Your Room .410
Grayson Construction Co. Inc. 154,206
Gregory Allan Cramer & Company 208
Gullans & Brooks Associates, Inc. 82,83

H

H.J. Luciano 254
HADCO 328,329
Hampton Court Interiors 220,221
Handwright Gallery & Framing L.L.C. 449
Harbor View Center For Antiques 455
Haverson Architecture and Design, PC 87
Richard F. Hein 85
Hobbs Incorporated 147
Hoffman Contracting LLC 175
Home Builders
    Association of Fairfield 155
Home Gym Design, Inc. 432
Home Works 430
Homefires 439
HomeTronics Lifestyles 476
House of Fins 408
House of Tibet Rugs Inc. 385
Huestis-Tucker Architects, LLC 92

I

I.K. Builders LLC 164,165
Interstate Lumber/
    Lakeland Lumber 361,363

J

J.S.J. Window Treatments 428,429
Jason Roberts, Inc. 259
Jerry Liotta Decorative Artist 423

K

K.L.R. Woodworking 339
Karen Houghton Interiors 223
Karp Associates, Inc. 136,137
Katherine Cowdin, Inc.,
    Interior Design 227
Kent Greenhouse & Gardens 244,245
Kent Pruzan Interiors, LLC 222
Kitchen & Bath Center 281-283
Kitchen & Bath Creations, LLC 298
Kitchen Company, The 302,303
Kitchen Factor, The 296
Kitchens By Benson 281-283
Kitchens By Deane 299
Kling Brothers Builders Inc. 144,145

L

Lakeland Lumber 361,363
Lang Pools, Inc. 263
Le Barn 459
LoParco Associates, Inc. 160,161
Lowenthal Partners Interior Design 224

M

Mark P. Finlay Architects, AIA 84
Masterworks Cabinetry, Inc. 348,349
Mayfair Construction 162,163
Meinke Associates Inc. 159
Miele 321
Mingolello & Hayes Architects 62,63
Moisan Architects 72,73

N

New Canaan Marble & Tile 388,389
New England
    Kitchen Design Center 305
New England
    Stair Company, Inc. 331-333,355-359

O

Olson DeBeradinis Development, LLC 172
Opus Audio/Video/Control Inc. 470,471
Opus Lighting LLC 470,471

P

Palladio Interior Design 228
Paramount Stone Co 387
Paul Dolan Company, Inc. 308
Perdikaris - Constantine
    Developers, Inc. 130,131
Perfect Plantings .255
Performance Imaging 465-467
Phoenix Hardwood Flooring 391
Pianeta Legno Floors USA Inc. 394
Pierre Gagnon Interiors 422
Planet TV & Appliance 325,480
Post Road Homes .134

ProSource Wholesale
  Floor Covering 383
Prosperity Interiors, Inc. 229
Putnam Kitchens Inc. 300-303

Q

Quai Voltaire Antiques 452,453

R

R.B. Benson & Co. 146
R.C. Torre Construction Corp. 148,149
Radcliff Interiors, Inc. 230
Red Sun Studio, The 101
Richard F. Hein 247
Rings End Lumber 366
Rings End Lumber 366
Robin McGarry & Associates 202,203
Ronco Building Corporation 483,484
Rooms of England 290,291
Rose Adams Cabinetry 306
Rose Adams Design Cabinetry 306
Rosenblum Architects 96

S

Sachs Plumbing Supplies 319
SBD Kitchens, LLC 294,295
Sean O'Kane AIA Architects PC 68,69
SGDA 243
Sheridan Interiors 196,197
Studio Snaidero Greenwich 307
Summer Rain 260

T

T.O. Gronlund Co. 292,293
TDS Home Line
  Designing & Building 170
Top Drawer Custom
  Cabinetry Corp. 312
Turnkey Associates 150,151

V

V. W. Interiors LLC 231
Vallin Galleries LLC 462
Vandamm Interiors of Greenwich 225
Vigneau & Associates 70

W

Walpole Woodworkers 270,271
Wayne Pratt Interiors 460,461
Westchester Design
  Center/Empire 310,311,352,353
Westfair TV 469
Wilton Lamp Light & Shade 437
Woodbury Antiques
  Dealers Association 457
Wright Brothers Builders Inc. 112,113

Z

Zoltan European Floors, Inc. 392,393

Professional Index

Architects

Richard F. Hein 85

Agrarian
Haverson Architecture and Design, PC 87
Mark P. Finlay Architects, AIA 84
Red Sun Studio, The 101

American Traditional
Albis Turlington Architects, LLC 71
Architects' Guild 94
Austin Patterson Disston 89
Banks Design Associates, Ltd 57
Building Designs, LLC 98,99
Chary & Sigüenza Architects, LLP . . . . .95 →
Cole Harris CH2K
    Architecture Interiors 64,65
Contadino Architects, AIA 86
Country Club Homes, Inc. 152,153
De Motte Architects, PC 67
Eric Michaels Architects, LLC 55,56,88
Gary Neil Savitzy/
    Woodsmith Building Corp. 483,484
Geitz Design Associates 93
Grayson Construction Co. Inc. 154,206
Haverson Architecture
    and Design, PC 87
Huestis-Tucker Architects, LLC 92
Mark P. Finlay Architects, AIA 84
Red Sun Studio, The 101
Ronco Building Corporation 483,484
Rosenblum Architects 96
Sean O'Kane AIA Architects PC 68,69

Cape Cod
Austin Patterson Disston 89
Building Designs, LLC 98,99
Cole Harris CH2K
    Architecture Interiors 64,65
Eric Michaels Architects, LLC 55,56,88
Geitz Design Associates 93
Grayson Construction Co. Inc. 154,206
Gullans & Brooks Associates, Inc. 82,83
Haverson Architecture and Design, PC 87
Huestis-Tucker Architects, LLC 92
Mark P. Finlay Architects, AIA 84
Mingolello & Hayes Architects 62,63
Red Sun Studio, The 101
Rosenblum Architects 96

Colonial
Austin Patterson Disston 89
Banks Design Associates, Ltd 57
Building Designs, LLC 98,99
Cole Harris CH2K
    Architecture Interiors 64,65
Contadino Architects, AIA 86
Country Club Homes, Inc. 152,153
Daniel L. Colbert, Architect 91
De Motte Architects, PC 67
Eric Michaels Architects, LLC 55,56,88
Geitz Design Associates 93
Grayson Construction Co. Inc. 154,206
Gullans & Brooks Associates, Inc. 82,83
Haverson Architecture and Design, PC 87
Huestis-Tucker Architects, LLC 92
Mark P. Finlay Architects, AIA 84
Mingolello & Hayes Architects 62,63
Moisan Architects 72,73
Red Sun Studio, The 101
Rosenblum Architects 96
Sean O'Kane AIA Architects PC 68,69

Contemporary
Albis Turlington Architects, LLC 71
Architects' Guild 94
Austin Patterson Disston 89
Building Designs, LLC 98,99
Chary & Sigüenza Architects, LLP 95
Cole Harris CH2K
    Architecture Interiors 64,65
Daniel L. Colbert, Architect 91
Eric Michaels Architects, LLC 55,56,88
Geitz Design Associates 93
Grayson Construction Co. Inc. 154,206
Haverson Architecture and Design, PC 87
Mark P. Finlay Architects, AIA 84
Mingolello & Hayes Architects 62,63
Red Sun Studio, The 101
Rosenblum Architects 96
Sean O'Kane AIA Architects PC 68,69

Country
Austin Patterson Disston 89
Banks Design Associates, Ltd 57
Building Designs, LLC 98,99
Chary & Sigüenza Architects, LLP 95
Cole Harris CH2K
    Architecture Interiors 64,65
Contadino Architects, AIA 86
Country Club Homes, Inc. 152,153
De Motte Architects, PC 67
Eric Michaels Architects, LLC 55,56,88
Gary Neil Savitzy/
    Woodsmith Building Corp. 483,484
Grayson Construction Co. Inc. 154,206
Gullans & Brooks Associates, Inc. 82,83
Haverson Architecture and Design, PC 87
Mark P. Finlay Architects, AIA 84
Mingolello & Hayes Architects 62,63
Red Sun Studio, The 101
Ronco Building Corporation 483,484
Rosenblum Architects 96
Sean O'Kane AIA Architects PC 68,69

English
Austin Patterson Disston 89
Chary & Sigüenza Architects, LLP 95
Cole Harris CH2K
    Architecture Interiors 64,65
Country Club Homes, Inc. 152,153
Daniel L. Colbert, Architect 91
Eric Michaels Architects, LLC 55,56,88
Gary Neil Savitzy/
    Woodsmith Building Corp. 483,484
Grayson Construction Co. Inc. 154,206
Gullans & Brooks Associates, Inc. 82,83
Haverson Architecture and Design, PC 87
Huestis-Tucker Architects, LLC 92
Mark P. Finlay Architects, AIA 84
Moisan Architects 72,73
Red Sun Studio, The 101
Ronco Building Corporation 483,484
Rosenblum Architects 96
Sean O'Kane AIA Architects PC 68,69

Farmhouse
Architects' Guild 94
Austin Patterson Disston 89
Banks Design Associates, Ltd 57
Building Designs, LLC 98,99
Chary & Sigüenza Architects, LLP 95
Cole Harris CH2K
    Architecture Interiors 64,65
Contadino Architects, AIA 86

Country Club Homes, Inc. 152,153
Daniel L. Colbert, Architect 91
De Motte Architects, PC 67
Eric Michaels Architects, LLC 55,56,88
Gary Neil Savitzy/
    Woodsmith Building Corp. 483,484
Geitz Design Associates 93
Grayson Construction Co. Inc. 154,206
Gullans & Brooks Associates, Inc. 82,83
Haverson Architecture and Design, PC . . .87
Huestis-Tucker Architects, LLC 92
Mark P. Finlay Architects, AIA 84
Mingolello & Hayes Architects 62,63
Moisan Architects 72,73
Red Sun Studio, The 101
Ronco Building Corporation 483,484
Rosenblum Architects 96
Sean O'Kane AIA Architects PC 68,69

French

Austin Patterson Disston 89
Chary & Sigüenza Architects, LLP 95
Country Club Homes, Inc. 152,153
De Motte Architects, PC 67
Eric Michaels Architects, LLC 55,56,88
Gary Neil Savitzy/
    Woodsmith Building Corp. 483,484
Grayson Construction Co. Inc. 154,206
Haverson Architecture and Design, PC . . .87
Homefires 439
Huestis-Tucker Architects, LLC 92
Mark P. Finlay Architects, AIA 84
Moisan Architects 72,73
Red Sun Studio, The 101
Ronco Building Corporation 483,484
Rosenblum Architects 96
Sean O'Kane AIA Architects PC 68,69

Georgian

Austin Patterson Disston 89
Building Designs, LLC 98,99
Chary & Sigüenza Architects, LLP 95
Contadino Architects, AIA 86
Country Club Homes, Inc. 152,153
Eric Michaels Architects, LLC 55,56,88
Gary Neil Savitzy/
    Woodsmith Building Corp. 483,484
Geitz Design Associates 93
Grayson Construction Co. Inc. 154,206
Gullans & Brooks Associates, Inc. 82,83
Haverson Architecture and Design, PC . . .87
Huestis-Tucker Architects, LLC 92
Mark P. Finlay Architects, AIA 84
Moisan Architects 72,73
Red Sun Studio, The 101
Ronco Building Corporation 483,484
Rosenblum Architects 96
Sean O'Kane AIA Architects PC 68,69

Historic Renovation

Albis Turlington Architects, LLC 71
Austin Patterson Disston 89
Building Designs, LLC 98,99
Chary & Sigüenza Architects, LLP 95
Cole Harris CH2K
    Architecture Interiors 64,65
Eric Michaels Architects, LLC 55,56,88
Gary Neil Savitzy/
    Woodsmith Building Corp. 483,484
Geitz Design Associates 93
Grayson Construction Co. Inc. 154,206
Haverson Architecture and Design, PC . . .87

Mark P. Finlay Architects, AIA 84
Mingolello & Hayes Architects 62,63
Moisan Architects 72,73
Red Sun Studio, The 101
Ronco Building Corporation 483,484
Rosenblum Architects 96
Sean O'Kane AIA Architects PC 68,69

Historical

Huestis-Tucker Architects, LLC 92

Modern

Albis Turlington Architects, LLC 71
Austin Patterson Disston 89
Building Designs, LLC 98,99
Chary & Sigüenza Architects, LLP 95
Cole Harris CH2K
    Architecture Interiors 64,65
Daniel L. Colbert, Architect 91
Eric Michaels Architects, LLC 55,56,88
Grayson Construction Co. Inc. 154,206
Haverson Architecture and Design, PC . . .87
Mark P. Finlay Architects, AIA 84
Red Sun Studio, The 101
Rosenblum Architects 96
Sean O'Kane AIA Architects PC 68,69

Neo-Classical

Anthony Totilo, Architect 90
Austin Patterson Disston 89
Building Designs, LLC 98,99
Chary & Sigüenza Architects, LLP 95
De Motte Architects, PC 67
Eric Michaels Architects, LLC 55,56,88
Gary Neil Savitzy/
    Woodsmith Building Corp. 483,484
Grayson Construction Co. Inc. 154,206
Gullans & Brooks Associates, Inc. 82,83
Haverson Architecture and Design, PC . . .87
Mark P. Finlay Architects, AIA 84
Red Sun Studio, The 101
Ronco Building Corporation 483,484
Sean O'Kane AIA Architects PC 68,69

Neo-Traditional

Albis Turlington Architects, LLC 71
Banks Design Associates, Ltd 57
Chary & Sigüenza Architects, LLP 95
Cole Harris CH2K
    Architecture Interiors 64,65
De Motte Architects, PC 67
Eric Michaels Architects, LLC 55,56,88
Grayson Construction Co. Inc. 154,206
Haverson Architecture and Design, PC . . .87
Mark P. Finlay Architects, AIA 84
Red Sun Studio, The 101
Sean O'Kane AIA Architects PC 68,69

Prairie

Albis Turlington Architects, LLC 71
Architects' Guild 94
Eric Michaels Architects, LLC 55,56,88
Geitz Design Associates 93
Grayson Construction Co. Inc. 154,206
Haverson Architecture and Design, PC . . .87
Mark P. Finlay Architects, AIA 84
Red Sun Studio, The 101
Rosenblum Architects 96

Ranch

Building Designs, LLC 98,99
Grayson Construction Co. Inc. 154,206
Haverson Architecture and Design, PC . . .87
Mark P. Finlay Architects, AIA 84
Red Sun Studio, The 101

Professional Index

Rosenblum Architects 96

Salt Box

Architects' Guild 94
Austin Patterson Disston 89
Building Designs, LLC 98,99
Chary & Sigüenza Architects, LLP 95
Eric Michaels Architects, LLC 55,56,88
Geitz Design Associates 93
Grayson Construction Co. Inc. 154,206
Haverson Architecture and Design, PC 87
Mark P. Finlay Architects, AIA 84
Mingolello & Hayes Architects 62,63
Red Sun Studio, The 101
Sean O'Kane AIA Architects PC 68,69

Shaker

Albis Turlington Architects, LLC 71

Shingle Style

Anthony Totilo, Architect 90
Architects' Guild 94
Austin Patterson Disston 89
Banks Design Associates, Ltd 57
Building Designs, LLC 98,99
Chary & Sigüenza Architects, LLP 95
Cole Harris CH2K
      Architecture Interiors 64,65
Contadino Architects, AIA 86
Country Club Homes, Inc. 152,153
Daniel L. Colbert, Architect 91
De Motte Architects, PC 67
Eric Michaels Architects, LLC 55,56,88
Gary Neil Savitzy/
      Woodsmith Building Corp. 483,484
Geitz Design Associates 93
Grayson Construction Co. Inc. 154,206
Gullans & Brooks Associates, Inc. 82,83
Haverson Architecture and Design, PC 87
Huestis-Tucker Architects, LLC 92
Mark P. Finlay Architects, AIA 84
Mingolello & Hayes Architects 62,63
Moisan Architects 72,73
Red Sun Studio, The 101
Ronco Building Corporation 483,484
Rosenblum Architects 96
Sean O'Kane AIA Architects PC 68,69

Specialty Rooms

Architects' Guild 94
Austin Patterson Disston 89
Building Designs, LLC 98,99
Chary & Sigüenza Architects, LLP 95
Cole Harris CH2K
      Architecture Interiors 64,65
Daniel L. Colbert, Architect 91
Eric Michaels Architects, LLC 55,56,88
Gary Neil Savitzy/
      Woodsmith Building Corp. 483,484
Geitz Design Associates 93
Grayson Construction Co. Inc. 154,206
Gullans & Brooks Associates, Inc. 82,83
Haverson Architecture and Design, PC 87
Mark P. Finlay Architects, AIA 84
Red Sun Studio, The 101
Ronco Building Corporation 483,484
Sean O'Kane AIA Architects PC 68,69

Traditional

Anthony Totilo, Architect 90
Architects' Guild 94
Austin Patterson Disston 89
Banks Design Associates, Ltd 57
Banks Design Associates, Ltd 57
Chary & Sigüenza Architects, LLP 95

Cole Harris CH2K
      Architecture Interiors 64,65
Contadino Architects, AIA 86
Country Club Homes, Inc. 152,153
De Motte Architects, PC 67
Eric Michaels Architects, LLC 55,56,88
Gary Neil Savitzy/
      Woodsmith Building Corp. 483,484
Geitz Design Associates 93
Grayson Construction Co. Inc. 154,206
Gullans & Brooks Associates, Inc. 82,83
Haverson Architecture and Design, PC 87
Huestis-Tucker Architects, LLC 92
Mark P. Finlay Architects, AIA 84
Moisan Architects 72,73
Red Sun Studio, The 101
Ronco Building Corporation 483,484
Rosenblum Architects 96
Sean O'Kane AIA Architects PC 68,69
Vigneau & Associates 70

Tudor

Austin Patterson Disston 89
Building Designs, LLC 98,99
Chary & Sigüenza Architects, LLP 95
Eric Michaels Architects, LLC 55,56,88
Gary Neil Savitzy/
      Woodsmith Building Corp. 483,484
Grayson Construction Co. Inc. 154,206
Haverson Architecture and Design, PC 87
Mark P. Finlay Architects, AIA 84
Red Sun Studio, The 101
Ronco Building Corporation 483,484
Rosenblum Architects 96
Sean O'Kane AIA Architects PC 68,69

Vacation

Albis Turlington Architects, LLC 71
Architects' Guild 94
Austin Patterson Disston 89
Banks Design Associates, Ltd 57
Chary & Sigüenza Architects, LLP 95
Cole Harris CH2K
      Architecture Interiors 64,65
Eric Michaels Architects, LLC 55,56,88
Gary Neil Savitzy/
      Woodsmith Building Corp. 483,484
Geitz Design Associates 93
Grayson Construction Co. Inc. 154,206
Gullans & Brooks Associates, Inc. 82,83
Haverson Architecture and Design, PC 87
Red Sun Studio, The 101
Ronco Building Corporation 483,484
Rosenblum Architects 96
Sean O'Kane AIA Architects PC 68,69

Victorian

Austin Patterson Disston 89
Building Designs, LLC 98,99
Chary & Sigüenza Architects, LLP 95
Cole Harris CH2K
      Architecture Interiors 64,65
Eric Michaels Architects, LLC 55,56,88
Gary Neil Savitzy/
      Woodsmith Building Corp. 483,484
Grayson Construction Co. Inc. 154,206
Haverson Architecture and Design, PC 87
Huestis-Tucker Architects, LLC 92
Mark P. Finlay Architects, AIA 84
Red Sun Studio, The 101
Ronco Building Corporation 483,484
Rosenblum Architects 96
Sean O'Kane AIA Architects PC 68,69

Art & Antiques

American Traditional
Handwright Gallery & Framing L.L.C. 449
Le Barn 459

Antiques
Alexa Wheeler Interiors 195
Asian Collectibles 405
B & D Johnson Antiques, LLC 458
Briggs House Antiques 463
Eleish Van Breems Antiques 454
G. Sergeant Antiques 441-443
Harbor View Center For Antiques 455
Le Barn 459
Quai Voltaire Antiques 452,453
Vallin Galleries LLC 462
Wayne Pratt Interiors 460,461
Woodbury Antiques
      Dealers Association 457

Art Galleries
Accent Picture Framing 450
Barney's Place 447
Geary Gallery 450
Handwright Gallery & Framing L.L.C. 449
Le Barn 459

Artists, Commissioned
Handwright Gallery & Framing L.L.C. 449

Asian
Asian Collectibles 405

English
Le Barn 459

Framing
Accent Picture Framing 450
Barney's Place 447
Geary Gallery 450
Handwright Gallery & Framing L.L.C. 449

French
Le Barn 459

International
Harbor View Center For Antiques 455

Repair & Restoration
Accent Picture Framing 450
Geary Gallery 450
Handwright Gallery & Framing L.L.C. 449
Le Barn 459

Vanity / Cabinetry, Antique
Westchester Design Center/
      Empire Kitchens 310,311,352,353

Contractors

Advanced Roofing Inc. 179
Chris Carlo Electrical Contractors, Inc. 177

Design/Build
A & G Contracting Inc. 174
A.P. Savino LLC 133
ACI General Contracting, Inc. 128,129
Bamman Building .171
Benchmark Builders, LLC 173
Building Designs, LLC 98,99
Clarke Builders Inc. 140
Construction Concepts Corp. 135,199,289
Country Club Homes, Inc. 152,153
Gary Neil Savitzy/
      Woodsmith Building Corp. 483,484
Grayson Construction Co. Inc. 154,206
Kling Brothers Builders Inc. 144,145
Post Road Homes .134
R.C. Torre Construction Corp. 148,149

Ronco Building Corporation 483,484
Rose Adams Cabinetry 306
Rose Adams Design Cabinetry 306
Turnkey Associates 150,151

Designers
Blansfield Builders, Inc. 116, 117
Girouard Associates, Inc. 103,104,168

Home Builders, Custom
A & G Contracting Inc. 174
A.P. Savino LLC 133
ACI General Contracting, Inc. 128,129
American Development
      Corporation 166,167
Artisans, Inc. 114, 115
Barrington Building Company, LLC 143
Blansfield Builders, Inc. 116, 117
Bourke & Mathews 157
Brenner Builders 138,139
Brindisi & Yaroscak LLC 141
Cannondale Building & Design 111
Clarke Builders Inc. 140
Construction Concepts Corp. 135,199,289
Cornerstone Building, LLC 126,127
Country Club Homes, Inc. 152,153
Davenport Contracting, Inc. 158
E.M. Rose Builders, Inc. 105
Gary Neil Savitzy/
      Woodsmith Building Corp. 483,484
Girouard Associates, Inc. 103,104,168
Grayson Construction Co. Inc. 154,206
Hobbs Incorporated 147
Home Builders Association
      of Fairfield County 155
I.K. Builders LLC 164,165
Karp Associates, Inc. 136,137
Kling Brothers Builders Inc. 144,145
LoParco Associates, Inc. 160,161
Mayfair Construction 162,163
Meinke Associates Inc. 159
Olson DeBeradinis Development, LLC 172
Perdikaris - Constantine
      Developers, Inc. 130,131
Post Road Homes .134
R.B. Benson & Co. 146
R.C. Torre Construction Corp. 148,149
Ronco Building Corporation 483,484
Rose Adams Cabinetry 306
Rose Adams Design Cabinetry 306
TDS Home Line Designing
      & Building Services 170
Turnkey Associates 150,151
Wright Brothers Builders Inc. 112,113

Plastering
ACI General Contracting, Inc. 128,129
Bamman Building .171
Benchmark Builders, LLC 173
Gary Neil Savitzy/
      Woodsmith Building Corp. 483,484
Kling Brothers Builders Inc. 144,145
Ronco Building Corporation 483,484
TDS Home Line Designing
      & Building Services 170

Remodeling Specialists
A & G Contracting Inc. 174
A.P. Savino LLC 133
ACI General Contracting, Inc. 128,129
American Development
      Corporation 166,167
Bamman Building .171

Professional Index

Benchmark Builders, LLC 173
Blansfield Builders, Inc. 116, 117
Brenner Builders 138,139
Brindisi & Yaroscak LLC 141
Clarke Builders Inc. 140
Construction Concepts Corp. 135,199,289
Country Club Homes, Inc. 152,153
Davenport Contracting, Inc. 158
E.M. Rose Builders, Inc. 105
Fenimore Plumbing Supply 318
Gary Neil Savitzy/
  Woodsmith Building Corp. 483,484
Grayson Construction Co. Inc. 154,206
Hobbs Incorporated 147
Hoffman Contracting, LLC 175
I.K. Builders LLC 164,165
Karp Associates, Inc. 136,137
Kitchen & Bath Center 281-283
Kitchens By Benson 281-283
Kling Brothers Builders Inc. 144,145
LoParco Associates, Inc. 160,161
Meinke Associates Inc. 159
Olson DeBeradinis Development, LLC 172
Perdikaris - Constantine
  Developers, Inc. 130,131
R.C. Torre Construction Corp. 148,149
Ronco Building Corporation 483,484
Rose Adams Cabinetry 306
Rose Adams Design Cabinetry 306
TDS Home Line Designing &
  Building Services 170
Turnkey Associates 150,151

Repair & Restoration

ACI General Contracting, Inc. 128,129
American Development Corporation . . .166,167
Bamman Building 171
Benchmark Builders, LLC 173
Brenner Builders 138,139
Country Club Homes, Inc. 152,153
Davenport Contracting, Inc. 158
Gary Neil Savitzy/
  Woodsmith Building Corp. 483,484
Kling Brothers Builders Inc. 144,145
LoParco Associates, Inc. 160,161
Meinke Associates Inc. 159
R.C. Torre Construction Corp. 148,149
Ronco Building Corporation 483,484
TDS Home Line Designing &
  Building Services 170

Custom Woodworking, Metal, Hardware &

Cabinets, Custom

All Star Woodworking 342
Bloom Design LLC 341
Bloom Design LLC 341
Closet Factory 415
Descom Woodworking Company . . .344,345
Drexel S. Frye, Inc. 350,351
Fairfield County Millwork 346
Kitchen & Bath Center 281-283
Kitchens By Benson 281-283
Kling Brothers Builders Inc. 144,145
Masterworks Cabinetry, Inc. 348,349
Rooms of England 290,291
Rose Adams Cabinetry 306
Rose Adams Design Cabinetry 306
Top Drawer Custom Cabinetry Corp. 312

Westchester Design Center/
  Empire Kitchens 310,311,352,353

Furniture, Custom

Bayberry Woodworking, LLC 343

Glass & Mirrors, Decorative

Christianson Lee Studios, Inc. 421

Hardware

Interstate Lumber/Lakeland Lumber . . .361,363
Lakeland Lumber 361,363

Mantels

All Star Woodworking 342
Beautiful Home .191
Drexel S. Frye, Inc. 350,351
Kitchen & Bath Center 281-283
Kitchens By Benson 281-283

Metalworking, Custom

Artistic Iron Works, LLC 370
Creative Metal Fab, LLC 368,369
Garon Fence Company Inc. 279
Kling Brothers Builders Inc. 144,145

Millwork

All Star Woodworking 342
Bloom Design LLC 341
Crane Woodworking, Inc. 340
Drexel S. Frye, Inc. 350,351
Fairfield County Millwork 346
K.L.R. Woodworking 339
Kitchen & Bath Center 281-283
Kitchens By Benson 281-283
Kling Brothers Builders Inc. 144,145
Rose Adams Cabinetry 306
Rose Adams Design Cabinetry 306
Westchester Design Center/
  Empire Kitchens 310,311,352,353

Radiator Covers

All Star Woodworking 342
Beautiful Home .191

Stairs & Railings

Artistic Iron Works, LLC 370
Bloom Design LLC 341
Creative Metal Fab, LLC 368,369
Garon Fence Company Inc. 279
Kling Brothers Builders Inc. 144,145
New England Stair
  Company, Inc. 331-333,355-359

Windows & Doors

American Frameless 364,365
Beautiful Home .191
Bloom Design LLC 341
Danbury Overhead Door 372
Ed's Garage Doors 373
Interstate Lumber/
  Lakeland Lumber 361,363
Rings End Lumber 366

Woodworking, Custom

All Star Woodworking 342
Beautiful Home .191
Bloom Design LLC 341
Closet Factory 415
Designs By Kaye 434,435
Drexel S. Frye, Inc. 350,351
Fairfield County Millwork 346
Masterworks Cabinetry, Inc. 348,349
Rose Adams Cabinetry 306
Rose Adams Design Cabinetry 306
Westchester Design Center/
  Empire Kitchens 310,311,352,353

490

Flooring & Countertops

Carpeting / Custom Carpeting
A.T. Proudian Inc. 375,376
CCA Carpet Co-Op of America 383
Classic Carpet & Rug 384
Dorello Carpets & Area Rugs 377
ProSource Wholesale Floor Covering 383

Countertops
All Star Woodworking 342
Closet Factory 415
Kitchen & Bath Center 281-283
Kitchens By Benson 281-283
Kling Brothers Builders Inc. 144,145
Paramount Stone Co. 387
Rose Adams Cabinetry 306
Rose Adams Design Cabinetry 306

Flooring
Hoffman Contracting LLC 175
Kitchen & Bath Center 281-283
Kitchens By Benson 281-283
Kling Brothers Builders Inc. 144,145
Paramount Stone Co 387
Phoenix Hardwood Flooring 391
Pianeta Legno Floors USA Inc. 394
Zoltan European Floors 392,393
Zoltan European Floors, Inc. 392,393

Hardwood
Hoffman Contracting LLC 175
Kitchen & Bath Center 281-283
Kitchens By Benson 281-283
Kling Brothers Builders Inc. 144,145
Phoenix Hardwood Flooring 391
Zoltan European Floors, Inc. 392,393

Marble & Granite
Kitchen & Bath Center 281-283
Kitchens By Benson 281-283
New Canaan Marble & Tile 388,389
Paramount Stone Co 387
Zoltan European Floors 392,393

Rugs, Contemporary
Dorello Carpets & Area Rugs 377

Rugs, Oriental
Dorello Carpets & Area Rugs 377
House of Tibet Rugs Inc. 385

Solid Surfaces
All Star Woodworking 342
Paramount Stone Co 387

Stone, Slate, Concrete
Connecticut Bomanite Systems, Inc. 261
Jason Roberts, Inc. 259
Kitchen & Bath Center 281-283
Kitchens By Benson 281-283
Kling Brothers Builders Inc. 144,145
Paramount Stone Co 387
Zoltan European Floors, Inc. 392,393

Stonecare Products
Paramount Stone Co 387
Zoltan European Floors, Inc. 392,393

Tile, Ceramic
Kitchen & Bath Center 281-283
Kitchens By Benson 281-283
Paramount Stone Co. 387
Zoltan European Floors, Inc. 392,393

Tile, Glass & Metal
Kling Brothers Builders Inc. 144,145

Home Furnishing & Decorating

Accessories
Budd & Allardyce Interiors LLC 188,189
Colonial Collections
    of New England, Inc. 418
Connecticut Design Center 397-399
Country Design, Inc. 207
Garage Tek 416
Go To Your Room 410
Homefires 439
House of Fins 408
Wilton Lamp Light & Shade 437

American Traditional
Colonial Collections
    of New England, Inc. 418
Connecticut Design Center 397-399
Wilton Lamp Light & Shade 437

Art Deco
Connecticut Design Center 397-399
Wilton Lamp Light & Shade 437

Artisan
Christianson Lee Studios, Inc. 421
Wilton Lamp Light & Shade 437

Arts & Crafts
Asian Collectibles 405
Wilton Lamp Light & Shade 437

Asian
Asian Collectibles 405
Connecticut Design Center 397-399
Wilton Lamp Light & Shade 437
Closet Designers
California Closets 412,413
Classy Closets 414

Colonial
Colonial Collections of New England, Inc. . .418
Wilton Lamp Light & Shade 437

Commercial
Bloom Design LLC 341
Garage Tek 416

Contemporary
Connecticut Design Center 397-399
Garage Tek 416
Wilton Lamp Light & Shade 437

Country
Colonial Collections
    of New England, Inc. 418
Connecticut Design Center 397-399
French Country Living 406,407

Eclectic
Connecticut Design Center 397-399
Wilton Lamp Light & Shade 437

English
Budd & Allardyce Interiors LLC 188,189
Connecticut Design Center 397-399
Wilton Lamp Light & Shade 437
Fabrics & Upholstery
Connecticut Design Center 397-399
Country Design, Inc. 207
Giorgio's Upholstery
    Interior Decorating Inc. 427

Faux Painting
Burdo Painting Company, LLC 420
Christianson Lee Studios, Inc. 421
Connecticut Design Center 397-399
Couleur Provence 422
Country Design, Inc. 207

Professional Index

Fireplaces
All Star Woodworking 342
Homefires 439
Kitchen & Bath Center 281-283
Kitchens By Benson 281-283

French
Connecticut Design Center 397-399
Couleur Provence 422
French Country Living 406,407

Furniture, Custom
All Star Woodworking 342
Bloom Design LLC 341
Classic Sofa 409
Closet Factory .415
Connecticut Design Center 397-399
Country Design, Inc. 207
Designs By Kaye 434,435
Go To Your Room 410

Garage Designers
Closet Factory .415
Garage Tek 416

Home Library
All Star Woodworking 342
Bloom Design LLC 341
Closet Factory .415
Connecticut Design Center 397-399
Kitchen & Bath Center 281-283
Kitchens By Benson 281-283
Westchester Design Center/
    Empire Kitchens 310,311,352,353
Wilton Lamp Light & Shade 437

Home Office
All Star Woodworking 342
Bloom Design LLC 341
Budd & Allardyce Interiors LLC 188,189
Closet Factory .415
Connecticut Design Center 397-399
Kitchen & Bath Center 281-283
Kitchens By Benson 281-283

Integrated Home Systems
Audiodesign, Inc. 472

Lifestyle Furnishings
Bloom Design LLC 341
Closet Factory .415
Go To Your Room 410

Lighting
Colonial Collections
    of New England, Inc. 418
Connecticut Design Center 397-399
Wilton Lamp Light & Shade 437

Modern
Connecticut Design Center 397-399
Wilton Lamp Light & Shade 437
Neo-Classical
Connecticut Design Center 397-399
Wilton Lamp Light & Shade 437

Oriental
Vallin Galleries LLC 462
Wilton Lamp Light & Shade 437

Repair & Restoration
Connecticut Design Center 397-399
Connecticut Design Center 397-399
Giorgio's Upholstery
    Interior Decorating Inc. 427

Retro
Connecticut Design Center 397-399
Wilton Lamp Light & Shade 437

Sculpture
Connecticut Design Center 397-399
Vallin Galleries LLC 462

Shaker
Wilton Lamp Light & Shade 437

Shutters
J.S.J. Window Treatments 428,429

Specialty Painters
Christianson Lee Studios, Inc. 421
Couleur Provence 422

Specialty Wall Finishes
Christianson Lee Studios, Inc. 421
Connecticut Design Center 397-399
Couleur Provence 422
Garage Tek 416
Jerry Liotta Decorative Artist 423
Pierre Gagnon Interiors 422

Sport Facilities
Home Gym Design, Inc. 432

Traditional
Budd & Allardyce Interiors LLC 188,189
Connecticut Design Center 397-399
Giorgio's Upholstery
    Interior Decorating Inc. 427
Wilton Lamp Light & Shade 437

Victorian
Wilton Lamp Light & Shade 437

Window Coverings
Connecticut Design Center 397-399
Country Design, Inc. 207
Giorgio's Upholstery
    Interior Decorating Inc. 427
Home Works 430
J.S.J. Window Treatments 428,429

Home Theater & Sound

Accessories
Audio Video Excellence, LLC 477
Audiodesign, Inc. 472
Electronics Connection, The 475

Audio/Video Retailers
Audio Video Excellence, LLC 477
Audiodesign, Inc. 472
Electronics Connection, The 475

Audio/Video, Custom
A-Arch, Inc. 478,479
Audio Video Excellence, LLC 477
Audiodesign, Inc. 472
Design Installations 474
Electronics Connection, The 475
Opus Audio/Video/Control Inc. 470,471

Entertainment Centers
All Star Woodworking 342
Audio Video Excellence, LLC 477
Audiodesign, Inc. 472
Closet Factory .415
Electronics Connection, The 475
Kling Brothers Builders Inc. 144,145
Westchester Design Center/
    Empire Kitchens 310,311,352,353

Home Theater Design
A-Arch, Inc. 478,479
Audio Video Excellence, LLC 477
Audiodesign, Inc. 472
Closet Factory .415
County TV & Appliance 324
Design Installations 474
Electronics Connection, The 475

Professional Index

HomeTronics Lifestyles 476
Kitchen & Bath Center 281-283
Kitchens By Benson 281-283
Opus Audio/Video/Control Inc. 470,471
Performance Imaging 465-467
Westfair TV 469

Integrated Home Systems
A-Arch, Inc. 478,479
Audio Video Excellence, LLC 477
Design Installations 474
Electronics Connection, The 475
HomeTronics Lifestyles 476
Opus Audio/Video/Control Inc. 470,471
Opus Lighting LLC 470,471
Planet TV & Appliance 325,480

Security System Contractors
Audio Video Excellence, LLC 477

Shaker
Connecticut Design Center 397-399

Specialty Painters
Connecticut Design Center 397-399

Telecom Systems
A-Arch, Inc. 478,479
Electronics Connection, The 475

Interior Designers

Davenport & Co. 192, 193
Vandamm Interiors of Greenwich 225

American Traditional
Alexa Wheeler Interiors 195
Architreasures Interiors 200
Audrey Morgan Interiors 181-183
Banks Design Associates, Ltd 57
Beautiful Home 191
Budd & Allardyce Interiors LLC 188,189
Champa Interiors 201
Connecticut Design Center 397-399
Country Design, Inc. 207
Décor of Greenwich 190
Dujardin Design Associates 204
Edelmann Kitchen,
    Bath & Interior Design 209,297
Grayson Construction Co. Inc. 154,206
Gregory Allan Cramer & Company 208
Hampton Court Interiors 220,221
Haverson Architecture and Design, PC 87
Karen Houghton Interiors 223
Katherine Cowdin, Inc., Interior Design 227
Kent Pruzan Interiors, LLC 222
Lowenthal Partners Interior Design 224
Palladio Interior Design 228
Prosperity Interiors, Inc. 229
Radcliff Interiors, Inc. 230
Robin McGarry & Associates 202,203

Art Deco
Alexa Wheeler Interiors 195
Audrey Morgan Interiors 181-183
Beautiful Home 191
Connecticut Design Center 397-399
Décor of Greenwich 190
Grayson Construction Co. Inc. 154,206
Gregory Allan Cramer & Company 208
Kent Pruzan Interiors, LLC 222
Palladio Interior Design 228

Asian
Audrey Morgan Interiors 181-183
Beautiful Home 191
Connecticut Design Center 397-399

Décor of Greenwich 190
Dujardin Design Associates 204
Grayson Construction Co. Inc. 154,206
Haverson Architecture and Design, PC 87
Kent Pruzan Interiors, LLC 222
Lowenthal Partners Interior Design 224
Palladio Interior Design 228
Vallin Galleries LLC 462

Classic Modern
Alexa Wheeler Interiors 195
Audrey Morgan Interiors 181-183
Beautiful Home 191
Champa Interiors 201
Connecticut Design Center 397-399
Country Design, Inc. 207
Décor of Greenwich 190
Dujardin Design Associates 204
Edelmann Kitchen, Bath &
    Interior Design 209,297
Grayson Construction Co. Inc. 154,206
Gregory Allan Cramer & Company 208
Hampton Court Interiors 220,221
Haverson Architecture and Design, PC 87
Karen Houghton Interiors 223
Kent Pruzan Interiors, LLC 222
Lowenthal Partners Interior Design 224
Palladio Interior Design 228
Robin McGarry & Associates 202,203

Colonial
Alexa Wheeler Interiors 195
Architreasures Interiors 200
Audrey Morgan Interiors 181-183
Champa Interiors 201
Connecticut Design Center 397-399
Country Design, Inc. 207
Décor of Greenwich 190
Edelmann Kitchen, Bath &
    Interior Design 209,297
Grayson Construction Co. Inc. 154,206
Hampton Court Interiors 220,221
Haverson Architecture and Design, PC 87
Palladio Interior Design 228

Contemporary
Alexa Wheeler Interiors 195
Audrey Morgan Interiors 181-183
Beautiful Home 191
Champa Interiors 201
Connecticut Design Center 397-399
Décor of Greenwich 190
Diana Sawicki Interior Design, Inc. 194
Dujardin Design Associates 204
Edelmann Kitchen, Bath &
    Interior Design 209,297
Grayson Construction Co. Inc. 154,206
Gregory Allan Cramer & Company 208
Hampton Court Interiors 220,221
Haverson Architecture and Design, PC 87
Kent Pruzan Interiors, LLC 222
Lowenthal Partners Interior Design 224
Palladio Interior Design 228
Prosperity Interiors, Inc. 229
Robin McGarry & Associates 202,203

493

Professional Index

Country

Alexa Wheeler Interiors 195
Architreasures Interiors 200
Audrey Morgan Interiors 181-183
Banks Design Associates, Ltd 57
Beautiful Home 191
Champa Interiors .201
Connecticut Design Center 397-399
Country Design, Inc. 207
Décor of Greenwich 190
Edelmann Kitchen, Bath &
     Interior Design 209,297
Grayson Construction Co. Inc. 154,206
Hampton Court Interiors 220,221
Haverson Architecture and Design, PC 87
Kent Pruzan Interiors, LLC 222
Lowenthal Partners Interior Design 224
Palladio Interior Design 228
Prosperity Interiors, Inc. 229
Radcliff Interiors, Inc. 230
Robin McGarry & Associates 202,203

Eclectic

Alexa Wheeler Interiors 195
Architreasures Interiors 200
Audrey Morgan Interiors 181-183
Banks Design Associates, Ltd 57
Beautiful Home 191
Champa Interiors .201
Christman Stuart Interiors 205
Connecticut Design Center 397-399
Construction Concepts Corp. 135,199,289
Country Design, Inc. 207
Décor of Greenwich 190
Diana Sawicki Interior Design, Inc. 194
Dujardin Design Associates 204
Grayson Construction Co. Inc. 154,206
Gregory Allan Cramer & Company 208
Hampton Court Interiors 220,221
Haverson Architecture and Design, PC 87
Kent Pruzan Interiors, LLC 222
Lowenthal Partners Interior Design 224
Palladio Interior Design 228
Prosperity Interiors, Inc. 229
Robin McGarry & Associates 202,203
V. W. Interiors LLC 231

English

Alexa Wheeler Interiors 195
Audrey Morgan Interiors 181-183
Beautiful Home 191
Budd & Allardyce Interiors LLC 188,189
Champa Interiors .201
Christman Stuart Interiors 205
Connecticut Design Center 397-399
Country Design, Inc. 207
Décor of Greenwich 190
Dujardin Design Associates 204
Grayson Construction Co. Inc. 154,206
Gregory Allan Cramer & Company 208
Hampton Court Interiors 220,221
Haverson Architecture and Design, PC 87
Homefires 439
Karen Houghton Interiors 223
Katherine Cowdin, Inc., Interior Design . . .227
Kent Pruzan Interiors, LLC 222
Lowenthal Partners Interior Design 224
Palladio Interior Design 228
Prosperity Interiors, Inc. 229
Radcliff Interiors, Inc. 230
Robin McGarry & Associates 202,203

Federal

Alexa Wheeler Interiors 195
Audrey Morgan Interiors 181-183
Beautiful Home 191
Champa Interiors .201
Christman Stuart Interiors 205
Connecticut Design Center 397-399
Country Design, Inc. 207
Décor of Greenwich 190
Dujardin Design Associates 204
Grayson Construction Co. Inc. 154,206
Hampton Court Interiors 220,221
Haverson Architecture and Design, PC 87
Karen Houghton Interiors 223
Kent Pruzan Interiors, LLC 222
Lowenthal Partners Interior Design 224
Palladio Interior Design 228

Feng Shui

Christman Stuart Interiors 205
Connecticut Design Center 397-399
Dujardin Design Associates 204
Kent Pruzan Interiors, LLC 222
Vallin Galleries LLC 462

French

Alexa Wheeler Interiors 195
Architreasures Interiors 200
Audrey Morgan Interiors 181-183
Beautiful Home 191
Budd & Allardyce Interiors LLC 188,189
Champa Interiors .201
Christman Stuart Interiors 205
Connecticut Design Center 397-399
Country Design, Inc. 207
Décor of Greenwich 190
Edelmann Kitchen, Bath &
     Interior Design 209,297
Grayson Construction Co. Inc. 154,206
Gregory Allan Cramer & Company 208
Hampton Court Interiors 220,221
Katherine Cowdin, Inc., Interior Design . . .227
Kent Pruzan Interiors, LLC 222
Lowenthal Partners Interior Design 224
Palladio Interior Design 228
Prosperity Interiors, Inc. 229
Radcliff Interiors, Inc. 230
Robin McGarry & Associates 202,203

Historic Renovation

Alexa Wheeler Interiors 195
Audrey Morgan Interiors 181-183
Dujardin Design Associates 204
Gregory Allan Cramer & Company 208
Hampton Court Interiors 220,221
Haverson Architecture and Design, PC 87
Katherine Cowdin, Inc., Interior Design . . .227
Lowenthal Partners Interior Design 224
Palladio Interior Design 228
Robin McGarry & Associates 202,203

Historical

Alexa Wheeler Interiors 195
Architreasures Interiors 200
Audrey Morgan Interiors 181-183
Champa Interiors .201
Christman Stuart Interiors 205
Décor of Greenwich 190
Dujardin Design Associates 204
Gregory Allan Cramer & Company 208
Hampton Court Interiors 220,221
Haverson Architecture and Design, PC 87
Katherine Cowdin, Inc., Interior Design . . .227

494

Lowenthal Partners Interior Design 224
Palladio Interior Design 228

Home Office
Alexa Wheeler Interiors 195
Audrey Morgan Interiors 181-183
Beautiful Home 191
Budd & Allardyce Interiors LLC 188,189
Christman Stuart Interiors 205
Closet Factory 415
Connecticut Design Center 397-399
Country Design, Inc. 207
Décor of Greenwich 190
Dujardin Design Associates 204
Grayson Construction Co. Inc. 154,206
Hampton Court Interiors 220,221
Haverson Architecture and Design, PC 87
Katherine Cowdin, Inc., Interior Design . . .227
Kent Pruzan Interiors, LLC 222
Lowenthal Partners Interior Design 224
Palladio Interior Design 228
Radcliff Interiors, Inc. 230
Robin McGarry & Associates 202,203

Mission
Alexa Wheeler Interiors 195
Beautiful Home 191
Connecticut Design Center 397-399
Décor of Greenwich 190
Grayson Construction Co. Inc. 154,206
Haverson Architecture and Design, PC 87
Lowenthal Partners Interior Design 224
Palladio Interior Design 228

Modern
Alexa Wheeler Interiors 195
Audrey Morgan Interiors 181-183
Beautiful Home 191
Connecticut Design Center 397-399
Décor of Greenwich 190
Grayson Construction Co. Inc. 154,206
Haverson Architecture and Design, PC 87
Kent Pruzan Interiors, LLC 222
Lowenthal Partners Interior Design 224
Palladio Interior Design 228

Neo-Classical
Alexa Wheeler Interiors 195
Audrey Morgan Interiors 181-183
Beautiful Home 191
Champa Interiors 201
Connecticut Design Center 397-399
Décor of Greenwich 190
Grayson Construction Co. Inc. 154,206
Hampton Court Interiors 220,221
Haverson Architecture and Design, PC 87
Kent Pruzan Interiors, LLC 222
Lowenthal Partners Interior Design 224
Palladio Interior Design 228
Robin McGarry & Associates 202,203

Neo-Traditional
Alexa Wheeler Interiors 195
Audrey Morgan Interiors 181-183
Banks Design Associates, Ltd 57
Beautiful Home 191
Connecticut Design Center 397-399
Diana Sawicki Interior Design, Inc. 194
Dujardin Design Associates 204
Grayson Construction Co. Inc. 154,206
Hampton Court Interiors 220,221
Haverson Architecture and Design, PC 87
Kent Pruzan Interiors, LLC 222
Lowenthal Partners Interior Design 224

Palladio Interior Design 228
Robin McGarry & Associates 202,203

One Day Makeovers
Prosperity Interiors, Inc. 229
Radcliff Interiors, Inc. 230

Prairie
Grayson Construction Co. Inc. 154,206
Haverson Architecture and Design, PC 87
Lowenthal Partners Interior Design 224
Palladio Interior Design 228

Southwestern
Audrey Morgan Interiors 181-183
Beautiful Home 191
Connecticut Design Center 397-399
Décor of Greenwich 190
Grayson Construction Co. Inc. 154,206
Haverson Architecture and Design, PC 87
Kent Pruzan Interiors, LLC 222
Lowenthal Partners Interior Design 224
Palladio Interior Design 228

Traditional
Alexa Wheeler Interiors 195
Audrey Morgan Interiors 181-183
Banks Design Associates, Ltd 57
Beautiful Home 191
Budd & Allardyce Interiors LLC 188,189
Champa Interiors 201
Christman Stuart Interiors 205
Connecticut Design Center 397-399
Country Design, Inc. 207
Décor of Greenwich 190
Diana Sawicki Interior Design, Inc. 194
Dujardin Design Associates 204
Grayson Construction Co. Inc. 154,206
Hampton Court Interiors 220,221
Haverson Architecture and Design, PC 87
Karen Houghton Interiors 223
Katherine Cowdin, Inc., Interior Design . . .227
Lowenthal Partners Interior Design 224
Palladio Interior Design 228
Prosperity Interiors, Inc. 229
Radcliff Interiors, Inc. 230
Robin McGarry & Associates 202,203
Sheridan Interiors 196,197
V. W. Interiors LLC 231

Transitional
Alexa Wheeler Interiors 195
Audrey Morgan Interiors 181-183
Banks Design Associates, Ltd 57
Beautiful Home 191
Connecticut Design Center 397-399
Décor of Greenwich 190
Grayson Construction Co. Inc. 154,206
Gregory Allan Cramer & Company 208
Hampton Court Interiors 220,221
Kent Pruzan Interiors, LLC 222
Lowenthal Partners Interior Design 224
Palladio Interior Design 228
Prosperity Interiors, Inc. 229
Robin McGarry & Associates 202,203
Sheridan Interiors 196,197

Kitchen & Bath

Appliances
A Matter of Style 309
Albano Appliance & Service, LLC 326,327
Clarke 324-331
Country Kitchens, LLC 313
County TV & Appliance 324
Dacor 322,323
HADCO 328,329
Kitchen & Bath Center 281-283
Kitchen Factor, The 296
Kitchens By Benson 281-283
Miele 321
Planet TV & Appliance 325,480
Putnam Kitchens Inc. 300-303
SBD Kitchens, LLC 294,295

Bath Accessories
Country Kitchens, LLC 313
Creative Bath At Danbury
    Plumbing Supply 317
Fenimore Plumbing Supply 318
Kitchen & Bath Center 281-283
Kitchen & Bath Creations, LLC 298
Kitchens By Benson 281-283
Putnam Kitchens Inc. 300-303
Sachs Plumbing Supplies 319
SBD Kitchens, LLC 294,295

Cabinets, Custom
Empire Kitchens 310,311,352,353
Gallery of Kitchens 290,291
New England Kitchen Design Center 305
Paul Dolan Company, Inc. 308

Fixtures
Albano Appliance & Service, LLC 326,327
Country Kitchens, LLC 313
Creative Bath At Danbury
    Plumbing Supply 317
Fenimore Plumbing Supply 318
Kitchen & Bath Center 281-283
Kitchen & Bath Creations, LLC 298
Kitchen Factor, The 296
Kitchens By Benson 281-283
Putnam Kitchens Inc. 300-303
Sachs Plumbing Supplies 319
SBD Kitchens, LLC 294,295

Hardware
A Matter of Style .309
Country Kitchens, LLC 313
Fenimore Plumbing Supply 318
Kitchen & Bath Creations, LLC 298
Kitchen & Bath Creations, LLC 298
Kitchen Factor, The 296
Putnam Kitchens Inc. 300-303
Sachs Plumbing Supplies 319
SBD Kitchens, LLC 294,295

Home Library
Kitchens By Deane 299

Kitchen & Bath Designers &
A Matter of Style .309
All Star Woodworking 342
Bilotta Home Center 301
Connecticut Kitchen & Bath 312-319
Construction Concepts Corp. 135,199,289
Country Kitchens, LLC 313
Custom Kitchens & Baths 304

Edelmann Kitchen, Bath &
Interior Design 209,297
Empire Kitchens 310,311,352,353

Gallery of Kitchens 290,291
Hoffman Contracting, LLC 175
Katherine Cowdin, Inc., Interior Design 227
Kitchen & Bath Center 281-283
Kitchen & Bath Creations, LLC 298
Kitchen Company, The 302,303
Kitchen Factor, The 296
Kitchens By Benson 281-283
Kitchens By Deane 299
Masterworks Cabinetry, Inc. 348,349
New Canaan Marble & Tile 388,389
New England Kitchen Design Center 305
Paul Dolan Company, Inc. 308
Putnam Kitchens Inc. 300-303
Rings End Lumber 366
Rooms of England 290,291
Rose Adams Cabinetry 306
Rose Adams Design Cabinetry 306
SBD Kitchens, LLC 294,295
Studio Snaidero Greenwich 307
T.O. Gronlund Co. 292,293
Top Drawer Custom Cabinetry Corp. 312
Westchester Design Center/
    Empire Kitchens 310,311,352,353

Kitchen & Bath Surfaces
A Matter of Style .309
Country Kitchens, LLC 313
Kitchen & Bath Center 281-283
Kitchen & Bath Creations, LLC 298
Kitchens By Benson 281-283
Putnam Kitchens Inc. 300-303
SBD Kitchens, LLC 294,295

Shower Doors
Country Kitchens, LLC 313
Creative Bath At Danbury
    Plumbing Supply 317
Fenimore Plumbing Supply 318
Kitchen & Bath Center 281-283
Kitchen & Bath Creations, LLC 298
Kitchens By Benson 281-283
SBD Kitchens, LLC 294,295

Shower Enclosures
Country Kitchens, LLC 313
Creative Bath At Danbury
    Plumbing Supply 317
Fenimore Plumbing Supply 318
Kitchen & Bath Center 281-283
Kitchen & Bath Creations, LLC 298
Kitchens By Benson 281-283
SBD Kitchens, LLC 294,295

Landscaping

Arborists
Kent Greenhouse & Gardens 244,245

Architectural Elements
Alfredo LDC .235-237
Femia Landscaping, Inc. 253
Garon Fence Company Inc. 279
Kent Greenhouse & Gardens 244,245
SGDA 243

Basketball Courts
Barchella Contracting
    Company, Inc. 250,251
Connecticut Fencemen, Inc, The 272
Kent Greenhouse & Gardens 244,245

Conservatories
Kent Greenhouse & Gardens 244,245

Professional Index

Decks
Barchella Contracting
Company, Inc. 250,251
Cardillo Pools & Spas LLC 265
Kent Greenhouse & Gardens 244,245
Kling Brothers Builders Inc. 144,145
Paramount Stone Co 387

Fencing & Gates, Decorative
Alfredo LDC 235-237
Connecticut Fencemen, Inc, The 272
Femia Landscaping, Inc. 253
Garon Fence Company Inc. 279
Kent Greenhouse & Gardens 244,245
SGDA 243
Walpole Woodworkers 270,271

Fountains
Alfredo LDC 235-237
Cardillo Pools & Spas LLC 265
Fishe Bros., Merchants of Interest 269
Kent Greenhouse & Gardens 244,245
Paramount Stone Co 387

Garden Centers
Kent Greenhouse & Gardens 244,245

Garden Ornaments
Bedford Stone & Masonry 252-259
Colonial Collections of
New England, Inc. 418
Femia Landscaping, Inc. 253
Fishe Bros., Merchants of Interest 269
Kent Greenhouse & Gardens 244,245
Vallin Galleries LLC 462

Hardscape Contractors
Alfredo LDC 235-237
B. Hirsch Landworks, LLC 249,257
Barchella Contracting
Company, Inc. 250,251
Bedford Stone & Masonry 252-259
Connecticut Bomanite
Systems, Inc. 261
Coppola & Sons
Construction Co. Inc. 258
D.L.T.C., Inc. 246
D.L.T.C., Inc. 246
Femia Landscaping, Inc. 253
H.J. Luciano 254
Jason Roberts, Inc. 259
Kent Greenhouse & Gardens 244,245
Perfect Plantings 255
SGDA 243

Irrigation
Kent Greenhouse & Gardens 244,245
SGDA 243
Summer Rain 260

Landscape Architects
B. Hirsch Landworks, LLC 249,257
Connecticut Fencemen, Inc, The 272
D.L.T.C., Inc. 246
Richard F. Hein 85
SGDA 243

Landscape Contractors
Alfredo LDC 235-237
B. Hirsch Landworks, LLC 249,257
Barchella Contracting
Company, Inc. 250,251
D.L.T.C., Inc. 246
Femia Landscaping, Inc. 253
Kent Greenhouse & Gardens 244,245
Perfect Plantings 255

Landscape Lighting
Alfredo LDC 235-237
Custom Landscape &
Lighting, LLC 274,275
Design Lighting By Marks 276,277
Kent Greenhouse & Gardens 244,245
SGDA 243

Landscape Maintenance
Alfredo LDC 235-237
B. Hirsch Landworks, LLC 249,257
Barchella Contracting
Company, Inc. 250,251
Femia Landscaping, Inc. 253
Perfect Plantings 255

Mailboxes
Colonial Collections of
New England, Inc. 418
H.J. Luciano 254

Sport Facilities
Kent Greenhouse & Gardens 244,245

Swimming Pools & Spas
Alfredo LDC 235-237
All American Custom
Pool & Spas, Inc. 266,267
Anthony & Sylvan Pools 264
Cardillo Pools & Spas LLC 265
Connecticut Fencemen, Inc, The 272
Femia Landscaping, Inc. 253
Kent Greenhouse & Gardens 244,245
Lang Pools, Inc. .263
Paramount Stone Co 387
SGDA 243

Tennis Courts
Connecticut Fencemen, Inc, The 272
Kent Greenhouse & Gardens 244,245

Underground Sprinklers
Kent Greenhouse & Gardens 244,245
Summer Rain 260

Water Gardens
Alfredo LDC 235-237
B. Hirsch Landworks, LLC 249,257
Femia Landscaping, Inc. 253
Kent Greenhouse & Gardens 244,245
Paramount Stone Co 387

Notes

499

500

501

502